There's

GOT TO BE

MORE

There's GOT TO BE MORE

MELISSA EBY
as told by Reuben Yoder

ISBN: 978-1-941213-69-8

Cover design and layout: Teresa Sommers

Printed in the USA

Published by:
TGS International
P.O. Box 355
Berlin, Ohio 44610 USA
Phone: 330-893-4828
Fax: 330-893-2305
www.tgsinternational.com

TGS001027

Publisher's Note:

THE STORIES TOLD IN THIS book are based on true-life experiences in the lives of the main characters. However, at times, happenings have been combined, dialogue has been altered, and sequence rearranged in the telling of these stories. For security reasons, the names of some characters, organizations, and locations have been changed.

Table of Contents

TABLE OF CONTENTS

Introduction

THE ROAD BETWEEN THE BUS stand and our apartment swarmed with the normal combination of trucks, buses, rickshaws, cattle, and people. It was late forenoon, and my wife and I were returning from the market with plans to attend a Bengali wedding in the next hour. Suddenly a rickshaw swerved off the road in front of us and a man jumped off. I quickly observed that something unusual had happened or was about to happen.

Excitedly, the man extended his hand to us and exclaimed, "I need blood!" I was thankful it wasn't dark. After all, this was Bangladesh, and this fellow was a total stranger. "My wife had a baby, and they had to make this big cut," he demonstrated. "She's lost blood and needs some now. The baby is doing fine, but my wife may die if I don't get blood soon."

"What kind do you need?" I asked.

"Type O positive," he replied as the urgency in his demeanor intensified.

"Mine is red, and I know it's good, but I don't know what type I have."

The man shifted nervously from one foot to the other as I searched for a phone number. Thankfully, our mission team leader was within reach. "Is there anyone on our team with type O positive blood?"

Brian wasn't sure but suggested I call Lydia, one of the teachers.

"I have the right kind," Lydia replied in answer to my query.

"Would you like to give some of your life away?" I asked. "The mother of a newborn baby girl has been hemorrhaging and needs blood."

Lydia's answer was confident. "I will give her blood."

"Where are you now?"

"I'm walking toward the apartment with two other team girls."

"We'll be there soon," I assured her.

My wife and I joined the man on the rickshaw and went to find Lydia. The man was happy to meet her and invited her to hop onto the already crowded conveyance. We stopped briefly to see the mother. By her side lay a lovely little girl with coal black curls and eyes like miniature chocolate mint patties. Introductions were brief. There was no time for delay. The donor gave her blood, and a precious life was spared.

~~~~~~

The world is crying for life. The great Blood Donor who came from the heart of Father God continues to call people from every kindred, people, tongue, and nation to experience the ultimate blood transfusion and be redeemed.

We are living in an era of unprecedented opportunity to reach the world with the love of Jesus. Cyclones, earthquakes, and tsunamis are breaking barred doors and calling attention to a sovereign God.

The work of God's children is to show forth the glorious presence of God and wear the face of Jesus in a way that draws people into His kingdom. They are called to make the Lord Jesus visible, intelligible, and desirable to all people. All men need to know Christ, and it is our opportunity and duty to take that knowledge to them. Perhaps you are the one whom God wants to use to point the next seeker to the ultimate sacrifice of Jesus' blood and the gift of eternal life.

If the heart of the Father toward a broken world doesn't kindle the fire of compassion in our hearts, perhaps our wood is wet. The purpose of this story is to encourage cooperation with God so that His kingdom might be extended and His name glorified.

Walking on the water with God requires getting out of the boat. We began this journey on the water with voluntary service experiences in our youth. Later, we were called to ministry as a family. During those years, we felt a growing interest in international missions. As our children grew up and moved on to lives of their own, doors opened for us to transition to various international crisis projects. While our present focus is in Bangladesh, our future is in God's hands and we are convinced that there is more to be done for the kingdom of God.

—Reuben Yoder

CHAPTER 1

Minnesota Virginia Pakistan Ukraine Afghanistan Israel Haiti Bangladesh

Young Men Dream Dreams

YOUNG MEN DREAM MANY DREAMS. The world is before them, and they want to go see it. They peer around bends in the road and climb hills, looking ahead, thinking, *There's got to be more.*

Reuben Yoder may or may not have thought of himself as seeing the world the day he was ordered off the bus with a rabble of youth in Minneapolis. Certainly this wasn't what he had thought he would be seeing. He observed the gigantic warehouse, stolidly awaiting the droves of young men about to be regimented in her echoing spaces. Reuben sized up the place as he joined the crowd filing through the pickets to toe the yellow dotted lines marked on the concrete.

It was 1969, and the Vietnam War was sweeping the fit men of America into its ranks. The year was young, just March. Although the Communist ranks had suffered crippling losses during the Tet Offensive and peace talks had begun earlier, Nixon had yet to announce that American troops would begin to withdraw from the man-eating conflict. The war was old and infuriating to the American homeland. They were tired of war. Their men had been going overseas for years, many of them never to return. But the draft was still in effect, and Reuben had been drafted.

Raised on a farm in Minnesota by Mennonite parents, Reuben figured he'd be a farmer someday. At eighteen, he was tall and lean, used to working hard. Growing up in a home where a meager farm income had been stretched to meet the needs of eight children had taught Reuben to make do with what he had and think around the hard places. The government, however, couldn't be improvised around, and drafts couldn't be vaulted over. There had been no choice but to come to Minneapolis.

Upon arrival, Reuben was assigned a tiny room with another young man. There was only one double bed. Reuben didn't know much about hippies, but by the looks of it, his roommate was one. Jude was gaunt and longhaired, disposed to be friendly.

"Let's go out," Jude suggested, so Reuben joined him for a walk. It was a quiet walk. Reuben watched the tops of the bare trees against the spring evening and looked the grounds over, curious about his present predicament, and his future. When they reached the entrance of their sprawling complex, Jude wanted to go farther, in the mood for a movie.

"No, thanks," Reuben said. "I'll just go back to the room. May I have the key?"

"Okay!" Jude replied, peeved. "But you'd better unlock the door when I get back."

"I'll unlock it," Reuben told him.

Reuben went back to the stuffy room. Since there was nothing to do, he crawled into bed and fell asleep.

It was midnight when he roused to the sound of someone beating down the door. "Wait!" Reuben hollered. He rolled out to unlock the door, eyes dull with sleep. Jude brushed by him into the room and knelt down by his pack.

Reuben dropped back into bed, but sleep had fled. He lay there in the dark, listening to his roommate muttering and tossing items around. Eventually Jude must have found what he wanted. A match scratched, and thick cigarette smoke filtered under the blankets and permeated the air. Jude stretched out on the bed and set an ashtray on his chest. Reuben stirred ever so slightly, and his roommate's breathing stopped. Then it began again.

"You awake?" the gravelly voice inquired.

Reuben sat up, glaring into the darkness, and moved to the edge of the bed. "Yes."

"You a Mennonite?"

"Yes."

"So you what . . . live next to the earth, grew up on a farm milking cows, walked to school, can ride any animal in sight?"

Reuben thought Jude was going a little far, but he only replied, "Yes." His voice choked on the cigarette smoke. A brief silence followed, and he waited, his muscles tense. The abrupt end to his slumber had his adrenaline racing.

"Hmm . . ." the voice murmured from the darkness. Reuben wasn't normally a fearful person, but he would have given a lot to see the morning. This was getting eerie. Frozen, he sat on the bed. For some reason, at that unhandy moment, he was wondering about this man's soul. Movies and cigarettes and long hair. *This man is not saved,* Reuben guessed. *I wonder what Christ would have said to him.*

Whatever Christ would have said, Reuben was reluctant to pursue Jude further at the moment. He felt far outside his boundaries of comfort. Were hippies ever violent? Only when they needed a cigarette?

"Hmm . . ." Jude murmured again. "We're kind of alike, you and me. Big family?"

"Yes."

"I have three brothers. Yeah, we're a lot alike."

Reuben disagreed, but he only said, "You want to open the window?"

"Sure." Jude rose from the bed, and Reuben spied his shadow as it moved by the glass. The hippie leaned out the window, smoking like a chimney. Most of the smoke drifted back into the room on the night breeze.

"I come from the hills of Missouri," Jude remarked, "but I was born in Los Angeles. Still go there sometimes, but I'm a country boy. Like the country. You can breathe there. It's nice there are places like that. Goin' back as soon as possible. This war business lacks, man. You and I don't wanna be in it. Makes a man wonder what he's made for. Maybe you know . . ."

The statement hung in the air.

After a while Reuben answered, "Well, there are important things like God and family and love and truth . . ." It sounded weak even to Reuben's ears.

"Wonder what's gonna last. What'll be important later, after we're dead." This was said so softly that Reuben strained to hear Jude's words.

"Yes." Reuben wasn't prepared to debate that. A man needed to face those things, but it was a mighty personal subject to jump into without knowing the man's background.

The next morning Reuben found himself tromping through shuffling lines of men stripped to their shorts and shoes, toting bags with their belongings, standing in line to get their physicals. They were shoved along queues past holes in the glass. Hands shot out from the holes to grab Reuben's arm. A needle pinched his vein, and vials filled with blood. It was a system, and Reuben didn't resist it.

Looking about him occasionally, Reuben reflected on all the men around him—men of different ages, backgrounds, and life experiences. Perhaps, like him, they had thought they knew what the future held. Maybe they had jobs they were really good at, but when their country had called, there they were. That kind of summons couldn't be ignored. No one argued. Maybe they didn't come willingly, but after all, something higher than their own plans had demanded their attention.

Reuben figured it would soon get interesting when he started to explain his higher calling. With his conservative Anabaptist perspective of Christianity, he could not take part in war. Conscientious objectors were not unheard of in the 1960s, but they were uncommon. Reuben had a suspicion that his beliefs would be subjected to heavy scrutiny.

~~~~~~

After the experience in Minneapolis, Reuben returned to farm life, and several weeks passed until the draft board notified him of the results of his physical. Of course, he had passed. Reuben's health, always good, had been fostered to brawn by his next-to-earth upbringing. He made an appointment with the county draft board, and standing before them, he explained that he valued human life and could not participate in war. He told the board that rather, he was willing to serve his country in ways that would benefit his fellow humans.

Then Reuben sat down and clenched his hands. He was nervous. He couldn't help it. There were all sorts of misunderstandings in these cases. What if he hadn't explained clearly enough?

However, the board said little about his position. They allowed him to file as a conscientious objector and take the routine steps. Finding a place to do voluntary service was up to Reuben.

Not long after this, Abe Schwartz, director of River Forest Nursing Home in Michigan, visited Reuben's community of Grove City on a speaking tour. He stopped by Reuben's home one evening, and Reuben and Abe talked over the backs of the milk cows. Abe, a small man with a lot of gray hair, displayed a zeal for getting folks to work at his nursing home.

"You ought to come," Abe urged.

Reuben remained silent for a bit, not ready to get anyone's hopes up. He thought it over, though, and began to see it as a possibility. He did need a place to do his voluntary service. He didn't really have a particular place or nursing home in mind, but he was willing to consider the idea.

"It would be an excellent thing to have on your résumé in case you get drafted," Abe continued.

Abe had nailed the crux of the matter without knowing it. "I *have* been drafted," Reuben admitted. "What would I do there?" He knew how to milk cows. He didn't know how to take care of old people.

Reuben accepted Abe's invitation, but he didn't end up taking care of old people. He spent fifteen months working in the kitchen, making salads and rotating as dining room attendant. He set the tables, cleaned the floors, and became second cook. He could think of worse jobs to do in a nursing home than chopping lettuce, and the kitchen served as a gathering place for the staff. The nurse's aides were always hungry, and that was how Mary Ann tripped into his world, her dark eyes snapping and glowing with life.

Reuben had met Mary Ann before. She had traveled from her Pennsylvania home with three of her friends the previous summer to attend a wedding in Minnesota. His parents had offered the four girls lodging, and they had stayed with Reuben's family for a few days. Their

Lancaster County upbringing provided glimpses of another world to Reuben, who had been mostly confined to Minnesota. The girls had enjoyed each other's company and the later hours of the night. Through a thin wall, Reuben and his brothers had listened silently to their merriment and tried to sleep.

Reuben spent two years at River Forest, and Mary Ann spent sixteen months there during his term, volunteering as a nurse's aide. Mary Ann thought of Reuben as her brother. They were good friends.

After Reuben's term of service ended, a winter or so passed before a wedding of two River Forest colleagues drew a group of former nursing home staff to Iowa. Reuben and Mary Ann served guests together at the wedding.

By the time the wedding was over, enough had occurred to convince Reuben that the time had come. The next line was his, and he was determined to say it. The Sunday after the wedding, he sat with his friends, fidgeting. The atmosphere at the fellowship meal began to annoy him. He wanted out, he wanted fresh air, and he wanted something to happen.

All afternoon Mary Ann had been with her girlfriends, laughing and enjoying herself. Reuben had not had so much as a chance to speak to her. Soon she and her friend would be leaving for Pennsylvania, and he had no idea when he would see her again.

Then, without warning, she was going for her coat.

Pennsylvania! Prodded by that thought, Reuben stood to follow Mary Ann as she and her friend, Carol Dean, were leaving the big lunchroom. Young people's heads swiveled in surprise at his abrupt departure, but he didn't give them a backward glance.

Carol Dean saw him coming first and nudged Mary Ann. Reuben noticed, and he also thought Carol Dean looked surprised. Mary Ann only reached for her coat, bestowing a small smile upon him. Reuben took the bags the girls had bent to pick up. Mary Ann was such a little bird-like girl, but her eyes were as bright as a chipmunk's.

The three young people sauntered out into the golden sunshine of the winter afternoon. Reuben hoped Carol Dean would get the point, and soon enough, she recollected something she had left somewhere and traipsed off.

Carol Dean was a smart girl, and Reuben silently wished her well as Mary Ann chattered on about the weekend and the drive back to Pennsylvania. They stood by the car, parked by a windbreak of evergreens.

There by the car, with a robin hopping about on the sidewalk and the branches waving above them in an endless dance, Reuben told Mary Ann of his wishes and dreams, struggling to keep from laying out to her all the reasons why she should become his girlfriend. He had plenty of reasons, and they were all lined up, but Reuben knew it would take more than the right words to make Mary Ann say yes.

It happened that Mary Ann would say yes, but it took her long enough to tell him. Those dark eyes popped and crackled with life, but standing there by the car, all she would say was that she would let him know in a few weeks. She would write him a letter.

Several weeks passed before Mary Ann felt it was time to respond, expressing in prim words that she, too, felt that there could be a future together for the two of them.

Five months passed, and the summer had aged before they saw each other again. Mary Ann made a trip to Montana to care for an elderly Amish lady and stopped in to see Reuben. There on the Minnesota farm, time snapped out of its lethargy. Two months later, Reuben asked Mary Ann to marry him. She said yes.

By the time he had begun angling for Mary Ann's friendship, Reuben had acquired a small farm close to where he grew up. It was a nice piece of land, but the house on it was an old Sears & Roebuck modular home. The kitchen had a porcelain sink in the corner where the door opened onto the rickety porch. The stairs housed a toilet underneath, but no shower, and the old ceiling was built high above the floor. An electrical wire ran down one of the walls. With a marker, Reuben had written on the wall by the wire, "Happiness is being content."

Reuben introduced the house and Mary Ann to each other when she came to visit again that winter before their marriage. The drifts on the south side of the tree windbreak glared in the windows of the upper floor as they clambered about the house. It had been a phenomenally hard winter, even for Minnesota.

The Yoder farm was just inside the northern tip of the Corn Belt. It was corn and hog country, but the killing frost had come in early September, and the corn and soybeans had frozen where they languished in late summer ripeness.

Reuben had been worried about the contrast between Mary Ann's manicured Lancaster home and his Sears & Roebuck modular on the Minnesota farm.

"I'll live anywhere with you, Reuben," Mary Ann said. "Even in a mud hut—as long as we're together."

Reuben grinned down at her. "That's all that matters."

This became their life. Together they would do everything. They returned from their honeymoon in the spring of 1975 to find three feet of water in their cellar from melting snowdrifts around the house. The only thing to do was to put on their boots and get to work.

Spring on the farm demanded all of their energy. From morning till night they tackled the work together, and together they made it fun. Wherever Reuben was, Mary Ann was right beside him. They tilled and planted and harvested, nurturing live plants from dormant seeds, breaking crusty ground into fertile soil.

They converted the ancient chicken house into a delivery room for the sows. The first batch of piglets astounded them. Their sows birthed one hundred forty-six babies within forty-eight hours, and Mary Ann's tiny hands served as forceps in the difficult deliveries.

When Mary Ann was expecting their first baby, the farm work and a handful of crackers seemed to be the best cure for the sickness she felt. She rose early in the morning to go out to the barn, preferring the cold fresh air.

Darrell was born, and then Darlene. For five years the crops yielded substantial harvest, but good crops meant good fodder for the pigs—not necessarily cash. It paid better to feed their corn to the pigs and market them than to sell the corn as a cash crop. During this time, they poured all their resources into developing their herd of hogs.

Little could daunt Reuben, and Mary Ann's enthusiasm added life to his determination.

"Is it doable?" Reuben would ask. "If it is, then let's do it." Together they shouldered the load. With a work ethic handed down through generations, with the vision of pioneers, the strategy of conquerors, and the faith of prophets, the world was at their fingertips. What couldn't they do? With God at the helm, what couldn't they survive? But there *were* limits, as they began to find out.

A step forward usually meant a step backward, and major losses kept their dreams and plans tuned to reality. A hailstorm destroyed some of the soybean crop, and a virus, sweeping through the community, claimed nearly a hundred piglets. One night some ornery neighbor boys opened the gates of three wagons of shelled corn, dumping the corn out onto the gravel drive. Only parts of the loads were recoverable.

Then one day a pink slip arrived from the bank for an overdraft, and for the rest of that day they worked soberly, not calling back and forth to each other as usual. Finally, at the end of the day, Reuben caught Mary Ann by the hand and tugged her out into the woods where they went to escape sometimes. They rested together underneath the boughs of the oaks, leaning against the rough bark that scratched their arms.

"What do we do?" they asked each other. "Where do we go?" The crops weren't ready to harvest yet. They stood together, silhouetted against the darkening glow of the west. Time passed before Mary Ann stirred, "Dear, we need to remember God."

Reuben squeezed his hand around her fingers, looking at the two hands, large and little, melded together. It was his family—his responsibility.

"You're right," he said at last. "We should pray."

Down by the house, spitting gravel disturbed the moment. Reuben lifted his bowed head, and Mary Ann was already listening. "Visitors." Together they walked back to the house, which rose small but sheltering among the trees. Together they had made it a wonderful home.

The two rounded the house and found the neighbor man standing beside his truck. They didn't know him well, but he had come to make them an offer. He was selling his dairy next February, and until then, he needed someone to milk his cows.

Before they call, I will answer. Reuben liked that verse. He agreed to milk for the neighbor. The cash would help out a lot.

Reuben and Mary Ann had been busy before, but now "busy" redefined itself. With so much to do, life slid by rapidly—very rapidly. The fieldwork and the hogs sapped their daylight hours, and now, come evening, away went Reuben to work at the neighbor's farm.

Two more daughters, Lavonna and Connie, were born, but more than just the family was growing.

The goal of raising piglets to market weight had finally materialized. The operation of the herd had grown predictable to the point that Reuben could sell a few pigs regularly. As Reuben's schedule was already so demanding, Mary Ann often delivered the pigs to market, twenty miles away. Loading the pigs into the back of the farm pickup, a four-speed manual, Mary Ann climbed in behind the wheel, tucking her children around her, and away they rolled. The children liked to stand up and hang onto the dash—they could see better that way. The truck could go fast, and Mary Ann told stories and sang with the little ones. Hair blew and skirts flapped, and at the stop signs, Mary Ann downshifted, raising an arm to steady the children.

In this way their little kingdom compounded and grew. Years of farming stretched out before them. Life was good, but a question began niggling in the back of their minds. They could do this, but was this all there was to life? Farming, crops, pigs—season after season. Was this what was most important? The first five years had been difficult. It was easier now. Maybe after a while it would become even easier. They could make this farm profitable. They could expand and build until eventually they would have everything they wanted—but where would it end? Was there more? Was there more to life?

One Sunday afternoon the young couple had sprawled under the big tree behind the house. Their littlest ones were sleeping, and Darrell was playing in the loose dirt by the porch. This moment of leisure was rare, and Reuben, lying on his back with his hands laced under his head, pretended to himself that it would last. Mary Ann sat upright, plucking grass incessantly with her fingers.

"This is nice," she said at last. "It's peaceful."

"It is," Reuben replied. "Stop pulling all the grass and stretch out like me. It'll be even more peaceful."

She plopped down beside him but sat back up again. "We should do this more often."

"We should," Reuben agreed.

Mary Ann threw a handful of grass at him. "We work awfully hard."

"We do."

"Do you think work is all there is to life?"

Reuben focused his eyes on her face, and she stilled. "I wonder . . ." Reuben's tone changed, no longer bantering.

"It seems kind of pointless, doesn't it?"

"Sometimes."

"I mean, we can do this. But where does it end? We have enough here to live on. You work hard. I work hard. We've got the farm . . ."

Reuben looked at her.

"Okay, so it's not paid for, but it will be after a while. We can make this farm roll. To what end? Are we going to get rich and prosperous and try to marry our girls off to someone richer and more prosperous? And set Darrell up with a nice big farm when he's about eighteen and marrying the girl he liked in third grade?"

"My parents knew each other in third grade. You make it sound bad." Reuben laughed.

"It's not . . . it's just . . . isn't there more to life? Don't laugh at me."

Reuben grabbed her hand. "I'm just teasing you, dear. I like to hear you talk. You're completely right. I've often wondered . . ." He rolled over and pulled out one single blade of grass to examine. "I've wondered if this is the place for us for a lifetime. You know, there's got to be more—more to life than this."

They fell silent for the space of a couple minutes before Reuben continued, "Well! If there is something more, I guess God will show us. He'll fix something to give us an idea of where He wants us."

Mary Ann nodded. "He will. We can pray. Oh, dear, I hear the baby. I know where God wants *me* right now."

She jumped up, and Reuben stood with her. Hand in hand they strolled across the yard. For the moment, the farm and all its duties seemed far away.

Only a month later, Reuben's brother Nathan came home for a visit. He was volunteering at Faith Mission Home in Virginia, caring for mentally handicapped children. Speaking of his experiences over a Sunday lunch at Reuben's parents' place, Nathan mentioned that the Home needed house parents.

Something leaped inside Mary Ann. The same feeling surged inside Reuben, she discovered later. *What about Faith Mission? What about it?*

CHAPTER 2

Jabbok—
A Change of Course

IT WASN'T AN EASY DECISION. The two of them had labored long and hard to master the farm and make it produce. Now, at the moment when they were reaching their long-sought goals, when the farm was beginning to pay for itself, Reuben and Mary Ann were walking away into volunteer service. But these thoughts couldn't linger now. There was only a week of farm life left, and Mary Ann was packing.

Connie, the baby, was fighting a cold that was keeping them both up at night. Mary Ann felt tired. She leaned her head against the chest of drawers and closed her eyes, wishing for a nap. She thought of Reuben's determination through all of these changes. She was thankful for him and his quiet strength and support that boosted her through. She had come to depend on that.

They were moving, but life still felt singularly normal. Sometimes Mary Ann looked out at the frozen fields and the brown of the harvested cornfields and wondered why it didn't tug at her heart more. Gamely, she went on packing, caring for the four children as though they prepared to move twelve hundred miles to a new life every week. When she got to Virginia she would better understand the changes—what she was losing and what she was gaining—but as of now, life seemed about the same.

Still, she thought as she bent over the dresser drawers in her room, *something ought to feel like it's changing. If I felt that, maybe I would feel more equipped for the life ahead.*

Mary Ann had always known that God uses people He has prepared for His work. Well, now that the time had come, she didn't feel a bit prepared. Was she ready to meet the challenges of Faith Mission Home? Honestly, she didn't even care that much. She was just going to do what needed to be done.

Mary Ann sighed and pushed her hair away from her face. She was so tired that she was thinking in circles. *Lord, however you want us, we'll come. You do the rest.*

A voice shouting downstairs shattered the train of her thoughts. "Ma'am! Ma'am! Mrs. Yoder!"

Mary Ann's heart froze. A person can go a whole lifetime without experiencing tragedy, but when that moment arrives, he recognizes tragedy for what it is.

Hearing the urgent voice, Mary Ann flung herself down the stairs as Cavendish, the neighbor's hired man, burst into the hallway. "Mrs. Yoder, you need to call the ambulance right away. Reuben's hurt. Bad!"

~~~~~~

Harvest was late that year, for it had been a wet fall. It was November 17, 1981, and Reuben was still bringing the corn in. He was unloading a final load into the crib. The stalks were as brown as the rest of the autumn world, and most of the fields were bared to the merciless sky. Clouds raced high, and a sharp wind snapped at Reuben's coat. "Hurry," it hissed, "hurry!" The hard clumps of the ground, frozen after a muddy rain, had loosened the turf and caught at Reuben's boots, trying to trip him. Reuben, intent on getting done, paid them no mind. It was evening—of the day and of the year. It was time to finish.

Reuben had been working since daylight. He usually worked from daylight to dark, but this late in the year, the daylight didn't last. Already the shadows had gathered. Reuben jogged about the elevator, figuring that he had spent most of the day running. He could get a lot done in one day. His mind scrolled ahead to the next job, to the new life approaching. What would it be like in Virginia, teaching handicapped boys and managing a farm for the mission? Would he be bored? Would it bother him to be around people all the time? Reuben brushed the thought away. Secretly he suspected that he would miss being out on the farm with just his wife. He didn't mind people. He wasn't anti-social, but . . .

Reuben was just about done harvesting the field by the road. His corn picker was slower than the big rigs, but he had a corn sheller that he sometimes took around to the neighbors to help them out.

Jerry Burke, on the neighboring farm, wasn't doing too badly. Burke had passed by earlier on his way to town with a load of corn, and Burke's hired man, Cavendish, was already plowing in the field across the road. Now the Burke truck was trundling back down the country road hauling an empty wagon. Reuben waved. It would soon be too dark to work. Racing along, he kicked the corner of his five-horsepower stationary engine that he usually used to run the elevator. That morning it had stopped running, so Reuben had set it aside and had hooked up the tractor to power the elevator.

Reuben noticed that the elevator was jamming up at the top. He stepped onto the chain in the elevator. Along the side, he had a place to stride up to the top. The corn rattled as it fell into the bin on top of the other corn. The corn was piling just under the roof of the bin. The elevator creaked; the tractor thrummed away. Reuben eyed the chain, assessing the problem. The chain was running over the top of an ear of corn, and he reached out with his boot to push the chain down. He pressed on it, bullying it back under the corn.

My boot's tight. Anxiously, Reuben glanced down. *My boot is tight!* It was under the chain, and his foot was stuck crossways. He tugged briefly. A horrible twist wrenched his body as his foot traveled around the end of the elevator where the chain disappeared into the channel, and he toppled forward. The grinding and turning of the chain jerked at his boot. The chain wrenched, dragging him down. Blood burst over the corn and the roof of the bin.

My leg! My leg is gone! The flesh had been ripped from the knee down.

Reuben saw—through horror—the bare bone shaft protruding below his knee. Broken, Reuben caught himself. Swaying, he sat down on the fluted rim of the elevator before sliding down.

On the ground, he tried to stand up, knowing he needed help. Reuben's mind shrieked that he needed to get someone's attention immediately. He needed to run to the house and tell Mary Ann. Hoisting himself up, he started to walk—to run. But he fell. There was no left leg.

The house was only about three hundred feet away. Reuben crawled, calling for help and dragging himself to the tractor. He pulled himself up to turn the key. The engine died, leaving silence. His voice echoed in the thin, cold air, calling for help as he crept toward the house, dragging his bleeding leg. It wasn't very far. He tried to go on, but he couldn't. Bleeding out of the main artery in his leg, he struggled to pull himself along. He was fading fast, clinging to only a thread of consciousness. He drifted in and out—in and out.

Jerry Burke crawled out of his truck to unhook his trailer just beyond the road. The hitch clanged as he wrestled with it. There was a weak wail to the racket of unfastening the trailer as iron rubbed on iron. Then a moan startled him. Burke forgot the hitch and turned. There was no sound now, but his mind shrieked at him that something was wrong. Mr. Yoder's tractor wasn't running.

Jogging down to the field, Burke listened above the rasp of the corn stalks he bounded through. The night breeze around him gobbled and moaned. "Help! Help!" Weeping, a tree branch scraped another, and the wind brought a shriek out of them.

Reuben's corn picker and tractor stood abandoned and silent under the deepening sky. Burke saw in a glance that the trouble was not there.

Breathlessly, he dashed to the elevator, his eyes sweeping the ground around the silent equipment. He ducked under the elevator between the shaft and the bins. Slipping around the tractor, Burke at last spotted the outline of a figure crumpled on the ground. A dark shadow at the bottom of the figure leaped out at Burke. *Blood!* He yelled as he reached the hurt man, "Where is your leg?"

Reuben stirred at the sound of the panicky voice. "Probably in the corncrib." The words were touched with pain, and the last word died away in his breath. He fainted then. Burke heard running feet, and Cavendish appeared at his elbow, eyes bulging.

"What's wrong!"

There was a warm spot at the bottom of the elevator where the boot and mangled leg had jammed the chain. The chain links were bent out of square from the tension of tightening around the leg, and the elevator had stalled. Had the elevator been driven by the stationary engine, almost certainly it would not have had the power to tear a leg off. The tractor had.

Burke took one look at the leg and galloped back to Reuben. *We need an ambulance, now!*

"Go get his wife to call the ambulance," he ordered Cavendish.

"Where is he?" Mary Ann demanded when Cavendish blurted out that Reuben was hurt.

Cavendish doubled over the banister, gasping. "Out by the driveway. You need to call an ambulance now. You need to call for it right *now!*" He stabbed his finger for emphasis, almost sobbing.

I need to go to Reuben. It was the only thing immediately on Mary Ann's mind. She dashed past him to the door. "You call the ambulance."

"No, you do!"

Mary Ann paused, her hand on the knob, looking wildly back at the hired man. He was breathing hard, deathly white.

Cavendish pulled himself up and faced the woman. "There's blood everywhere. It's ugly, Mrs. Yoder. Let me go back to him. You stay here with the little ones and call an ambulance. I need something to tie . . ." Distraught, he looked down at Darrell and Darlene, standing there. Their eyes were huge.

Mary Ann made up her mind. *I will call, but then I am going to my husband.* She looked around for some cloth, pouncing on a scarf in an open box by the coat rack where she had been packing earlier. "Here. Take this."

Her mind was racing, and she wondered if she could pull herself together enough to instruct an ambulance on how to come. She dialed Reuben's mom who lived just across the field. "Reuben's hurt bad, and I need you to call an ambulance."

There. Reuben's mom can manage things. "Stay in here and watch Connie," Mary Ann told Darrell, who looked as though he might cry. Snatching a blanket, she ran outside.

As Mary Ann crossed the frozen ground toward her husband's dark form, her heart was crying, *Lord! Lord! Where are you? Be strong and comfort us.* Kneeling by Reuben, she barely noticed the blood, calling his name. "Reuben!"

Reuben's eyes opened suddenly, and he saw his wife. Eyes dark with horror and pupils dilated, he focused on her face. "I don't think I will make it," he said.

"You *will* make it," Mary Ann replied stubbornly, and paused before adding in a choked voice, "God is with us."

Reuben's eyes seemed to grow larger before they fell shut, and he smiled. Again he lost consciousness, sliding away, and his features relaxed.

In the minutes before the ambulance came, they tucked a blanket around him. Burke had tied the scarf above the stump. Mary Ann clung to Reuben's hand and fought grief. Praying silently, she implored, *Help us, Lord.*

At last the ambulance arrived with a sheriff escort. Other people were there now. Reuben's parents had come, along with some of the neighbors who had followed the ambulance. Reuben was mercifully unaware of everything, but as they prepared to raise him onto the stretcher, he came to consciousness enough to hear them say, "Now!" and lift him. The crushed and ripped nerve endings twanged with movement, and incredible pain shot through his body. Reuben had never experienced anything like it. No numbness came to aid him.

It was a fast ride. The sheriff's car went first, with the severed leg on ice. Mary Ann had been permitted to ride in the ambulance, and she watched the medic like a hawk. "He's doing okay, Mrs.," the medic said, noticing Mary Ann's keen gaze. "He's stable."

Mary Ann sat back and thought about it. She caught a glimpse of the speedometer, pushing eighty miles an hour. *He's doing okay . . . ? Possibly. The Lord is at the helm, but I don't think the medic knows that.*

"Yes, ma'am," Mary Ann agreed. "The Lord is taking care of him."

The medic nodded. She was used to agonizing families.

At the hospital, everything happened at once. Doctors and nurses surrounded Reuben, clipping away his clothes and attaching wires to him. Then they rolled him off, and Mary Ann trotted to keep up with the wheeled stretcher. The doctors took Reuben right into the operating room, and the minutes stretched into hours. After all the activity and the adrenaline of finding and transporting Reuben, the world went still. Mary Ann sat alone outside the operating room and cried.

A man exited the operating room and paused to say, "You've got quite the husband, ma'am. He must be a hard worker."

"He's the best worker I know," she replied drearily.

"He must be! One of his lungs collapsed. We're guessing it's from going from a dead run to falling over when his leg was torn off, and from just lying there in the cold."

Hours passed, and Mary Ann waited, exhausted. At long last the doctor stepped out of the operating room. His eyes were kind. "All things work together for good to them that love God, to them who are the called according to his purpose."

"Oh, sir!" Mary Ann roused. "Are you a Christian?"

"Yes," he replied, his eyes crinkling.

〰〰〰〰〰〰〰〰〰〰〰〰〰〰〰〰〰〰〰

On the floor where Reuben was hospitalized, there were seven hundred beds, and in those beds were all shapes and sizes of amputations—seven hundred broken bodies and seven hundred broken spirits. There were many bitter patients in that ward.

Reuben wrestled just like the others. He had faith in God, but faith didn't remove the struggle—it only gave him a tool with which to fight it. For the first several days, Reuben drifted in and out, his senses dulled with strong painkillers. The days were one long, misty night to him. Yet throughout the haze there were moments of crystal clarity, and in those moments he fought. With what, he couldn't have said, but he battled with his whole body, holding death at bay.

As time went on, Reuben came to view these battles as visitations from the Lord. A war both physical and spiritual was being waged, and he was determined to get something out of the struggle. His old life was dead. He had no leg, and in his dreams he fought for a new lease on life. On and on he fought until the wrestling wore him back into a daze, but again the battle returned. At last he accepted these dream-like struggles. Something bigger and stronger than himself was holding onto him. Still he tussled with his angel, clinging and crying, "I will not let you go unless you bless me!"

When the first days had passed and the blur was clearing, Reuben was weak but exultant. The snowy world outside the ward window shone so brightly that he hid his face against it. Color and smell and sound filled his senses as though he had come out of a cold, dark, silent valley into a warmly lit home. Triumph was his. The struggle leaped into his memory, and he thought of Jacob at the brook Jabbok. Why he should think of Jacob immediately, he wasn't sure, but it was as clear as the new day to him that he had crossed the brook Jabbok, wrestling with the angel of the Lord—the Lord who wanted more of him. Yes, the angel had left his mark. Never again would Reuben walk the same. But he had the promise of blessing.

A young Jewish orderly worked among the amputees. A mild-mannered young man with a gentle face, he passed through the ward on his rounds, stopping to listen sympathetically to a complaining patient or to exchange pleasantries with another. He often seemed sad, and even after seeing scores of hurting people, each individual's suffering appeared to weigh on him. His name was Nicholas.

Walking in one day, he caught Reuben and an old family friend laughing. Nicholas checked the charts and then watched Reuben, puzzled. "How can you smile like that? You've lost a leg."

Reuben stopped laughing to look at the young orderly, thinking back to those first days, to his dreams. He had passed from death unto life. "My friend," he said, "only because of Jesus Christ. Compared to what the Lord suffered, I can only be thankful for what He bore for me."

"Doesn't it ever bother you?" Nicholas motioned to the rest of the ward. "There are so many sad people here."

"Yes," Reuben replied honestly. "Every day I have to choose not to be bitter and not to wish I would have quit working earlier that night. It can't be changed. It is what it is."

Steadily and gradually, Nicholas formed a friendship with Reuben. It was not a deeply conversant relationship. But he would always stop to say good morning and ask about the pain. Sometimes he would stand, shifting from foot to foot, listening to Reuben's answers to his simple questions about the farm and country life. At times he barely seemed to listen, responding little and looking out at the wintry hospital grounds.

Mary Ann spent her days by Reuben's side at the hospital in Minneapolis. Friends or relatives coming in to visit would bring nine-month-old Connie every day for her to nurse. Reuben's mother kept the other three children, and Connie went back to her at night.

With the visitors came many blessings and many opinions.

"Of course you won't go to Faith Mission now."

"I guess Virginia will be out for you."

"Too bad this happened before you got a chance to try Faith Mission."

Reuben and Mary Ann listened to these remarks and said nothing.

A fund was started for people to contribute to Reuben's medical costs. Reuben knew his neighbors. It wasn't uncommon for him to help them out with one service or another, and now people came out of the cracks and crannies to assist him financially. It was a huge boost to Reuben and Mary Ann.

Eight days after the accident, Reuben wanted to go home. The doctor listened doubtfully. The majority of amputees spent considerably more time under supervised care, but Reuben didn't have much money, and no insurance.

"I have a nurse to take care of me," Reuben implored, stopping to take Mary Ann's hand. They exchanged glances of adoration that made the doctor polish his glasses with great attention. "She's a great nurse, a really good one."

"I bet you would be a good nurse," the doctor agreed.

"Oh, my! It's not me . . . it's something else. I mean, we should give all the glory to God," Mary Ann said, flustered for the moment. She busied herself with Connie.

The doctor was weakening. He polished his glasses again. "I will agree on that condition, and on this observation. Mr. Yoder, I have seldom seen an amputee come out of the initial trauma as you have. You have exhibited a tremendous attitude and a will to recover. If the other men here would have half the grit that you have, most of them would be out of here by now. Instead, they stay, nursing their wounds in bitterness and fighting infection . . ." The doctor paused as Reuben raised his hand.

"Only because of God," Reuben explained.

"Yes, well, be that as it may." This doctor was not a Christian, but he was flexible about such things. After all, he had just said that it was an above-average recovery. "But listen to me; you're not out of the woods yet. That stump still worries me."

The stump had been a point of much discussion. The amputation had left Reuben his knee, but just barely. Little had been left with which to form a healthy stump. The doctors had wanted to cut the leg above the knee, but Reuben had wanted the knee preserved. Not only would it save him from a painful surgery, but it was just that much more of him. The doctors had pointed out that what was left was only marginally functional.

"If it's marginally functional, it's doable," Reuben had maintained, trying not to sound stubborn.

"If there is any infection or any more loss of tissue," the doctor was saying, "we *will* have to remove the knee. That stump needs to stay clean, and you can't risk getting more infection.

"We've done the best we could with the surgery," the doctor continued, "but this is what I would like to propose. We put a cast on the stump to protect it and put a drainage tube in. Another thing, you've had the maximum amount of morphine that you can have. There's another drug, not as strong, that I can prescribe for a time, but after that you will need to manage on over-the-counter drugs. Hopefully the cast will protect the stump to some extent."

So it was agreed. They put a cast on Reuben's stump, and in the afternoon, Reuben's father arrived to take his son home. A nurse pulled out all of Reuben's IVs and helped him put his shirt on. Eight days after being delivered in an ambulance, Reuben was ushered out in a wheelchair. Mary Ann carried the suitcase.

It had snowed recently, and when Reuben arrived home, the world was whited out. The countryside was fresh and pure; the fields lay quietly under the winter sky, content to have the summer work completed. The bare branches reached out in a friendly way to the home comers.

"Look, sweetie." Reuben turned Mary Ann to look out toward the corn bins. "The blood stains are covered in snow."

The next day was Thanksgiving. Reuben's family brought the Thanksgiving dinner, and neighbors drifted in throughout the day. Mary Ann waited on Reuben, and Reuben rested in a hide-a-bed couch near the kitchen. When she wasn't busy, Mary Ann sat by him, and sometimes they talked. Mostly, they were just thankful. Through the tragedy of what had been and the pain of what now was, there was soft rejoicing. It hurt. There were changes ahead. Something was gone that would always be missing. But the first day home after the terrible event was an occasion of joy.

~~~~~~~~~~~~~~~~~~~~~~~~~~~~~~~~~~~~~~

The winter was challenging. With plans to leave for Faith Mission Home indefinitely postponed, the normal jobs swarmed up around Mary Ann. There were still pigs to feed, and snow fell and piled up and fell and piled up. Reuben could entertain the children, and Mary Ann left them with him while she did the chores. The children were at an age where games could occupy them for hours. Darlene especially loved Memory, and she beat her father consistently. Storybooks and toys cluttered the old sofa, and the children crawled all around him. Sometimes, though, being inside was just too much for Reuben, and he would hobble out to the barnyard on his crutches and hoist himself onto the skid loader to work.

The stump continued to heal. After a month, the cast came off, and Reuben wrapped the stump with an ACE bandage to form it for a prosthesis. Phantom pain haunted him. When it flared up, Reuben tried to hide it, but invariably, its intensity caught him off guard. He would grab his leg, sweat breaking out on his skin.

The time came to be fitted for a prosthesis. During the process, Reuben's stump opened and drained a little. Likely a pebble was still in there. The doctor suggested that he soak it with Dreft detergent. This seemed like an odd remedy, but it worked. Soon the stump healed completely.

There was a particular nerve at the end of the stump that troubled Reuben. It bothered him because he could feel exactly where it was. Time and again he pointed out the spot to Mary Ann. One day when it was paining him again, Mary Ann found Reuben studying the stump of his leg with a razor in his hand.

"Dear!" she cried, alarmed.

Reuben looked up at her energetically. "Look," he explained, "it's right there. I can feel it. I could cut it with this razor, and then it wouldn't give me so much trouble."

Mary Ann did not like the idea. "Oh my, no. That's not a good idea. What if you bled to death?"

This outburst made Reuben laugh, but Mary Ann took the razor from him.

Another new adjustment presented itself. Reuben spent the nights on the cot in the living room as he tossed and turned, unable to sleep because of the pain. One night as he lay there counting the seconds and praying for release from the pain, a sound made him forget it. The front door latch clicked. It must not have been latched quite right, but the lock caught in the door. Reuben stopped breathing. He heard no other sounds, but he longed for his old agility. There was no way he could slip over to the door on crutches without alerting whoever was there. It was awful to lie there helplessly, thinking of his sleeping family under his protection, with him crippled on his cot. They were sitting ducks, vulnerable to whoever or whatever. Reuben couldn't even run.

Reuben heard no more sounds, but the next morning he hobbled out on his crutches to take a look. There were spots of blood on the front doorstep. From what, they were never to know.

As spring approached, Reuben and Mary Ann continued preparing to leave for Virginia, five months later than they had intended. So many people had helped them. When the banker showed them the list of people who had donated money, they were amazed to see that they didn't recognize even half of the names.

When people help, they also feel they have a right to offer their opinions, and as it became clear that Reuben and Mary Ann still intended to go to Faith Mission Home, many people were surprised. Some strongly felt they should not go, suggesting that the Yoders were ignoring God's leading.

"God is trying to stop you. He's saying not to go. How can you go as an amputee?" a good friend shared one night in the Yoders' living room.

Reuben adjusted his coffee cup on his lap. "We feel we are still called to go," he explained. His steady words belied the agitation in his mind, and he stared into the coffee. The clock ticked on into the silence.

Mary Ann turned to her husband, but touching her fingers to her lips and sitting back, she waited.

Reuben was thinking of those dark days after his accident when he had drifted into another world. He put his hand on his knee to brace himself and flung his head back. "By this handicap, God has changed my life and is preparing me to minister to other handicapped people. Before this I was like Jacob. I knew how to arrange to get more goats. I could manage my own life. The night of my accident, I crossed a brook like Jacob. I wrestled with the angel and was lamed, and it changed me forever. I am now lame, but from this brook on, my course is different."

CHAPTER 3

Minnesota Virginia Pakistan Ukraine Afghanistan Israel Haiti Bangladesh

Of Airports and Birthdays, Coffee and Socks

REUBEN SET DOWN HIS CUP of coffee by the newspaper that secretary Lauren had thrown on his desk. The snappishness of fall outside made the buzzing interior of the mission seem cozy. The distant chatter, the racket of breakfast dishes being cleared away, and the speakers announcing phone calls all contributed to the hum of Mission Home life. The wind slammed against the panes of the door, making it creak, and some leaves clattered against the window. *Edwin is probably getting cold,* Reuben guessed, turning to observe the young black man just outside his office, running on the track.

Edwin had been at Faith Mission Home for a number of years, having come there as a small boy. Now he was a young man, and an athletic one at that. Because he often had seizures, it was important to get a good deal of oxygen to his brain, and the staff encouraged his outdoor activities. Most mornings, Edwin ran twenty-one laps on the track just outside Reuben's office. Twenty-one laps equaled a mile, and Edwin could run that mile pretty fast. He could also do double flips on a trampoline.

Two years of managing Rocky Bar Farm at Faith Mission Home had come and gone. There Reuben had supervised as cottage boys learned the vocational skills of planting corn, gathering rocks, baling hay, feeding cattle, and raising feeder pigs. Faith Mission was a residence for the mentally handicapped, and the higher-functioning residents lived in cottages where they learned vocational skills that allowed them to be more independent. Reuben had worked with the young men in his care until life had taken another twist. Reuben had just accepted the position of director at Faith Mission Home. The Home in Virginia had truly become a home to his family, which now numbered seven. Since their move, their fifth child had been born, a little girl they named Celena.

It seemed like much longer than two years since they had made that trip of twelve hundred miles. Reuben had driven a pickup pulling a farm trailer and had managed a clutch with his new wooden leg the whole way to Virginia.

The Yoder family in their younger years.

Reuben looked out the window and took a long drink of coffee, watching the blowing leaves and the gray morning clouds roiling across the hills. Tucked away in the woods across from the main grounds of Faith Mission, the little log house that had become their home awaited Reuben at the end of the day. There, where Mary Ann and the children spent their days, the lights sprang out to greet him at night when he walked in, and in the morning, the jolly lily pond by the walk sent him on his way. Across the winding lanes, the sprawling Home of brown stones rested on the top of a rise, and all around in the dips and hollows were cottages, tucked away.

The Yoders' home in Virginia.

Edwin must have been cold, for he came in from the track without lingering. Reuben knew what he wanted. He picked up the newspaper from his desk. "Here, Lauren." He handed the newspaper to the secretary, minus the sports section. Reuben screened the newspapers and removed the sports section before he turned it over to the staff. It was the board's idea that the staff had better things to do than stand around with their nose buried in articles about the Dallas Cowboys.

Reuben left the sports section on his desk, knowing the ritual. Edwin slapped his cheeks, wandering about the small enclosure of Reuben's office. Then he picked up the sports section, rifled through it, his head swaying from side to side. "Oh, they're good at it . . . they're having a good day, they're winning. They are good. Okay that's good." Closing the paper, he scooted on his way.

Reuben took his seat at his desk and rubbed the stump of his amputation. The swelling had gone down finally. Just the other week he had come striding through the dining room to attend to something. The cleanup crew had left a patch of water on which Reuben had slipped. His leg had snapped off and hurtled off to the side. He had smacked his stump on the floor so hard that he had passed out from the pain. When he had regained consciousness a minute later, he had become vaguely aware of another presence in the room. No one else had been around when he had fallen, and he had wondered who was there now. Opening his eyes, he had looked straight into the anxious faces of Edwin and another resident boy. They were mightily disturbed by something. Not having been aware that Reuben's leg could come off, they had stepped over to have a look at it, returning Reuben's gaze and thinking hard.

"Reuben?" Edwin asked, puzzled. "You okay?"

He had been okay, but the stump had swelled up with blue and purple bruises that took two weeks to heal.

Reuben smiled, sipping his coffee. He liked to watch things happen in their time, in their place. Little rituals pleased him, like watching Edwin run his laps or reading the sports section, drinking coffee, Sunday afternoon naps, pizza on Saturday evenings . . . He set the coffee down. Too much ritual could also be a bad thing. He was getting as bad as the children, all excited about Saturday pizza, and paperwork was waiting for him.

~~~~~~

The Home, nestled under the shadow of the Blue Ridge Mountains, drew in special needs children from all over, including a few foreign countries.

A peaceful place, the therapeutic environment wasn't cluttered with the raucous effects of the American dream. Youth came to serve, investing their lives to provide care, training, and quality of life for the less fortunate. Here structure, discipline, and love found good soil to root in, both in the residents and the staff.

Reuben smiled again, thinking about it. He enjoyed working with young people. He liked watching them find their niche, and was especially interested in the way young people found each other at Faith Mission. "Without decrying the wholesome position of singlehood and the things an unmarried man can accomplish for the Lord," he had told Mary Ann once, "this is a good place for young people to find spouses, and I like to see it happen—though they don't come serve for that reason."

"Unmarried women can accomplish a lot for the Lord too," Mary Ann had reminded him. "Oh, my! A family ties a person down. Sometimes I look at the young girls over at the Home and wonder if they realize . . ."

Once, a young man from Canada arrived to serve a term. When he noticed a girl from New Jersey, he stopped by Reuben's office and asked, "Reuben, what do you think?"

"Well, God called you here, and I wouldn't doubt that God called her here. Maybe this is one of God's ways of bringing people together."

The Canadian was gratified with this view of things.

Reuben watched many couples come together. Happily married himself, he found this to be a real blessing. *People's search for ministry leads them in greater paths of service,* he thought. *If that boy had stayed at home in Canada and spent all his money on a fancy pickup instead of coming to Faith Mission, he never would have met that girl from New Jersey.*

Reuben oversaw the young people as a man sees to a garden, nurturing it, trying not to be rough on the tender plants. Sometimes, however, a bit of firmness was in place. Reuben was intrigued by the letters that came back from the volunteers. One volunteer wrote, "There were things I did not understand, things I wanted ten reasons for, but now I understand. I will never be the same. It's the result of having subjected myself to the influence of someone who I thought was lesser than me . . ."

The residents taught the staff so much. With their humble appreciation for care and universal love and affection, they broke down the reserved emotions and dignity of the workers, showing them the joy and beauty of service.

Ministry changed the minister. Reuben watched as the young people trailed into Faith Mission Home, intending to benefit the residents. Yet often the givers benefited more than those who received. The residents received love and care, of course, but the caregivers received something greater. They learned the secret truths of service, love, patience, and self-lessness, and became better people in the process. They found they couldn't make a difference in the world without first having experienced a difference themselves.

Reuben thought of Terry. Terry was severely limited physically, but he had great mental abilities. He loved matchbox toys and periodicals like the daily newspaper, *The Budget*, the almanac, and encyclopedias. Over and over, he would repeat, "I came to Faith Mission Home on Saturday, April 17, 1971, at 3:50 p.m."

Of the one thousand staff who had come and gone in his time there, Terry knew the day that each one had arrived and the day they had left. He could list his own childcare workers in order. Most incredible of all, upon hearing a person's birthdate, he could tell him which day of the week he had been born.

Who is mentally handicapped anyway? Reuben wondered as he took another sip of coffee.

Reuben thought of how Mary Ann enjoyed relating to the staff. She had her set of nine staff girls to mentor and meet with, and she also liked the way the mission brought company to their home. Often the overflow of visitors from the Home was put up at their house. Reuben liked company, he supposed, though he could get tired of it. He admired his wife who loved people and company, but he occasionally wished she didn't like them quite so much. One summer they had guests at their place every weekend they were home except one. Mary Ann had not stressed about it. She had scorned the housewifely obsession over cooking fancy meals for guests. She had shared whatever they had and then spent her time with her friends.

Reuben frowned and shifted in his chair, looking at the blueprints for the new living room and bedroom for Roselane Cottage. *Concentrate, Reuben,* he told himself. *What was the contractor thinking, putting a window here?*

These cottages were Reuben's special interest. He had conceived the ideas for most of them, and he continued to shepherd their operation. In the Home's beginning, the residents had all been young and new to the program, so the administration had focused on training them in skills like speech, crafts, and basic academics. As the years had passed, a need for something new had developed. Reuben and the board envisioned facilities for vocational training and independent living skills. A cottage at the foot of the hill had become home to resident girls and their staff caretakers who busied themselves with baking, sewing, and continued academics. Similar programs had developed for the boys, teaching them the skills required for woodcrafts, broom winding, grounds maintenance, and care of livestock and laying hens.

Reuben took another sip of his coffee. It was cooling, but Lauren was calling him. He set it aside and got up to see what she wanted. Matt Forbes peeked around the corner just then, startling him.

"Good morning, Matt," Reuben said, grinning down at him. "Nope, nope, no you don't."

Matt was trying to slide under Reuben's arm and into his office. He had smelled the coffee. Matt had a radar for coffee that astounded the staff and befuddled their attempts to hide it. Matt could smell coffee a mile away.

Matt kept coming. "Oh, all right," Reuben relented. He let him in and gave him the coffee.

One day the Cincinnati airport called Faith Mission Home. Reuben was tempted not to answer, supposing it was a telemarketer, not a call from an Ohio airport, but he answered anyway.

"We have a non-verbal resident of yours—Joey Markle is his name—who refused to get on his connecting flight to Charlottesville, Virginia. You'll have to come for this boy. There is only one more Charlottesville flight this afternoon." The airline representative sounded harassed beyond the point of thinking anything was funny. Most likely she wasn't used to having residents of homes for the handicapped hang out at her gate.

Reuben called Joey's father. Joey was apparently making his way back to Virginia at his leisure after a visit home. "Get your credit card and run," Joey's dad said. "We'll settle up later."

Reuben got the credit card and ran accordingly. He passed his children walking home from school. "Tell Mom I've got to go to Cincinnati." He reached the Charlottesville airport at the last minute and would not have made it on the plane if it had not been for his handicapped parking pass. The plane was about to leave, but the attendants put him on.

After they landed in Cincinnati, a minivan scooted over the tarmac to meet them. "Is there a Mr. Yoder on this flight?" The stewardess beckoned Reuben forward, and they whisked him across the tarmac to the terminals. He was surprised at how fast they got him off that plane and into the terminal. He didn't have to wait on anyone or anything.

At the gate, Reuben found Joey and his entourage. Someone had given him a bag of popcorn, which he was eating in great handfuls as he jerked around the airport. Airport personnel tiptoed in his wake. When Joey turned, they froze, and when he ambled on, they crept behind him. Joey was humming to himself, and he paused at a doorway, seeming inclined to enter it. A chubby lady with a distressed look stood directly behind Joey, making a helpless gesture as if to restrain him, but her arms fell back at her side. Joey forgot about the doorway, reached deep into the bag, and then wheeled abruptly. All the personnel jumped, and Joey waved the empty bag at them.

Reuben was disgusted at the scene, and a little alarmed. Joey could be difficult. He had just been home for two weeks, which meant he had been allowed free rein. For the past several hours, strangers had been jumping to his every whim. Now, reveling in the sensation of being able to do exactly what he wanted, Joey would be reluctant to return to the structure of Faith Mission Home. Reuben thought he could manage Joey, but a public airport was not an ideal setting to adjust Joey's ideas.

"Joey," Reuben said, taking the boy by the arm, "how do you like Cincinnati?"

Joey twisted around to see who it was. Not expecting Reuben, he stopped and stared, his mouth working. Joey could not talk, but a moan escaped him, and his lower lip began to protrude. Joey backed away and made for a nearby escalator. Reuben followed him. "Come on, Joey. We need to go home."

Joey eyed him as the escalator carried him up. "C'mon, Joey." Reuben's voice was soft but inexorable as he followed. "C'mon." Joey paused at the top of the escalator, and Reuben joined him, hoping there wouldn't be a scene. Joey stepped back warily, but Reuben did not press him, mindful of the public's eye. The last thing he wanted was to be in the Cincinnati newspaper for violently apprehending a handicapped boy. "C'mon, Joey. Let's go home."

At last he convinced the boy to ride the escalators back down. "It's fun, isn't it, Joey? Do you want something to eat?" An airline representative had pressed a voucher into Reuben's hand before he had followed Joey up the escalator. The two stopped at McDonald's, and Joey began to soften toward his captor. Reuben bought them lunch, and Joey's stalkers met them as they returned with their hamburgers.

One lady was wringing her hands. "Oh, Mr. Yoder, we are so glad you came. We didn't know what to do!" Joey leaned close to her shoulder and mooed up at her. She shuddered visibly and regained her speech with difficulty. "Thank you." It was all she could manage.

The airport personnel took Reuben and his sulky captive to the pilot's lounge to wait for the return flight, saying they would board Reuben and Joey first. This proved a prudent arrangement because, as they made their way onto the plane, Joey protested in every non-verbal way that he could. Reuben was bigger than Joey and had the decided advantage.

"It's okay," Reuben said, holding on to the kicking, bawling Joey and looking over to the stewardess standing by, digging her nails into her palms. "He's going home with me. No options."

Joey's energy had dissipated with the close of his temporary freedom, and his tantrum had begun to wind out. Exhausted, he laid his head on Reuben's lap and fell asleep as the other passengers boarded. He slept for the entire flight, and it was nearly midnight when Reuben got him into his bed at Faith Mission Home.

~~~~~~

"Reubie, Reubie, Reubie." The door cracked slightly, and Debbie peered around it before puttering through.

"Ah, Debbie." Reuben put aside the blueprints. "And what can I do for you?"

Debbie's socks had the heels upside down. Reuben sat her down to take her shoes off and fix the socks. "How are you feeling today, Debbie? Stick your tongue out; there, that's good."

The purple tongue and lips reminded Reuben of the doctor's words. "Debbie, even under the best of circumstances, will have a short life." She was a severe diabetic with a defective heart. She was often away at the hospital, and the Home staff was always glad when she returned to their care.

Reuben loved this child. She was fond of everybody, but she was his own special friend. Debbie's favorite song was "Blessed Assurance," and she didn't mind singing it for other people. Neither did she mind starting her own applause afterward if the audience was tardy.

"There you go, Debbie!" Reuben patted her on the shoulder, and she wandered off to find someone else to chatter to. The smile she tossed him over her shoulder was priceless.

Upside-down socks and coffee, running laps and sports pages, Saturday evening pizza—all these rituals and routines made up life for the residents of Faith Mission Home. Love, grief, encouragement, and discipline followed to train the souls of all, from the residents to the staff to the administration. Reuben felt these things as keenly as anyone, even though his work involved extensive oversight and decisions far beyond coffee and socks. But the little things of the children's world wove their way into all of his responsibilities. Protecting the patterns of the Home was his biggest responsibility to these children.

CHAPTER 4

Minnesota Virginia Pakistan Ukraine Afghanistan Israel Haiti Bangladesh

Of Church and State

ONE EVENING TWO LADIES OUT for a drive through the country-side had stopped in to see Faith Mission Home. They were curious about the establishment. Reuben showed them around the place, and during the tour, the group paused at the dining room where the residents and their childcare workers were eating supper. Hungry after a busy day, the attention of the children was fastened on their food. They had macaroni and cheese that evening—a favorite. The staff leaned over their charges, helping to cut up food and reminding the children of their manners.

When Reuben arrived with the two spectators, the children looked up briefly but soon returned their gaze to the macaroni and cheese. The late evening sun streamed into the room. The two visitors watched in silence, even astonishment, it seemed.

Then one of them turned to Reuben and blurted, "But it's so orderly!"

"Is it?" Reuben looked over at the gaping, shaking, and moaning of some of the residents and their awkward handling of utensils and dishes. There were constant corrections and admonishing from the caretakers, and the harried kitchen staff trotted back and forth with more food. He wondered what had provoked the remark.

"Yes. I mean, I expected to find food spilled on the floor and the children in seizures or up walking around, doing whatever they want. Not this kind of peace."

"I see." Reuben shifted against the doorjamb he was leaning on. "Well, we like to create a peaceful environment through love and structure. The children are well-trained, and they expect the discipline and enjoy the routine."

Surprise visitors were becoming a theme. Reuben rubbed his face after the ladies left and found his way back to the office. Two representatives of the state agency that licensed facilities such as Faith Mission Home had dropped by the day before and had scheduled a meeting two days later. He dreaded the meeting.

In previous years, Faith Mission Home (FMH) had been recognized by the state as a "custodial care facility," meaning that the state was aware of the FMH program without actively regulating it. This recognition also qualified the Home for USDA commodities such as cheese and milk and some occasional funds.

Two years earlier, the issue of licensure had been brought up. "You must become licensed," the state voice had insisted.

The FMH board had been reluctant, not sure what licensure would involve. They were aware that through a license the state would be much more involved in procedures at the Home. Likely, a state presence would complicate their stand on discipline. The Home used physical punishment to train the residents, and historically it had brought about significant improvement in the behavior of handicapped children who previously had been allowed to do whatever they wanted. The FMH program had been built around the freedom to discipline as the administration and staff saw fit. Without that freedom, the Home would not have been able to offer the quality of training and lifestyle that made them stand out among homes for the handicapped.

The leading official of the state department two years earlier had been open-minded and offered them a loophole. He had said, "Well, look at it this way . . . punishment according to the state's definition is 'retributive, retaliatory, and sometimes harsh or abusive reactions to a child's misbehavior that primarily relieves adult frustration without being rationally designed to teach or correct the child's behavior.' In other words, punishment is something you use to get even with a child or make a child pay for his behavior to vent your anger or frustration. You can manage without that, can't you? In fact, what you call discipline or spanking is not even considered corporal punishment by this definition."

"Yes, this is true." The official and his Beachy-Amish counterparts had exchanged grins of complete accord, and the hearts of the bearded men had lightened. The Home had obtained a license, and under that official, everything had worked.

Not everyone at the state bureau saw the clause about discipline the same way that official did, however, and after two years the bridge that had so kindly spanned the fissure between the state and the church was beginning to crumble away. Inspections by the state were sores on the heels of Faith Mission, and Reuben's head ached now, thinking about it. They were walking a delicate balance on a treacherous tight rope, and while Reuben was not alone in facing the issue, sometimes he felt as though the weight of it all rested on him. He was the point around which the waters broke.

The routine inspections by the licensing agency were especially stressful for Reuben. Sometimes it was one representative; at other times it was a team. Sometimes they were from different departments. But they were all antagonistic.

The ladies tapped about in high heels with clipboards, carrying chips on their shoulders and brushing bleached wisps of hair out of their lipstick. The men weren't as classy in their dress, but they, too, carried clipboards. Some had cameras swinging from their necks.

Often the agents did not inspect much. They preferred meetings in the office, glancing over lists of questions which they fired like bullets while barely listening to the answers, needling Reuben, the director, and his brother Nathan, who had taken the role of administrator.

Not all the agents had behaved like professional peacocks, though. One lady, who had been in only yesterday, had been nice. "Mr. Yoder," she had said, "tell me what you hope to see this place accomplish in ten years."

"Ms. Jenkins," Reuben had politely addressed her, "we at Faith Mission have built a home with the goal of a safe, productive environment for these children, and I hope that will continue." Out of the corner of his eye he saw something that he hoped would go away, but it didn't. Matt was coming to share coffee.

"Step this way, Ms. Jenkins," Reuben suggested, motioning toward the dining hall. In that moment Matt peeked over the agent's shoulder and crowed.

"Oh, my!" she gasped, jerking her head around.

"Now, Matt," Reuben said. "Matt . . ." He convinced Matt to move away after giving him a sip of his own coffee.

The inspector looked thoughtful when Reuben had joined her again. "You know, don't you," she remarked, staring into the cup of coffee, "that in a state facility he would never have the freedom to do that to a guest." She had shaken her head as if to clear it of cobwebs. "And coffee. You gave him coffee! Isn't that bad for him?"

"This is a home, Ms. Jenkins," Reuben had replied and then immediately wished he hadn't said it. The state already viewed them as a foster granny, one who lived in a shoe and had so many residents that they didn't know what to do. Bread and milk, sound spankings, and early bedtimes—that was how the state saw their methods.

Reuben pushed his chair back now, trying not to worry about it. He knew the agents with clipboards didn't understand *how* the Home worked, but the agents knew that it *did* work. The state wasn't interested in closing the Mission. He had seen firsthand how awkward the agents were with the residents. They didn't want the responsibility of the handicapped children. They only wanted to stop the spanking.

Only the other day a doctor had found some bruises on one of the girl residents. The staff had taken her into the hospital because of uncontrolled seizures, and the evidence of excessive and unwarranted discipline had played against them. The spanking had been an isolated case. The staff worker had administered an unduly hard spanking that had been unauthorized, but there was no way to prove that this did not happen often. Undeniably, the bruises on the girl had come from a spanking.

The secretary's voice came over a loudspeaker, announcing a phone call for Reuben. The buzz of the cicadas outside thickened in Reuben's head, and suddenly the afternoon sunshine seemed oppressive. He stepped to the phone and lifted the receiver. "Reuben Yoder speaking."

The caller introduced himself as a reporter for the Charlottesville newspaper. "Faith Mission Home has been sued by the Department of Mental Health," the voice continued. "We would like your perspective."

Reuben steadied himself against the door. "I beg your pardon?"

A few moments later he stood, staring bug-eyed at the phone in his hands. Reuben heard nothing around him and did not notice the secretary approaching, her expression anxious. "Someone is here to see you."

There was no time to ask what the person wanted. Right on her heels followed the local sheriff. He entered and placed a court summons in front of him. "Mr. Yoder, this is an official warrant of suit against . . ."

So the doctor reported us to our own licensing agency. Reuben stared at the document. The state had petitioned the fourth circuit of Albemarle County to order all operations of the Mission to cease and to permanently close the Home. Feverishly he read on, his mind skipping about, barely reading the words. "Declare the use of corporal punishment . . . to be in violation of the law . . . poses threat to the health, safety, and welfare of the residents of Faith Mission Home."

The agency wanted to shut Faith Mission Home down on Friday, September 13, 1985, less than a week away. It was to become one of those moments of startling clarity in Reuben's memory, a moment that stood out to him as one of sinking failure.

"Sign this," the sheriff was saying.

An emergency board meeting was called. Parents of the residents came to the meeting and scorned the board's objection to legal involvement. "You may have religious scruples about going to law, but we have an interest here too. Suppose we hire a lawyer. They are our children, and Faith Mission Home is their home," the parents said.

The parents banded together to hire a local lawyer from Charlottesville named John Lowe, and he came for a meeting. Lowe, a big man, strode into the Home like the master lawyer that he was. Reuben, greeting him in the entrance along with Nathan, had just opened his mouth to say something pleasant.

"Look out," Nathan said in a sort of helpless monotone. A crack reverberated through the hallway.

Reuben looked just in time to see Lowe's forehead boomerang off the chandelier. One of the resident girls poked her head out of the kitchen.

When the vibrating had stopped, Lowe cocked his head to observe the low chandelier. "Why didn't they build this place for normal people?" he inquired. Rubbing his forehead, he trudged after Reuben to the office.

In the meeting, they discussed the lawsuit. Amazingly, the battle did not appear to be over the actions of the childcare worker who had spanked the resident, an action that the board admitted was wrong. That staff member had not been subpoenaed. The battle was over spanking itself, which the board said was right.

"It's like a Ford pickup has a wreck," Lowe explained, "and so you shut the Ford company down in case someone else gets hurt in a Ford pickup."

In the following days, the parents of the residents flooded in to overwhelm the board with thoughts and plans and arguments. Oblivious to whatever their previous objections to spanking had been, they were now defending FMH's practices. They liked what the Home had done for their children, many of them having been at their wits' ends trying to find a suitable facility before finding FMH. One of the parents said, "The government has gotten so corrupt these days. Where have the founding values of the country gone? George Washington himself would have been whipped had he not told the truth about cutting down a cherry tree. Now look at the government!"

The board discussed the appropriate actions in responding to the suit. They were going in defense, not in offense. "How can we portray the teachings of Christ in this situation?" the chairman asked in the course of another meeting of the board and parents. The Beachy-Amish men all looked at each other. It was a good question.

Mr. George, one of the most outspoken parents, spoke up. "Are you just going to stand there and let them take our children? How can you think about nonresistance when so much is at stake? Doesn't the Mission do enough good to deserve a little bit of compromise? We have a cause; let's take them on!"

The men paused the whole meeting to explain their position on lawsuits, feeling as though they themselves needed a fresh look at their beliefs.

None of these things changed the reality of the trial being only a few days away. The state was blitzing them, barely giving them time to involve legal counsel. Confused, the FMH side was staggering, trying to regain their foothold.

John Lowe came to visit Faith Mission one day. Professional down to the cufflinks, Lowe hadn't fussed much about himself or the case. Reuben wondered if he really supported their side or if he was embarrassed to represent them. The board had questioned Lowe's intentions too after the first meeting, asking each other if Lowe would work against them. Reuben sat on the other side of the desk from Lowe, and conversation faltered.

A few days later in the middle of a quiet Saturday afternoon at the Home, John Lowe made another abrupt appearance. Reuben, receiving him, noticed a change in the man. His sneakers squeaked on the hardwood floor, and he fiddled with the collar of his turtleneck, running his hands repeatedly through his wild bush of hair.

"Something from my earlier visit just won't go away," Lowe said as the men took their seats in the office. "I don't get it. I need to hear your story again and understand just exactly what is going on here."

Reuben looked him over from the blazing gray gaze to the broad shoulders on which criminal cross-examination sat. "It's a long story," he began, and then Reuben and his brother Nathan used the next several hours to explain their purpose, their faith, and their position on the lawsuit.

Outside, the trees became dim, and the rattle of supper dishes and the hum of a sweeper became background noise. They heard the children coming in from spending the day outside.

John was quiet when they were done. "I see," he said as if speaking into a deep current within himself. "I see." Raising his head, he spoke directly. "When I first read of this case in the papers, I thought it must be brutal of anyone to beat a mentally handicapped child. But I think I didn't understand. You must know that I was not at all anxious to take up this case, but . . ." He spread his fingers and shrugged. "Then I came here and saw your program. I didn't realize that it was possible to manage the handicapped without using physical or chemical restraints which, in my opinion, deprive them of their humanity."

God's found us a man! Reuben thought to himself.

Lowe left the FMH office that day committed to represent the cause of Faith Mission Home and the parents of the residents all the way to the Supreme Court if necessary, and he insisted on no further fees.

The board decided to agree to a consent order, put in place by the court. This was a process ordering an agreement by the Home to cease all forms of physical discipline, specifically spanking, until the time when the court reversed the order. The FMH counsel did not feel that their faith or commitment to discipline had changed but that the consent order was a temporary alternative to being shut down. The consent order went into place.

After the consent order, the state sat back, yawned, and stretched. Their work was over. They had FMH exactly where they wanted it. The Home was still operating, but it could not spank any of the residents.

Faith Mission Home was not happy, though. They tried, but all efforts to reverse the consent order failed. Not wanting to be legally aggressive, their hands were tied, and they did not think they could honor Scriptural practice without physical discipline. Besides, how could they be effective in managing the residents without it? The consent order was a form of oppression, religiously and practically.

At the Home itself, things were going from bad to worse. Jerry, a hyperactive resident, had been given his own room so that he did not destroy the entire Home in one swoop. In the days before he had been admitted to FMH, his parents had kept him in a crib with plywood nailed over the top. The Home had tried to do the same minus the plywood, but after a series of incidents, the plywood ended up on the window of his room. Jerry wasn't a great electrician, but that did not stop him from dissecting the electrical components of an outlet barehanded. Under discipline, he had bettered, and without it, he grew unmanageable again.

"What about Jerry?" a legal official asked one day as they were discussing other placements for the boy. "What will happen to him? How would he survive life at his parents' home?"

"He'll probably go back to his crib with plywood on top and live on behavior drugs," Reuben told her.

"That's terrible!"

Reuben agreed that it was.

Another resident discovered the absence of the once firm hand. She became so impossible that the staff had to admit her to a state institution where she could be drugged into pliability. Some other residents needed to leave the Mission because of uncooperative behavior. Despite efforts to encourage the staff throughout the stress, team spirit and the vision for training grew pale.

In the light of all this, Faith Mission Home decided not to renew their license, which expired in six months.

The state reminded them to renew the license. "Faith Mission must be licensed," they scolded, but the license ran out in the spring of 1986. The refusal to renew forced the state's hand, and the case would go to court.

CHAPTER 5

Minnesota Virginia Pakistan Ukraine Afghanistan Israel Haiti Bangladesh

37.1-188

THE CASE WENT TO COURT on June 29 that summer of 1986. The board, the FMH director and administrator, and the parents, along with the attorneys, met at the Holiday Inn in Charlottesville to prepare their case the night before the beginning of the trial. The meeting lasted late into the evening.

"If you need a place to sleep," Reuben said in an aside to Charles Craze of Gibbs and Craze Law Firm, "you are welcome to stay at the Mission with us." He extended the invitation in an offhand moment of hospitality, not really expecting Craze to take him seriously. Members of Gibbs and Craze slept in five star hotels and resorts, not in mountain missions.

"Oh, I'll come," Craze assured him. "A night in the mountains of Virginia! Who would turn that down?"

Half-delighted, half-alarmed, Reuben called back to the Mission to tell Mary Ann, who gulped and ran to change the sheets. Charles Craze slept in their bed that night.

The next morning the group met at Shoney's for breakfast, prayer, and encouragement. Then they walked to the courthouse together. The courtroom was packed. Mr. George, an involved parent of an FMH resident, pinned corsages on all FMH personnel and supporters who attended the trial. "It must be clear who is on whose side," he said.

As the trial came to order, the state representatives petitioned the judge to make room for their team in the courtroom. "Your Honor, there is not enough space. We are not represented well in the main room."

Judge Tremblay looked up from his conversation with John Lowe, his lip curling. He cocked his glasses at the crowd before directing them at the people representing the state. "This is America. The Mennonites and interested parties were here early and will retain their seats."

The state held a glaring minority.

John Lowe was holding himself back during the opening exercises, and as soon as was permitted, he wheeled to face the judge. "Your Honor, I petition that the parents of Faith Mission's residents be allowed to intervene on behalf of their children."

"Your Honor," the state lawyer, Carewe, objected, "the parents' testimonies are not relevant to the case, and you certainly cannot permit them to take the stand without proper witness review." The state representatives clamored, waving their pens and glasses and papers—anything that came into their grasp. Reuben, in spite of the dread he held on account of the trial, looked on in fascination.

The judge hushed them, pinching his pen between his fingers and rolling it. "Petition granted."

The parents testified, taking the stand one by one with fervent recitation of Faith Mission's virtues. All the state institutions they had looked into, they claimed, were negligent, poorly run affairs that they had never been able to bring themselves to admit their children into. At Faith Mission, they explained, they had found love and order. There, wisdom reigned and peace flowed! The staff was devoted to the residents, and the staff themselves gave a perfect example of healthy relationships. Reuben and Nathan looked at each other and hoped they could live up to the parents' descriptions. The parents were painting a flawless image.

Judge Tremblay narrowed the scope of the trial then, startling both sides, and reduced the arguments to one point. "Is discipline indispensable and effective when used as treatment?"

The parents came out clearly on the question. "Of course it's effective. Didn't it bring Jenny and Nick home to us in manageable form?"

The chime of the voices clashed again and again over one point and then another. The banter got so thick and twisted that Reuben sometimes forgot who was arguing what side. After a while it all began to sound similar, and annoyingly familiar. Reuben and the rest of the attending FMH board and staff went home that night with their heads ringing.

After four days of this clatter and fumbling through a ream of briefs, the court made its first ruling. "Discipline is indispensable and effective when used systematically and therapeutically as treatment." Amendments one and fourteen guaranteed free exercise of religion and the right to treatment.

The court gave the state ninety days to rewrite the codes for physical discipline. "Ninety days," the judge reiterated. During the ninety days, the process of issuing new discipline regulations required a public comment hearing.

After ninety days, the state introduced the regulations, and the Faith Mission board listened in horror as they heard the document read. "A behavior management plan . . . shall not be implemented with any resident until the Local Human Rights Committee has determined . . . recommended by a licensed clinical psychologist . . . physician check the resident within twenty-four hours after . . . program is developed, implemented, and monitored by staff professionally trained in behavior programming." The heavy wording fell on the ears of the board—incomprehensible.

"This is ridiculous," Nathan Yoder said flatly to his brother. Reuben re-read the regulations, but his mind didn't absorb them. He felt the burn of discrimination. He knew that a high school dropout and farmer would not be considered a trained professional. He would not be considered trained enough to know when a spanking should occur. Additional wording from the document rankled. The discipline was not to "involve a greater risk of physical or psychological injury or discomfort to the resident than the behaviors the plan is designed to modify."

Nathan had reread that item out loud twice, and now his eyes crinkled while a light turned on deep inside. "For example," he said, "the painful stimuli used to teach a child not to stick a pencil in his ear must not be greater than the pain he feels with the pencil in his ear."

One of the board members groaned, thinking about it. "If we fill out a request form in the triplicate and submit it to every state office between here and Richmond, we might get a child spanked before Christmas."

The Faith Mission board soon learned that the judge was as annoyed by the state's new version as they were.

"The new code hardly allows for discipline. Not only were Faith Mission's methods proven effective by the witness of the parents, but they were underscored by a history replete with goodwill and good works," Judge Tremblay said.

"Your Honor," a state representative replied, "it all comes down to the question of what is spiritual means or material means. Spanking is hardly a spiritual activity, so therefore it falls out of the religious bracket and under the jurisdiction of bureaucracy."

"How do you even begin to understand what makes up these men's faith without a Beachy-Amish bishop on your staff?" the judge retorted, rolling his pen between his fingertips. "While your thought holds some bullying weight, it's hardly an informed prerogative."

"Is it just me," Reuben asked as they were leaving a board meeting one day not long after the new regulations had been introduced, "or is the judge leaning toward our policies?"

"He might be," one board member admitted, "if only because our policies cause him less of a headache."

The judge handed the state the burden of proof to convince the court that professionalism and state control were the only solutions for the health, safety, and welfare of the children. This trial was to begin on a Monday morning that October.

The day before the trial of the burden of proof started, Reuben spied an interesting newspaper article. In one of the state's facilities for the hand-icapped, a childcare worker poured alcohol over a resident there and lit him on fire, causing second and third degree burns. Reuben took a copy of the article along to show John Lowe the next morning, but when he entered the attorney's office and set his coffee cup on his desk, John Lowe turned before Reuben could say anything. Lowe's eyes were blazing. "I

CHARLOTTESVILLE, VIRGINIA   TUESDAY, July 1, 1986

Progress Photo by Jim Carpenter

Representatives Of Faith Mission Home Take Break Monday From Court Proceedings
From Left To Right Are Owen Yoder, Nathan Yoder, Daniel Yoder And Elden Hochstetler

Cultures Clash As Mennonites Defend Spanking Use In Court

Used by permission of *The Daily Progress.*

have twenty copies!" His arms were loaded with newspapers.

"Twenty copies of what?"

"The article about the burning of the handicapped child."

"Oh, that!" Reuben exclaimed. "It's awful!"

"It is," Lowe agreed, "isn't it?" He smiled, baring his teeth. "It's terrible, but it couldn't have been timed better."

"It's from God," Reuben told him. As much as he hated the thought of such atrocity forwarding their cause, he knew that it would boost their case tremendously. Together, he and Lowe crossed the street to the now familiar courtroom. Judge Tremblay was calling the trial to order. The state's prime witness, standing in the witness box, adjusted his tie.

John Lowe stood. "Your Honor, with your permission, I have a document to present to the court." Tremblay granted the request.

Lowe and the associate lawyers spread the papers around the courtroom. Most of the FMH supporters had not seen the article, and their brows drew in confusion and horror as they read. The faces of the people from the state tightened. People began to talk among themselves, and a murmur rose among them. Everyone looked to the box to see what the judge would make of it. Judge Tremblay's expression was dry as paper, giving nothing away, but his eye glinted like Lowe's.

The state, trying to satisfy the burden of proof that state control and professional training were necessary for legal treatment, stumbled. At one point the judge called for a recess. "I think," Judge Tremblay said with a pitying look to the state witness who was brushing sweat, "we could all do with a break from drama."

After the recess, Lowe introduced the idea of complete exemption from license requirements for Faith Mission, proposing, "Every method the Mission incorporates in training and discipline is by spiritual motivation."

"Behavior modifications by intrusive aversive therapy—" Carewe, the state lawyer, began.

"Just say spanking," Lowe interrupted.

"Behavior modification," Carewe repeated, scowling, "is completely physical. It cannot be spiritual."

"How so, Mr. Carewe?" Judge Tremblay asked.

"Your Honor, any discipline involving touch is physical. As soon as it moves into the realm of the body, it must be physical."

"Your Honor," Lowe said, "I would like to give an illustration."

Tremblay held up his hand to Carewe and looked at Lowe. "Of spanking?"

"No, your Honor. I take the example of Communion." Lowe removed his glasses from his breast pocket with a flourish although he was not reading anything. His hair beamed around his head like the halo of a dandelion, and he bowed his head as though he were thinking. "Communion, your Honor, is a spiritual sacrament."

"Communion?" Tremblay frowned at Lowe.

"A Christian sacrament, your Honor. Perhaps you are familiar with Mass, the breaking of bread and drinking of wine?"

"Ah." The judge sat back and began swiveling the pen in his fingers again.

"There is nothing spiritual about bread and wine, nothing at all. But when these material objects are used in a spiritual exercise, they develop significance . . ." Lowe eyeballed the courtroom. A murmur arose from the state's quarters, but Lowe put up a finger and began to pace. "I would like to take this illustration one step further, your Honor, if you will permit." He wheeled to face the judge. "Do you permit?"

"Proceed."

Reuben heard the flutter of a bird's wings outside as it flew up into the eaves. The court waited.

"Should the priest's hand slip and his finger touch the tongue on which he places the bread, does Communion then become strictly a physical exercise?"

"Sir," Carewe said, looking over his glasses, "you are mixing apples with oranges."

"Apples with oranges; oranges with apples," Lowe fired back. "It's all fruit, sir, and about the same size. Now I ask you, when discipline is administered with goals of spiritual training in mind, is it fair, sir, to assume that the exercise is solely physical?"

Lowe next produced a state statute that said: "Any organization utilizing spiritual means as opposed to drugs and material remedies for the treatment of the handicapped is exempted from the mandates directed by state licensure." He was attempting to use this statute to separate the Mission from other facilities for the handicapped, to ultimately exempt the Mission from state control.

The state team bristled, and Carewe continued: "While it is hardly reasonable to expect that a farmer boy director with a ninth-grade education would choose anything beyond natural methods, herbs, and home remedies, including physical discipline, it would be possible to assume that there are further advanced technologies available today, technologies that have been researched by the best minds our nation has to offer.

Yet here untrained personnel try to offset these scientific advancements. Furthermore, we would like to point out that Faith Mission Home teaches their residents to pray. This is a spiritual activity. It could hardly be otherwise. But Faith Mission also uses drugs and medications. It involves self-care skills and tools for hand-eye coordination and brain development, among other things. These are all material remedies, not spiritual. And to revert back to the earlier question of 'spanking' as you term it, Mr. Yoder, may I ask you to explain what you use to 'spank,' as you say, and how you administer the 'spanking'?"

"Naturally, we use either a hand or a paddle to administer the discipline," Reuben said.

"Aha!" Carewe pounced. "What, I ask you, is a paddle if it's not a piece of material used to remedy a behavioral problem?"

"I, for one, would like to see this paddle," said Judge Tremblay.

"So," Lowe broke in, "the statute needs clarification. You said 'uses drugs and medications.' Mr. Yoder, do you prescribe drugs?"

"No."

"Do you know what drug a child should take? Say Jerry has a bipolar disorder. What drug would you give him to alleviate his symptoms?"

"I don't know, sir."

"So what do you do with drugs, exactly?"

"Every meal, a healthcare supervisor goes about distributing the medications that the various residents require."

"Where do you get those drugs?"

"From the doctor. A healthcare supervisor divvies them out in meal-by-meal doses."

"So you don't use drugs; you administer them," Lowe observed. "Your Honor, I would like to point out that if the Home needs a license to feed a child his doctor-prescribed medications, then you, sir," he spun about to face Carewe, "need a license to give your son or daughter an aspirin."

"This is not a family home, sir!"

"It is a refuge for the handicapped where these children find love and organized care which would be too great a burden for their parents to deliver! These people exemplify the heart of their religion by serving others. Faith Mission Home is a facility that uses physical things like gas, food, medications, or spankings, if you will, to accomplish the spiritual goal of serving the less fortunate and providing a high quality of life for them. As I may point out, Christ Jesus Himself fed five thousand people with material bread, and you can scarcely deny the spirituality of Christ's work on earth. This is a religious matter, sir, and not one for the state to dictate!"

There was not much to be said after that. The case rested. "With a state law in place protecting the freedom of institutions that treat by spiritual means," the judge said in the verdict, "I am citing the statute 37.1-188 to be applied in an unprecedented privilege to grant Faith Mission Home's exemption from state licensure. The court has found these judicial conclusions to be true. Number one: Only compelling state interest can overbalance legitimate claims to the free exercise of religion. Number two: Being licensed does not eliminate the possibility of abuse." The judge pointed his pen at the state legal team. "Number three: The state is declared unqualified to interpret the dictates of the members of Faith Mission Home's faith."

Faith Mission Home had been granted the right to discipline.

Judge Tremblay acknowledged, at the closing exercises of the second trial, that Faith Mission Home was a "religious community which had earned a fine reputation of historic and good works and goodwill using means of discipline with demonstrated benefits to those served."

The state called for an additional hearing to decipher the constitutional issues uncovered in the trial. Two days before Christmas, the case went to trial again to determine if the cited 37.1-188 really did extend to protect application of constitutional right to Anabaptist belief and practice. Immediately an attorney petitioned the court to extend the consent order, which had restricted all discipline at the Home, until the case could be resolved.

The judge barely heard the petition out. "In view of the emergency regulations set forth by the department, I will not extend the consent agreement injunction."

The right to train children in a way that honored the principles of God had been returned to Faith Mission Home. Christmas was just two days away.

The state promptly filed an appeal to the state Supreme Court. The Supreme Court agreed to juggle their trial schedule and hear the case within the month. The higher court upheld the ruling of the circuit court, allowing Faith Mission Home to remain unlicensed under the Virginia code 37.1-188. "There is no evidence of a threat of irreparable harm to the residents, and the health, safety, and welfare of the children is not an issue."

The state immediately re-appealed the case. The Supreme Court agreed to hear a second appeal, but this time the state would wait their turn. The appellate court entertained a backlog of cases that took nearly two years, so it was not until February of 1989 that the case was again heard.

The court was called to order. The prosecutor made a twenty-minute case as to why the findings of the circuit court were wrong, but when John Lowe, still the defense attorney, stood up to make his arguments, he found himself interrupted repeatedly by questions from the bench. Before he was able to make his case, the time was up.

That afternoon, Lowe called Reuben at his office at Faith Mission. His mood had plunged. "Mr. Yoder, we're going to lose. You heard me today. I couldn't get my case together in those twenty minutes. There were too many interruptions. I'm sorry. I've failed you. We're going to lose this final appeal."

Reuben said nothing. There was nothing to say.

Lowe continued, "You need to involve an expert in your training. You need to be ready with a backup plan that the state will recognize and approve. We're going to lose the case. Better get something together, or the state will shut you down as soon as they hear the ruling."

Reuben hesitated. "Mr. Lowe, I thank you for your concern and all you have done in our interest. But I can't do that. I can't say that God needs a backup plan. Look at the victories we've won here! The odds were that we wouldn't make it past the first hearing, but here we are at state level, and God's not finished. If I were to follow your advice, I would be telling God that He had been sufficient up to this point, but just in case He can't handle this one, we'll get a backup plan. Besides, how could we ever come up with a plan that we could follow and that the state would recognize? If that would have been

High Court Upholds Home's Right To Use Spankings

By Jane Dunlap Norris
of The Progress Staff

The Virginia Supreme Court's decision today to uphold a 1986 ruling exempting Albemarle County's Faith Mission Home from state regulations in caring for the disabled is a "David and Goliath"victory, says the lawyer who won the case.

The unanimous decision released today is "the most significant case I've been involved in in 21 years," said John C. Lowe, who represents parents of mentally retarded children at the home run by a Mennonite sect in the northwestern corner of Albemarle.

"This is a wonderful affirmation of the system where people who have no economic or political power can be protected from the overreaching of the government," Lowe said.

Lawyers for the state department of mental health and mental retardation had appealed the 1986 decision by Albemarle Circuit Judge E. Gerald Tremblay, who ruled the home for about 40 mentally retarded children and adults could use spankings as a treatment rather than as a punishment.

State mental health officials have been trying to close the home or change its spanking policy since 1985, when a resident, a mentally retarded woman in her 20s, was severely beaten on the buttocks.

Tremblay ruled that staff members did not violate state law by spanking the residents, saying that the home is exempt from regulation because it tries to "cure by mental or spiritual means without the use of drugs."

(The final ruling)

Used by permission of *The Daily Progress*.

possible, we would never have spent all this time in court."

"Okay," Lowe said, "I just wanted you to know how I feel. Attorneys make recommendations, but clients make the decisions."

Weeks passed. One April day in the middle of a warm, lackadaisical afternoon, the phone rang, and the secretary paged Reuben. "A call on line one for Reuben Yoder—that's a call on line one."

John Lowe's voice boomed through the earpiece when Reuben picked up the phone. "We've won a David and Goliath victory! The ruling from the Supreme Court of Virginia was not only unanimous, but was staged in a non-appealable form. Apparently the Commonwealth of Virginia was looking after its own best interests when they made the case non-appealable. Should this case go to the federal Supreme Court and win, it would change legislation in regards to these kinds of questions forever. With the direction the world of psychology is moving, this would have been devastating to their interests."

Years later after Reuben and Mary Ann had left Faith Mission Home, their daughter met up with David Gibbs of Gibbs and Craze Law Firm at a church in northern Virginia. "The case that your father was involved in with the Home," Gibbs told her, "is one of the most cited cases in the defense of religious freedom in the United States today."

In the aftermath of the lawsuit and in an effort to stay abreast, Reuben attended a comment hearing initiated by the state. Following the meeting, Reuben met the director of licensure as they exited the building. After the exchange of some pleasantries, the director of licensure remarked, "Well, the court told us to leave you alone, so I guess we'll continue to do what we need to do and leave you to continue doing what you need to do."

Reuben grinned and held out his hand. "Thank you. That is correct and good."

They parted ways where the sidewalk formed a T, travelling in opposite directions with opposite values and serving opposite kingdoms.

CHAPTER 6

Minnesota Virginia Pakistan Ukraine Afghanistan Israel Haiti Bangladesh

Beyond the Verdict

"YODER," GIBBS WAS SAYING, "THE world needs to hear about Faith Mission Home's legal battle."

The Christian Law Association was holding a seminar at a church in Fairfax, Virginia, that evening, and several attorneys had gathered before lunch to discuss the program. Reuben had been invited.

Soon after Reuben had arrived, David Gibbs Jr., a big man who liked to eat, had said, "Yoder, run down to McDonald's and get us some supper." Reuben had just returned with sacks of hamburgers to feed the attorneys and was settling in to eat his sandwich when Gibbs addressed him.

Reuben adjusted the wrapper on his burger. "What do you have in mind, Gibbs?"

"I want to propose—" The great attorney stopped. Reuben glanced up from the pickle in his burger to Gibbs' face. Gibbs' face, round and full with a large, laughing mouth, was perplexed. Raising the tablecloth, he looked under the table. Gibbs dropped his sandwich and shoved his chair back, catching the cloth and skewing everything.

"What?" One of the other attorneys snatched at a soda. Someone else complained, "Gibbs!"

Gibbs looked under the table again. Straightening, he swallowed. "In the name of all decency," he said to Reuben, "could you explain what that *thing* is? That *thing* I just kicked?"

"What thing?" an attorney asked.

"Under there," Gibbs said, pointing. The lawyers all shouted with laughter, and Reuben laid down his sandwich and laughed with them.

"It's my prosthesis," Reuben said. "I take it off when I sit down because my stump gets sore."

"Prosthesis!" Gibbs peeked under the table again. "Is that what that is? I would have never guessed—" He picked up his sandwich and resumed eating.

"Back to your original comment," Reuben said. "What did you have in mind?"

First Gibbs wanted to hear the story of Reuben's accident. He shook his head after hearing Reuben's brief account. "That's incredible, Mr. Yoder. God is using you, a handicapped man, as an advocate for the mentally handicapped. And that's what I was about to propose.

"I want to take the residents of FMH to Pastor's School in Hammond, Indiana, to create awareness of the Home's work and to share about the victory wrought by God in the legal battle with the Commonwealth of Virginia. The news needs to get out," Gibbs explained. "Oh, I know it was in the papers and *The Budget,* and the whole Mennonite world has breathlessly followed every event, but the world needs a face to put to the story. The children themselves could reach into hearts in a way that the newspaper or even a verbal report never will. And, most important, the Christian world needs to realize that God works in the legal realm as well."

Reuben was still thinking about Gibbs' remark about God using him. He slowly stirred his drink with his straw. "Isn't it amazing that God uses us untrained professionals—me, a backwoods farmer and amputee, and handicapped children to change a legal system? How did that happen? We have nothing to do with the law—know nothing about it. None of us ever dreamed of trying to change a law."

"Exactly," Gibbs said. "An amateur built the ark that survived the Flood, but an expert built the Titanic that sank crossing the Atlantic."

So it was to be. Several months later, the FMH staff was stowing residents and residents' belongings into two coaches. The coaches had arrived from Florida, hired by the CLA, to take the handicapped children to Hammond,

Indiana. As the buses had pulled up to the front door, it began to snow, and Edwin, FMH's self-appointed welcoming committee, had raced out. "Good to have you with us; nice to have you here."

Startled, the bus drivers stared down at Edwin, and from that moment, they were leery. No one had told them they were driving fifty mentally handicapped children, a fair definition of a madhouse, to Indiana. They looked at each other and cleared their throats, but the staff was already moving the mountain of luggage. The drivers climbed into their seats morosely, shaking their heads. As the trip passed, however, the drivers began to relax and proved helpful.

For the meals, the drivers called ahead to McDonald's and ordered all the food to be divided into boxes marked Bus A and Bus B. Late that night the two coaches arrived at a hotel in Indiana, and the staff members bedded their charges down and gathered in the lounge to revive themselves, beat by the strain of the trip.

In the morning, they were all up and ready on time. The Christian Law associates took the residents out for lunch and then ushered them into a Child's World toy store to buy each child a gift. The day grew topsy-turvy for the children in whom routine was deeply ingrained. In the afternoon they missed their naps, and to crown it all, they didn't have supper, as the program was to begin right over the supper hour. The loss of supper added injury to insult, and the children stared sadly out of the bus windows at the dreary rain of the early evening as they arrived at the huge church. All the staff could imagine was worst-case scenarios. On stage, tired and hungry handicapped children might refuse to cooperate, break down crying, or throw fits.

Their turn in the program came, a twenty-minute slot, and as the children entered, clapping began. All along the line, the children perked up and tensed, wondering what was happening. On and on the clapping rolled, and the crowd stood. Seven thousand five hundred pastors clapped and cheered. Shrinking back, the children appeared so startled that the staff members held their breath and reached out to offer comforting pats on their backs. As the residents mounted the stage, however, they pulled themselves together and did well. Still, the staff was worried about Susie. Susie was to sing her favorite round, but Susie was temperamental. Sometimes she would sing on request; sometimes she wouldn't. Only Susie knew when those times would be.

Susie sang perfectly in her sweet little voice. "God loves you, God loves me, God loves Susie . . ." The crowd went wild, whistling and stamping, and so the program at the pastors' seminar continued, a tremendous success.

~~~~~~

It was the kind of evening when the dark, damp air of winter pressed in and made a person think it might snow before morning. Already the blue shadows were embracing the barren landscape, and as Reuben closed the door of his van in the K-Mart parking lot, he was in a hurry. At home, Mary Ann, the children, and a hot supper waited. A little bit of business here, and he would be on his way. His two-way beeped as a man's voice garbled over the radio. "Resident missing! Come home as soon as possible."

Chills spread up Reuben's neck, and he shivered. *Out in this darkness and cold? Who?* Throwing his shopping list on the center console again, he restarted his van. *Where did she go?*

By the time he had navigated the curving roads between Charlottesville and the Home, he'd had ample time to worry. *Surely the staff has found the resident by now,* he thought, spitting gravel as he turned into the driveway.

One of the staff boys, Caleb, ran up the lane. Reuben slowed, and Caleb jumped in. "Still haven't found her."

"Who is it?" Reuben asked.

"Norma." Norma was young, about eighteen.

The staff was regrouping in front of the main building. They had made a small search, and now they gathered for a briefing. Norma had locked herself into a bathroom at the Roselane Cottage. Without a coat, she had climbed through a window and escaped into the woods. Reuben's heart sank.

Several of the higher-functioning girls had been having problems. Sylvia had been bucking the rules again and again, and then there was Lucy.

Lucy and Norma were great friends. Lucy, a mentally handicapped Amish girl, had been sent to FMH to break her off from a mentally handicapped boyfriend whom she insisted on seeing.

After Lucy had sneaked letters to her boyfriend through the mail, Lucy's family had asked FMH to keep an eye on her communications. Dismayed when she had realized her letters weren't making it to her boyfriend, she had told Norma about it. Norma was bright, and she had explained to Lucy that tampering with her mail was an infringement of her rights.

The girls had made a plan to run away by riding a little mustang pony that Lucy's father had sent her for a pet. Norma and Lucy typed a letter to the boyfriend to meet them at some exit off of a highway in Ohio. It was a wildly impossible plan, but when the two girls had been caught writing the letter, Norma had been infuriated. She made plans to escape.

Reuben asked if anyone had talked to Lucy. They had, but Lucy had declared that she knew nothing about Norma's plans. Reuben looked around at the looming mountain and felt the brisk air whooshing down the mountainside. It was cold. The porch lamps beamed against the winter night. It was dark.

Reuben made up his mind. "Norma is not brave enough to hide in the woods after dark. She didn't take a coat, so she'll try to find a warm place to go. Look, half of you go north on the road, and the other half take the road south and check every neighboring house within several miles. I'll call the police to help search, and then I'll stay at the office to coordinate."

Within forty minutes, Reuben's predictions had proved true. "You'd better come," Caleb's voice came over the phone.

Norma had slipped through the woods to a neighboring farm. Reuben groaned when he heard where she was. Mr. Lange was a relic of the decades gone by. Greene County had been such a remote county of Virginia that, in the old times, European countries had exported criminals there to free up their prisons. The descendants of those criminals had made up the wild clans of that region, and up until the mid-1900s, the people of Greene County had been inclined to settle disputes in the cornfield, flaming their passions with moonshine. Neighbors did not walk directly up to a house without announcing their arrival. Most of the community kept shotguns above the doors.

When the Mennonite missionaries had arrived in the community, the hollow had been full of family feuds. Lange had grown up in the thick of it, and he did not like Faith Mission Home. It brought too much bustle into the quiet hollow. FMH had a truck patch within view of Lange's house, where he lived with his handicapped sister. Lange had been difficult, calling the law out over a port-a-john set up by the patch and refusing to allow them to put birds out to eat bugs. He had said a feather might land in his yard.

Glad to know that Norma was at least safe and warm, Reuben drove to the farmhouse to join the search party. He found the staff standing about in the living room with awkward looks on their faces. Mr. Lange fidgeted as Reuben entered. "Is Norma here?" Reuben asked.

"She is."

"Norma is here," Caleb explained, "but she doesn't want to see us."

The farmer shifted in his chair. "Norma won't be speaking with you, Mistah Yoder. Social Services has been contacted, and we're standing with them to protect the rights of this girl."

Blackly, Reuben leaned back, shifting in his prosthesis. In the wink of an eye, he saw all their hard-won privileges swirling down a dark hole. He threw his head back. "I understand what you're saying, but I need to speak with Norma."

Norma had been in the kitchen, apparently, listening to the conversation, and now she entered the room with a flounce, tossing her braids and shaking her finger at Reuben. "You deserve to go to jail, and I am going to see that you get there."

Reuben answered softly. "That may be—"

Ring! Ring! Ring! The telephone rang just then. Mr. Lange handed it to Reuben. The lead investigator for the Social Services was calling, and he was not happy.

When the investigator had said everything he wanted to, Reuben asked, "Do you have time for a few questions?"

"I suppose." The investigator was sulky, hardly professional.

"Did you know that you accepted as fact a report from a mentally hand-icapped individual?"

"No."

"Were you aware that Norma is at Faith Mission by legal orders, and there will be no outside involvement without the consent of her parents?"

It was quiet on the other end.

"Were you?"

"No, I wasn't." The words were reluctant.

"Furthermore, if you were to come and take her for the night, are you prepared to sleep in the same room with her since she isn't able to care for herself?"

"Oh, we wouldn't take her for the night." This wasn't what the man had said two minutes earlier, but the investigator was beginning to sound as though he would like to lock himself in a bathroom and jump through the window too.

"But you promised Norma, didn't you?"

The animosity evaporated completely. "No, no, indeed. We simply want to make you understand that we've been notified. We'll contact you in the morning for an on-site investigation of the allegations. She will not be spending the night with us under any circumstances."

Reuben relented. He had wanted to tree the investigator, but he controlled himself. "Have a good night then," he told the caller coolly. "We'll see you in the morning." He was weary of the old story: bureaucracy wanting to dictate care but never wanting to touch handicapped people themselves. He turned to Norma. "I'm going to talk to your parents." She scowled, but Reuben ignored her.

He phoned Norma's parents, and they told Norma she must return to the Home for the night. To Reuben they said, "We'll be by in the morning."

Reuben could see Norma trying to build her attitude. Maybe the dark had worn her down, maybe she didn't like Mr. Lange, or maybe she was just hungry, but at any rate, Norma gave in. "All right." Her shoulders slumped.

Silently, they all took their leave of Lange's house and crawled into their vehicles. At the Home, Norma asked to sleep by herself and was allowed to do so. She slept on the floor with her head against the door all night.

Early the next morning, after extensive communication with Reuben, Norma's parents walked into the icing room at the bakery where Norma was working. "Pack up, Norma. We're leaving." Norma was surprised, but did not argue.

"We're so sorry about this," Norma's mother told Reuben.

"Yes," her dad agreed, "we'll do our best to fix the situation. We appreciate what you have done for Norma, and we'll stand behind you all the way." By seven-thirty that morning, Norma had ridden off to another state with her family. She had left Faith Mission for good.

Soon after Norma's departure, the Social Services phoned. "We want to know what time would suit for investigation."

"I have a meeting," Reuben stalled. "Can you call back at noon to discuss this?"

"I'm sorry," the investigator said, "we promised to investigate Norma's claims immediately."

"I doubt Norma will mind." Reuben winced, thinking of the coming storm. "She's not here."

"Not there!"

"Her parents removed her from the Home this morning for an indefinite time."

"Oh, I see." The social worker's tone was acid. "Do you think that was within your prerogative? Hardly, Mr. Yoder. You will not be viewed as cooperating with the department, of course."

"It was not my choice." Reuben tucked the phone between his shoulder and his ear, beginning to pace. "Norma's parents chose to take her. May I remind you that Norma is here by legal order, and without her parents' involvement, you will not be allowed to investigate."

"Norma is not the extent of this," the worker snapped. "Norma spoke to us about other residents whose rights are being violated. We will be following up on all of these complaints."

Sylvia, Reuben thought. He had hoped that Norma had confined herself to her own complaints. Norma had been at FMH long enough to know that everyone was loved and cared for, and that everyone was disciplined if they fought the rules. "I suppose you're referring to Sylvia . . . you won't be able to speak with her, of course," Reuben said. "She's non-verbal. I suppose you knew that. And before you come, I will have to arrange a time with my attorney so he can be here also."

The circling between Social Services and Reuben began. The caseworker wanted to see Sylvia badly, but Reuben would not agree to an investigation without a lawyer present. The caseworker called FMH's lawyer, Mr. Puryear, otherwise known as Bow. Mr. Puryear did not cooperate very well with the caseworker, and eventually the worker backed off.

In the meantime Sylvia became a problem, refusing to do as she was told and throwing tantrums. Everyone was scared to spank her. Any type of discipline showed on Sylvia's fair skin, and the board had instructed the staff to avoid discipline if at all possible, worried about where an investigation would lead. Some time passed, and Reuben did not hear from the Social Services. Finally Sylvia's house parents approached Reuben. Sylvia had become impossible to manage.

"In the fear of God," Reuben said slowly, "discipline Sylvia."

The very day after the spanking, the social worker called again. She wanted to schedule an investigation for that day. Reuben and the rest of the staff were sick at the thought. Reuben called Mr. Puryear. "What should we do?"

"I'm leaving town," Puryear said. "Really."

Reuben also had to go someplace on business, so he called the worker back. "It doesn't suit."

The social worker was unhappy, but she had left the investigation alone so long herself that she couldn't argue. A week later when Reuben returned from his business trip, he called and told the worker that she could come, but the social worker said she was leaving to visit her grandmother. Several weeks passed before the meeting occurred.

The morning of the investigation, Mr. Puryear arrived ahead of schedule. Reuben and Mr. Puryear retired to the office, talking in quiet voices.

"You know, Bow, Jesus told His disciples that they would be brought before authorities to testify for their actions, and He said it was a divinely given opportunity to testify of God and demonstrate kingdom values."

Mr. Puryear nodded. "You're right, Mr. Yoder."

Reuben tugged the newspaper over to have a look at it, trying to distract himself from the pressure. "Bow! Look at this." Leaning close, the two men read the article together.

Just as Mr. Puryear sat back and whistled, a tap on the door interrupted them.

Reuben sighed. "Well, here we go."

The Home's lack of filed documentation always brought them under fire, and that morning was no different. The lack of a paper trail raised the investigator's ire.

"Document, document!" the lead representative stormed. "Always document."

Legally, they were not required to document procedure, and Reuben pointed this out.

The woman grew cold and rigid. "But we *will* see the object you use for discipline."

"In three and a half years of trial, the court never asked to see that. It's a simple, light paddle, and these things are not available for public evaluation."

The caseworkers dropped the issue of viewing the paddle, but the woman, the lead investigator, took Sylvia into a private room for an examination.

Reuben took the newspaper from his desk and handed it to the other caseworker. "You're here because you're concerned about a mark on Sylvia from a simple spanking. Suppose you see how the state handles their residents." He pointed to the article he and Mr. Puryear had been reading. "In this article, professionals at a state facility tied a girl to a bed with a four-point restraint and a strap over her chest until she died from struggling against the restraints."

While the other caseworker was looking at the article, the lead investigator returned. Reuben turned to show her the article. "You've examined Sylvia now. She's clean, happy, enjoys life, and loves the people who discipline her.

Compare that with this. Could we agree that methods prescribed by God, the sovereign Creator of all things, are a suitable alternative?"

~~~~~~

Sanford Yoder, the founder of Faith Mission Home, came back to visit the Home one day after the crisis over Sylvia had melted away. Social Services had dropped the allegations and had not been back since. Reuben and Sanford roamed the premises together, looking over the cottages and ruminating over the past and future.

Reuben glanced at Sanford as they strolled up the hill after an investigation of the Roselane Cottage bakery. "What do you think? We've seen a lot of growth and program development here. Do you think FMH has reached the plateau it's going to operate on? Is this pretty much the way things are going to be here?"

Sanford rubbed his head with the heel of his palm and considered. "You know what? I doubt it. I've watched God work long enough to learn that God never leaves live things in the same place. He grows and prunes and waters. Things move forward, deepen, project, branch off, and break up. New things come, old things go. Our God is a mover and a shaker. I don't think Faith Mission has reached a plateau. There's got to be more."

~~~~~~

"Reuben, come!" One of the staff members called him from his office to see Debbie, newly returned to FMH from the university hospital following a bout with pneumonia.

Debbie was reuniting with the Home family in the reception room, delighted to be home again. She reached up to pat their cheeks one after another, but when Reuben came, she had eyes only for him. "Reubie," she said, and tucked her hand into his.

Her breath came hard, Reuben noticed. "Take her to her room," he ordered, sudden fear gripping his heart. They carried her into the girls' dorm, and everyone gathered around. Debbie sat on the edge of her little bed, smiling. She didn't seem inclined to talk, only smiled at them all, and then again at Reuben. Then she collapsed backward onto the bed. With a collective cry, the staff rushed forward. But Reuben stepped into the crush, holding his ground. Gradually they pulled back to give him room. Reuben bent over Debbie, his lean body trembling all over. She was gasping, her face a dreadful gray color.

"Debbie!" Reuben called. One of the staff girls moved in closer to take her hands. "Debbie?"

Debbie took one breath, smiled, and closed her eyes.

"She's gone," one of the girls choked. Someone rushed off to call a doctor.

Reuben called her name again. "Debbie!" Debbie did not answer.

Tears swarmed in Reuben's eyes. Debbie was his little friend. A sense of loss slammed into his chest, even as he knew the doctor would be of no use. Debbie was gone. What had originally been projected as a short-term stay at Faith Mission Home for Debbie had become a life of nearly thirty years. Her home had been Faith Mission, and now she truly was at another home—a home that she would never have to leave for the hospital.

CHAPTER 7

Withhold Not
Your Hand

THE BUDDING TREES OF SPRING drooped as the wind scattered a sudden shower of startled raindrops over the mountain. Mary Ann put her hand up to ward off the raindrops, but they blew on and did not disturb her again. The afternoon turned cold, and she propped her elbows on the fence like a little tomboy. The season as old as the years of the earth was about to bring forth new life, a pattern, a cycle that moved on after the pause of winter. Every year, a new harvest strove to come forth in the soil worn away and aged, farmed for years.

Mary Ann looked at her tall husband as he approached, taking each step as it came. His gaze was on the mountains around them. She knew that he grew restless each spring for about a week until the bees began to buzz and the sun grew warm with the hum of summer. This was the week between winter and summer that made Reuben's eyes search the skyline and trace the clouds. Reuben leaned against the fence post and looked at his wife. They had grown older. The years had fled like a deer on the run.

"How long have we been here?" he asked.

"You just came," she replied.

"No, here," he said, "at Faith Mission."

Mary Ann counted on fingers and pursed her lips. "Twenty-five years."

"Ah," Reuben said, "ah."

"Is it the old question?" she wanted to know.

"Yes," said Reuben. "Is there more?"

"There's got to be more." Mary Ann was stubborn on this point. They were silent as the clouds rolled overhead. "Do you think our children regret it?" Mary Ann asked him. "Growing up here, I mean. It's all they've known. Celena was born here, and she got married from this house."

"You think they would have preferred growing up on a farm?"

"That's reportedly the best place to raise a family," Mary Ann said.

"Why did we decide to come here anyway?" Reuben responded.

"We decided that there had to be more to life," Mary Ann reminded him.

Reuben looked up at the mountains again. Between the bare trees, they could faintly see Faith Mission Home. "He that observeth the wind shall not sow; and he that regardeth the clouds shall not reap. As thou knowest not what is the way of the spirit, nor how the bones do grow in the womb of her that is with child: even so thou knowest not the works of God who maketh all. In the morning sow thy seed, and in the evening withhold not thine hand . . ." He quoted the verse almost under his breath.

Mary Ann blinked. "You've got that down pat."

"It's Ecclesiastes," he told her. They sat on the high ground where it was not damp. "I've been thinking on it. Faith Mission was different when we first came here. Sanford Yoder started this place with a vision, but that vision wasn't complete. He didn't know what it would look like in the end. If he had set out to build a place like what it is now, he would never have gotten it accomplished. He started with what he had, a vision given by the Lord, and worked with the vision of others. See, the wind blew and the clouds came, but he sowed anyway, not knowing how the Spirit would move. It's just like the bones of a baby, Mary Ann. See, Faith Mission grew and grew. It had a heart, and branched out, limb by limb. It got a face, the lungs opened up, and it began breathing. It was a child, and now we're seeing what kind of adult it can be."

She shifted to look at him. "So, are you questioning why we came here?"

"No, I do not doubt how the Lord worked. I'm just wondering at it all. That's the way ministry is. You start out with an opportunity and a vision, and you have no idea how God will develop it. Pretty soon it gets a lot bigger than we are. I'm just wondering. Is there more? I used to ask, 'Is there more to life?' Now I ask, 'Is there more to do?' That's what I want to know."

"There's always more," Mary Ann said promptly.

"Do you know that, or are you just saying it? We're leaving Faith Mission, Mary Ann. We've already resigned. We agreed that it's time for some new blood around here. Celena is married; all the children are gone. What's next? A little cabin somewhere with books and grandchildren?"

"Grandchildren!" Mary Ann's eyes lit up, but she bit her lip.

"Now's the time, dear. Now is the time. If we want to serve anywhere else, we need to do it now. We won't be around forever." Reuben had watched his generation of men, boys he had grown up with. Over and over he had seen it. Men got to fifty and started to question their lives. He'd been there. He personally knew the feeling of panic. *My life is gone! But I never got to do this! And this! And this!*

"Men get to our age," he said aloud, "and they make silly decisions."

Mary Ann looked at him.

"How many couples our age do you know," he asked, "who just made some impossible investment and tied themselves down to debt for the rest of their working years? The world needs older couples who can sell out for the Lord."

"There's retirement to think about," Mary Ann reminded him. "Not everyone is financially stable."

"If they're not financially stable at fifty, they'll never be." Reuben was impatient. "You know, honey, there are ways to save money, even in volunteer service."

Reuben was riding his hobbyhorse. "There are too many people who have strapped themselves down financially so that nothing is ever an option. If only someone would teach teenagers how to make financial decisions that would free them up to be able to minister to others.

"The teenager could buy a brand new truck, or he could come to Faith Mission or teach school or go overseas. If he buys the new truck, he won't be as likely to do any of those other things. Neither will he meet that girl in service who has a vision for ministry. He'll marry the cute girl next door who likes new trucks too, and he'll raise children who want to buy new trucks when they're big.

"Then again, it doesn't completely rest on what we do or whom we marry. We can serve anywhere! We don't have to go to China, or even FMH. We could stay home and marry the neighbor girl and be totally involved in ministry in our own community. It's the focus!"

"Just think how much you could have done if you had stayed single. Maybe you should have stayed single so you could serve better." Mary Ann was provoking him.

Reuben grinned at her. Then he returned to his speech. "Noah was one of the first missionaries. He decided to save his family *and* build the ark. While he built the ark to save his family, he had a hundred years to tell others about God and offer them a chance at salvation."

"Do you think our children ever wished we had raised them in a different setting? Did they get tired of having you gone, away at meetings?" Mary Ann was sober.

"If they didn't, it was because you were behind me every time," Reuben said, taking her hand. "You made it easier for me to leave by always saying, 'Go, we'll be okay.' We did make plenty of mistakes, to be sure, but we tried hard and God helped us through."

The couple was silent, thinking. Finally Reuben said, "We've got to keep ministry on our desktop. If we don't, we'll forget it."

"We made mistakes," Mary Ann said, still thinking about the children. "But I think the children have done pretty well. They have all spent time in service or teaching school somewhere. And now Darrell is flying to Pakistan any day. I don't know, Reuben. I'm a bit anxious about him flying way over there."

Reuben smiled and patted her leg. "Now dear, it will be okay."

Mary Ann said nothing more. A major earthquake and huge landslides had struck Pakistan, and Darrell was leaving in a few days to work with a crew on a rebuilding project.

Summer came, but Reuben did not forget his restlessness. He lay awake many nights, praying, and Mary Ann would awaken sometimes too, knowing he was awake. She would put her hand in his, and together they would pray.

"You won't leave the Home," people had scoffed. "You'll run it from across the road."

"No, I won't," Reuben had replied, grinning. He was finished at Faith Mission.

"How will you help it?" they had wondered.

Indeed it did seem that something drastic was needed to break Reuben and Mary Ann away from the Home. They needed to jump off the end of the dock, so to speak.

In Pakistan, the first three months of Darrell's project were over, and the house parents for the project were leaving. Beacon of Light (BOL), the organization Darrell was working with, called Reuben and Mary Ann. "Would you consider being house parents in Pakistan?" they wondered.

Reuben and Mary Ann prayed about this responsibility, considering the options. Reuben's parents were getting older, and he didn't want to be negligent in caring for them. Yet he had plenty of brothers and sisters who would be able to help fill this role. As they prayed, Reuben and Mary Ann felt there was nothing to hold them back from going wherever the Lord was calling, even Pakistan.

They agreed to go to Pakistan for a few months. This was a radical change for them—they had never lived in a Third World country before. But the God who had led them this far would surely continue by their side.

Minnesota   Virginia   Pakistan   Ukraine   Afghanistan   Israel   Haiti   Bangladesh

What Are We Getting Into?

THE EARLY SUNSHINE IN THE streets of Abbottabad brought Reuben and Mary Ann out of the haze of their long trip from America to Pakistan. The night before, they had negotiated a maze from the airport in Islamabad, the capital city, to a guesthouse in Abbottabad. Reuben only barely remembered Mary Ann saying, "Dear . . ." before they had dropped away into an exhausted slumber. It had been morning before either of them had stirred enough for her to finish the thought. ". . . this is the beginning of something new for us."

Reuben supposed Mary Ann had been right about it being new, now gazing at the contraption that had stopped in front of them. It was filled with people waving at them to join—and one bad-tempered goat. There didn't appear to be any room, but the people insisted, and so up onto the conveyance they climbed. Reuben, reflecting that space was relative, tucked his feet under the goat, which opened its gray lips and moaned. He had never heard a goat moan before.

Reuben looked around him. The folks inside the motorized cart were also eyeing them, smiling with satisfaction at their ability to stuff extra people into the cracks. The women were all wrapped up just as he had been told they would be. The men wore something like a dress or a gown. Fascinated, Reuben wondered how they worked in such outfits. Mary Ann was tucked under his elbow on one side, primly observing their surroundings and working up courage to talk to the woman across from her. They were going to the bazaar now to shop and look around, and the brilliance of the morning enhanced the taste of adventure in the air.

Reuben peeked out over the shoulders of the other passengers to see the passing city. The streets whirred with traffic and pedestrians. Beyond the city, on the dull ridges around Abbottabad, gnarled trees waved in the wind, and white houses, strewn throughout the valley, baked in the sun.

Reuben and Mary Ann shopped, and the day waned. With it, the energy of the morning faded. Jet lag was an incomprehensible thing, worse than just missed sleep. Dizzy by early afternoon, Reuben and Mary Ann climbed into one of the taxi jeeps that would carry them up the mountain to the village of Galoosh, where BOL's project was underway. Darrell, who had come to meet them, was calm about it all—comfortable in fact—suggesting that if the landslides on the road weren't too bad, they should be there by nightfall.

The scenery along the way was stunning. Blue mountains were misted with green trees which staggered out along the upper slopes. In the distance, snow caps were visible, pulling their eyes away from the destruction of the earthquake that surrounded them. At first it didn't seem possible that such a tragedy had taken place here, but the farther they went, the more depressingly obvious the disaster became. The beauty of the surrounding country began to glare, sinister and menacing. In places, the road was cracked, and at one spot, the entire road had moved at angles to itself, about ten feet apart. The jagged ends appeared like a badly-fractured bone.

Farther into the mountains they encountered more and more landslides, many blocking the road. Apparently this was such a common problem that it had ceased to be a problem. The jeep would halt in front of a landslide, and the group would clamber over it and hire another jeep.

The ruin was seen in the splintered homes and the makeshift shelters along the road. It was also seen in the faces of the people. Hopelessness weighed in the eyes of the women, and desperation haunted the set of men's jaws. Only the goats seemed free of any concern. They leaped and frisked along the mountain paths, guided absently back into line by their shepherd.

It began to rain, slowly at first, and then harder as the jeeps wound deeper into the mountains where roads cut into their sides. Darrell said three of the main bridges on the road to Galoosh were out. Besides the earthquakes and the landslides, a once-in-a-hundred-year flood had come, and the waters had accomplished whatever damage the preceding disasters had not. Bulldozers worked above them now, carving out a route, and far below the narrow ledge where the road climbed, a yawning ravine beckoned to ridiculously impossible depths. Reuben leaned over to look and sat back, not wanting to alarm Mary Ann, but the distance to solid earth drew his gaze back, engrossing him. Mary Ann clutched his arm.

"If you go down, I am going with you." Mary Ann was gallant. The jeep fishtailed in the mud right then. It spun before the wheels caught, and the vehicle leaped forward.

It was dark by the time the last jeep halted. They had gotten completely stuck at least once, needing to be pushed out, and partially stuck more often than could be remembered. They stiffly crept out of their taxi in the damp, cool drizzle.

Mary Ann saw it first. "The camp's over there."

Through the darkness, they could make out something of a valley between them and the camp, and Darrell soon clarified what it was by saying, "The villagers will help carry the luggage across the river. Be careful on that plank, Dad, going across the ravine."

People were indeed surrounding them, and they whisked the suitcases away, trundling them across the ravine and over the river which Mary Ann and Reuben both heard, but couldn't see. Then as their flashlights marked out the plank across the river, they could see it boiling angrily below. There was nothing to do but cross the plank, and so they did. Reuben took his time stepping across, balancing with his wooden leg. Mary Ann followed with Darrell just behind, and they climbed through the village, terrace by terrace, until they reached the tents of the base camp. Ushered into the edge of the camp light, they paused as the group gathered under the tent.

Mary Ann huddled close to Reuben. *What on earth are we getting ourselves into?*

Reuben and Mary Ann were up early the next morning as the prayer call wafted down over the slopes. It was a low chant that rose to a mournful melody, calling the Muslims to their prayers.

Mary Ann combed her hair by flashlight, and she and Reuben began preparing breakfast down in the cook shack. At six o'clock they needed to have breakfast waiting for the crew, and by seven the men were supposed to be on their way to work. They walked to the work sites, carrying tools and supplies. They had to carry everything, since just beyond the camp, a landslide blocked all but foot traffic.

The morning was beautiful, and Mary Ann slipped out of the cook shack after breakfast to look about. The distant grandeur of the snowcaps and

Base camp at Galoosh.

the nearer blues and greens of the mountains sparkled under the clean air, promising a day of sunshine. The ominous dark rain of the night before was a distant memory. This was the land of the Taliban, home to religiously zealous fighters and fundamentalists. It was also the place where natural disaster had struck.

The scars, barely healed enough to be scars, lay open everywhere. Down in the village, a collapsed boys' school and shattered buildings all testified to what had happened. Across northern Pakistan, thousands of people had died. Slaughtering landslides had been their own gravedigger, burying many at the scene of death. Some bodies had been dragged out of the wreckage and laid to rest by grieving survivors. Floods had washed out some of the shallow graves. Corpses had been scattered to exposure to the elements.

Reuben and Mary Ann talked these things over that first morning in Galoosh when they found time to read their Bibles together. "Why do you suppose God allows this kind of destruction?" Mary Ann asked, twisting her pen in her hand.

Reuben did not answer immediately. All the standard replies of God being in control, of punishing the wicked, of trying to get sinners' attention rolled through his mind, but he ignored them. He had always thought that God used these natural disasters to open doors for the Gospel, and he still thought so. Since he had entered Pakistan, however, other ideas had been skipping around in his head, and he tried now to put words to them.

"In America we try to avoid pain and ugliness," he said slowly. "We have all sorts of medications to deal with pain and advanced procedures that delay death. We have sewer systems to get rid of filth and soft mattresses so our joints don't hurt. When we are hungry, we eat. We wall ourselves off from relationships that might hurt us and avoid people who will draw us into bad business deals. We have big machinery to do hard work for us. We wash our clothes and shower constantly so we don't smell bad . . ." Mary Ann waited for him to continue, clicking her pen.

"Maybe God sees how miserable our deteriorating bodies are and how far we go to hide that misery. Sometimes we have to face awful things like earthquakes. The very dirt we are made of kills thousands. Then maybe we become more honest about our world. We realize what we actually are when all the comforts are stripped away. And God says, 'There! Be real about who you are. Now let *me* work and clean up all the nastiness and heal the pain. Let *me* breathe life into your clay, or return to the dust.' He will only tolerate our mockery so long. See, Mary Ann, we're liars. We're false about what makes us happy; we pursue things that kill us—it's a mockery."

"So why doesn't this happen to us in America? Why don't we have earthquakes and lose our families all at once? It seems to me that we need it worse," Mary Ann said pertly.

"Oh, catastrophes will come—and when they do, they'll kill our soft society. But meanwhile, these disasters are open doors for us who are followers of Christ. We've got a message, and we have to walk through these open doors. The Gospel is for the beaten down and the poor, for folks that have been trampled by tragedy.

"A country opens its doors for help much quicker in broken times than it ever would in good times. These countries are just like people everywhere. See, people won't open the doors of their hearts to Christ until they are broken. Before that, they're just too proud. The Pakistanis are broken. Their doors are open. That's what we're getting into, Mary Ann. That's why we're here." He glanced at her to see what she was thinking.

"Well, I'm not too proud to ask for help," Mary Ann said, looking out the tent door into the sparkly morning. "I need some dirt spaded to plant my vegetable seeds."

As the morning progressed, loud roars startled Reuben and Mary Ann out of their tents three times. Before they could even move, pieces of a mountain beyond would cave away, churning down the mountainside. The noise was awful, sounding more dreadful because there was no way of knowing when they would be engulfed in one of these avalanches.

Reuben and Mary Ann paused their planting to watch as boulders rolled down the opposite mountainside. Mary Ann's hand fluttered to her mouth. "Lord," she breathed, "if you want us to build homes for these people, you had better keep us alive."

Shielding their eyes against the sun, the two became aware of a third person. A weathered Pakistani of indeterminate years had joined them, leaning on his stick, shading his eyes in imitation of them while goats jumped around him.

Sayyid, with scythe dangling from his collar,
preparing for a chai break with fellow countrymen.

The Pakistani noticed them staring across at the mountainside and chuckled a strange but infectious mirth. "Other side Osama bin Laden . . . problems . . . landslides. This side Americans . . . no landslides, no problems."

Reuben held out his hand. "My name is Reuben."

The Pakistani took the hand, and his eyes crinkled up. "Sayyid."

Sayyid became one of their dearest acquaintances in Galoosh. He was a middle-aged mountaineer with little to his name, but he owned the land that the camp was set upon—and the goats.

Sayyid lingered around the camp most days, observing and commenting. Evenings, he joined the crew around the campfire as though it were not a right but a duty, and he felt quite at home to voice whatever opinions he developed. Perhaps this came from the rather seer-like reputation he held among the villagers. He wasn't an important figure and occupied no position of authority, but oddly, his word counted with the village counsel, and even with BOL's crew leaders. Without knowing why they trusted his judgment, Sayyid's word swayed them.

Vague about his religious allegiances, he insisted that he was not a Muslim. But what this left him, no one knew. He certainly didn't profess Christianity, clinging to a few odd opinions. The villagers said, "Christians are good people with bad religion; Muslims are bad people with good religion." Maybe Sayyid agreed with them. He never said.

CHAPTER 9

Minnesota　Virginia　Pakistan　Ukraine　Afghanistan　Israel　Haiti　Bangladesh

He Needs Us

IN THE RIDGES THAT TOUCHED the sky above the plummeting ravines, Reuben and Mary Ann settled into a routine, rising every morning in the dark to start breakfast and working through the day till the campfire in the evenings when the men traipsed down from the heights, tired from their hard labor. In the dark evenings, they ate and talked, pulling close to the fire. Reuben listened to the chatter from his corner, and at first, the politics surrounding the rebuilding project in Galoosh confused Reuben mightily. He picked up that there was some sort of tension in the building project.

It was a few days after his arrival that he stumbled onto Darrell down in BOL's stockyard, talking with a Pakistani.

"But Darrell," the Pakistani was saying, scratching his great mop of curls, "we promised them a house. They are waiting for it. They are very patient people, and we promised."

"But they don't need it as badly as some other people, Tony," Darrell said. "We'll get there. They'll have to wait, so it's good they are patient people . . ." The two men turned as Reuben approached.

"Dad, this is Tony." Darrell gestured to the Pakistani. "He works with PCA."

"Hello." Reuben shook hands. Tony said hello and left.

"What is PCA?" Reuben wanted to know as they watched him go.

"Pakistan Christian Alliance," Darrell explained. "They were here in Galoosh before the earthquake, involved in some relief work, and they responded right after the earthquake. They sponsor us to be in the country. BOL donated money for their immediate crisis response, and they let us into Pakistan, sort of. Tony works with them and is a go-between for all of us."

Reuben sat down on a stack of boards, thinking. "Is that the group you and Chris were talking about last night? Are there problems?"

"Well," Darrell hesitated, sitting down too, "I guess you could say so. PCA knew the people in the community here, and so we used them to get a list of who should get houses. The problem is that they want to oversee who gets what, and there was a racket a couple of weeks ago. Still not sure what all was up . . . I thought I wrote home about that . . ."

"You mean about a fight?"

"Yeah, I wasn't here. Chris and Jake were. All of a sudden one day, a jeep

Pakistanis building trusses.

drove right into the stockyard here where our local workers were building trusses. The jeep drove right over a truss and broke it. All the workers ran off, scared. They came back while Jake was trying to convince the driver of the jeep to leave. The workers chased the jeep back out to the road, where they all started yelling at each other. It didn't take long for it to turn into an all-out fight. The driver of the jeep and all his cohorts were upset about something PCA had done, and all of our workers were telling them to knock it off. They fought and scrapped, beating each other up for half an hour before the jeep people got chased off. No one was hurt badly, but they took one of the council members to the hospital."

"What was the issue?" Reuben asked.

"Well there's this fella, Safeer, who is another PCA rep, and he's the one in charge of picking the people to get houses and benefits from the PCA projects in the valley. They were unhappy with the way something got distributed. We weren't clear on it all. That happened about nine o'clock in the morning, and no one would settle down to work again, so everyone went up to the camp to discuss what was up. Some people in this area just don't like PCA, and as a result, they don't like us either.

"By that time I was back, and we all went down to the army camp to talk to the colonel. The colonel did most of the talking, upset about all the reports he had been getting about PCA and us. Reportedly, we had been stealing wood and taking money to build the houses, and we're suspected of having converted some villagers to Christianity. That really got him going. We tried to patch things over and said that if we being here was an issue, we would pack up and leave tomorrow. That surprised the colonel, and he backed down."

Darrell stopped and shook his head. His face was frustrated. "We canceled the next team to give everything time to cool down and shake the community up a little. I don't know, Dad. The colonel understands now, and the village mostly supports us, but there are a couple of bad apples. I just don't know."

"Well, it's the Lord's work, son." Reuben stood, placing his hands on the stack of boards. He looked out across the valley. "You know that's what your mom would say. 'It's not about us; it's the Lord's work.' "

Darrell stared gloomily at the muddy ground. He sighed and shook himself like a dog coming out of water. "You're right. It is God's work. Nothing will happen here that God doesn't want to . . . oh, whatever." Darrell's voice trailed off. "We say that an awful lot, Dad. Do you believe it? Don't you think God ever allows things to happen that He doesn't want?"

"Well, I suppose so. I don't believe God wants evil to happen, but you can't deny that God works through bad circumstances." Suddenly it was as if they were back at FMH, chatting together while they worked, just as they had done after Darrell had finished school.

They were silent for a minute, and Darrell's tone changed. "We're fighting something more than flesh and blood here. And this isn't over. Not by a long shot. Those bad apples are still there, and they're rotting the rest. I don't trust PCA, not for a second. Even Tony . . . he's got a good heart, but he's a little unguided. He'll plan projects like a 'fun house' and then the villagers all fall out over whose land it should go on. And all this over something that isn't worth their time to begin with. The problem is, these are the people who decided who would get a house, and now we've got to untangle the mess. I don't know what criteria they were using to choose recipients, but it's not working."

"Do the villagers blame you for what PCA has done?" Reuben asked, taking his hands off the lumber pack. He looked up to the camp, thinking he should check on Mary Ann.

"No, not straight out. They understand that PCA is responsible for all the fighting, but there's still the odd rumor or lie floating around, and it clouds things."

Some men arrived to talk to Darrell, and Reuben went off to help Mary Ann. He was too busy for the rest of the day to think much about his conversation with Darrell. The building crew was leaving for America, and the next team would take its place soon. That evening, Darrell and the two other team leaders, Jake and Chris, delivered the departing team to Abbottabad and stayed to do some shopping. The two girls who helped with the cooking and laundry retired early, and Reuben and Mary Ann soon did as well.

Reuben didn't want to admit it, but he was nervous about being alone at the camp. He couldn't shake the sensation of being in Taliban country. The Taliban were allied with Al-Qaeda, and he knew what they thought of Americans. Were the villagers really, truly friendly? A few of them had dropped in to visit earlier in the evening, and Reuben had felt himself hurrying them out the door. He felt he just couldn't quite trust them. Lying on his cot in the tent, he tried not to think about the darkness outside and the girls sleeping beyond. Two girls, an old lady, and an amputee would be easy for anyone to terrorize. He didn't tell Mary Ann about his worries; he didn't want to scare her.

As it was, Mary Ann didn't seem a bit scared of the Taliban. What worried her were the jeeps. At bedtime she prayed, "Oh, Lord, keep Darrell and the boys safe on the road in those jeeps."

Irritably, Reuben rubbed his stump, sore after a day's work. "Oh, stop it," he told himself. "Fussing like a child in the dark." He started to pray, soon drifting off into a troubled sleep, tossing and turning as it began to rain slightly.

In the middle of the night he awoke, his thoughts clear as lightning on a dark night. Someone was outside the tent. He heard the footsteps coming closer. A light was shining. Reuben stiffened, adrenaline coursing through him. The light came nearer. The flap of their tent lifted. A figure ducked inside. The light was so bright he could not see who was behind it. Staring at the light, Reuben grasped for Mary Ann beside him. *Mary Ann isn't here!* he realized. Fear blazed in his brain.

Reuben heard a soft sigh, and then relief washed over him as the figure crawled into bed. "You should see the stars!" Mary Ann exclaimed.

~~~~~~

In the daytime, the fears became more reasonable, and there were other problems for Reuben to deal with, particularly something singular to him in the Pakistan North-West Frontier Province. The mountain paths were difficult enough for a person in his prime, but to be an amputee, skipping over the landslides, the rocks, and the impossibly steep mountainsides was nothing short of a marathon. He struggled, but he fought to keep from being a burden. Everyone else already carried so much.

One day the group was invited to a wedding high in the mountains. A new team had just arrived that morning, but many of them set out that afternoon with several village friends. The new watchman, Faruq, hired to keep guard over the inventory of building materials in the stockyard, went along. Darrell could not go. Reuben nearly didn't go, gazing up to where the peaks broke the clouds and imagining crossing those high places without Darrell's help. He hated being a drag on an expedition, and he never enjoyed depending on someone else to help him. Being in Pakistan had made him realize, more than ever, that he was an amputee. It was embarrassing to nearly fall, again and again, and the simple amount of effort it took to balance on his prosthesis was costly.

In the end, Reuben decided to go anyway. He patiently put aside his concerns and joined the party as they set out across the mountain. The twisting trails scaled higher and higher. He lagged a little. Determined to keep up, he tried to balance while keeping an efficient stride in the loose shale and slippery mud. The team moved out ahead, calling back and forth to each other, and the Pakistanis scampered even farther along, almost as nimble as the goats they so often drove along the slopes to graze. Several of them had already disappeared into the distant heights when Faruq and two other men came racing back to Reuben.

"Is there a problem with your foot?" They were concerned and curious.

"No," Reuben replied mildly, "I don't have a foot."

"Don't have a foot!" They were scandalized at his remark. Reuben tapped the problematic leg with a finger in answer to their exclamations and said simply, "This one is not real."

They eyed him in expanding horror before a short bark from Faruq brought another man to Reuben's side. Before Reuben could protest, Faruq and the man tucked themselves under his arms. Whether he wanted to or not, he flew away up the mountainside. The rocks on the path blurred under his feet, and he swung from their shoulders like a puppet. All things considering, they accomplished the journey rapidly, and at the top they set him down to walk into the tent of his own accord.

Reuben only said, "All right! Thank you!" and ducked into the tent, trying to find a quiet corner to remove his prosthesis. The walk back to camp would be a greater test, and he needed to rest his stump.

An old man of the house sized up the situation. "This man needs a cane. What were you all thinking?" He sent a runner racing over the lofty meadows to find one.

From then on, Reuben was nearly suffocated with their concern. Though he had provided amply for himself before, suddenly he wasn't allowed to do things for himself. The villagers waited on him hand and foot.

"He needs us!" they said, and they gathered around, trying to help. He was everyone's personal responsibility, and no longer was he allowed to traipse all over the land by himself. Those privileges were gone.

"He needs us," they nodded, watching him walk with a barely visible limp, which indeed had escaped their notice before.

For that matter, what was a one-legged man supposed to do for himself if troublemakers came at night? Or what about any of the other dangers that drifted about the mountain? What would he do if he heard a landslide coming? He couldn't run.

Faruq, the night watchman, was hired to watch the stockyard, but other villagers would gather in the evening and linger, ostensibly to visit. Wajid Sab,[1] a cultured teacher who interpreted between the BOL team and the Pakistanis, shook his head about it all. "In the village there are some good men and maybe some bad men. One night, the bad men might come. Maybe the Taliban will come. What will you do then?"

Sayyid was convinced that the whole arrangement was ridiculous. What in the world the Americans thought they could accomplish, sleeping unarmed in a tent with no protection, he wasn't sure, but he *was* sure that someone needed a better plan. "Osama!" he objected when Reuben thought the fuss wasn't necessary. "Osama stay that side . . . good." He gestured to the opposite mountain. "Osama come this side . . . bad problem.

---

1 In Pakistan, "Sab" is a title of respect, similar to the English word "Sir."

Maybe landslide there then come this side . . . big problem." He pointed to the village. "Many good . . . some bad."

Sayyid was not at all happy when an old man of eighty years or so made the fifty-mile trek from Abbottabad to Galoosh with the men who had gone into town to shop one day. The old man didn't look like a Pakistani, really, and never made much over himself or anything else, sitting about the camp for a day all by himself. His hair was longer than most and drooped around his ears under his cap. His white robe was worn and dirty. In fact, his whole appearance was sad except for the piercing black eyes that blazed from under the bushy brows. Sayyid objected to his presence with immoderate disapproval and dug out his father's old club in case he felt like using it. Reuben and one of the Pakistani helpers walked Sayyid back to his goats.

Sayyid shook his head and moved the goats just up the mountain from Reuben's tent, spending the nights nearly on their doorstep, even after the old man had left the camp. He would discreetly disappear farther up in the mornings until the teams had left for the work site. Then he would stroll into camp casually to discuss the weather, something he foretold with astonishing accuracy according to the way the smoke rose from the campfires.

Reuben always greeted him, "Good morning! Pakistani chai, Amer-r-rican coffee?"

This was always a great ceremony. Sayyid would shift from foot to foot nonchalantly, appear indifferent, tip his head to one side, and finally say vaguely, "Amer-r-rican coffee." Then he would glow with importance while a beaming Reuben poured his cup. Sayyid would drink the coffee, becoming sager with each swallow, and they would talk about as many different subjects as their limited vocabulary allowed.

Wajid Sab dropped by often for a cup of chai. He was young and married and held a degree in English, which made it easy for him and Reuben to communicate. He was an authoritative figure in the village, and the villagers respected him. Anyone who spoke English with the foreigners so easily was expected to know a lot. The village had had enough trouble with the language barrier to appreciate someone who could say "Thursday" and "purple." So Wajid Sab mediated between the people of Galoosh and the Americans, taking it upon himself to interpret and advise both sides. His advice swayed decisions often, and the Americans valued him as a friend. They needed someone on their side. The misunderstandings were growing.

"Ah, Reuben," Wajid Sab called out one day, finding Reuben out by the fire grilling burgers on the makeshift grill. Wajid Sab was walking home to his house far up in the mountains after a meeting in the village. "My good friend."

"Hello, Wajid Sab."

The night was quiet around them. The crews had still not arrived home. Twilight languished over the camp. "Reuben, my friend." Wajid Sab sounded serious. "You know that it is dangerous here."

"Of course."

"And you are a one-legged man. Maybe you should think carefully about this. If you do not care for your own safety, think of your wife. What a sweet woman. She should be safe."

"I've thought of it," Reuben told him, "but there is work to do here. Should I be a coward and run away? I have a big God who looks out for me. If I run away, I am saying that my God is smaller than the dangers here."

"That is true," Wajid Sab replied, "but you do not understand, my friend, how our world has changed. Our lives are cheap to the world. But the cost of pain is great to us. God may be bigger than an earthquake, but that did not stop the earthquake."

"But if there had never been an earthquake, we could never have come to help you. This is a great opportunity."

Wajid Sab considered. "Reuben, brother," he said, "in a tragedy that takes and destroys everything, men do two things. Sometimes they build again, bigger and stronger homes. They make their houses to stand again and last. But sometimes they say, 'If I build, then it will be destroyed again.' And they put up a piece of tin to live under. They think the whole world will steal from them, so they become thieves themselves. They steal everything precious because their own precious things are gone."

"Then those men need to see one man who will not steal from them," Reuben said. "How will they see that if I always hide and try to guard my things? Of course, they will want my things if they think I do not want them to take them. They will think that I must be rich to be hiding so much. But if I leave my belongings unlocked and walk about without a stick to guard myself, they will suppose that I have nothing more than they, and they won't bother me."

Wajid Sab only shook his head.

Minnesota Virginia Pakistan Ukraine Afghanistan Israel Haiti Bangladesh

Exodus

ON HIS WAY TO LOOK over a new work site one day, Darrell stumbled upon four little children. The children, scared and scrawny, dashed back to a ragged tent under the side of the mountain, where they stood peering out at the passing foreigner. They were so little and dirty and looked so much like forlorn rabbits that Darrell went out of his way to stop at the opening of the shelter. They shrank together.

"Where is your mother?" Darrell asked as well as he could in Urdu.

They only looked at him with big black eyes, and the littlest one put his finger in his mouth.

"Where is your father?" Darrell tried again.

One of the older ones pointed behind him after a long minute. Brushing aside the canvas flap that hung down, Darrell stooped and peered into the cold dimness. A figure under a blanket shifted, and sunken eyes looked out. It was a man, probably not as old as he looked, but consumed by a fever raging in his body.

Darrell tried to speak to him. "Hello!" he called. "Hello, how are you?"

Either the man was opposed to speaking with white men or else he couldn't understand the broken Urdu. Darrell got no response. He had no better luck with the children, and finally Darrell continued up the path, his chin sunk on his chest in thought. Why wasn't that family on the list of BOL recipients? Of course, there was a man in the household, and perhaps

Jesus loves them, but they don't know it yet.

he had not been ill at the time when the list had been made up. But . . .

Darrell had been headed to the work site of a house for a family of three. But that family appeared tolerably well off. The man had been laid up with a broken leg for a few months after the earthquake. Now healed, the man could walk again. One of the crews had been preparing to start on their house the week before, but the preparations had been interrupted when the tarp on the provisional shelter of a widow was torn by tumbling rocks. They had built her a home first.

Now Darrell, who had not been able to get the sick man and his children from his mind, persuaded the others that there was a serious need, and so the crew built a house for the poor family next. Unimpressed by this shifting around of plans, Tony did not say much, only reminding the crew occasionally of the house for the man with the broken leg.

When the sick man's house was finished, the man, dying of tuberculosis, wrung his hands in silence, too overcome to speak. The children moved about the studding of their new home as if in a dream, feeling the smooth wood. While the house was being built, they had spent their time watching from a short distance, piled together, as usual. Mary Ann and the girls, bringing lunch one day, tried to entice them with food. The children approached after some coaxing and ate, chewing the food rhythmically but rapidly before retiring by themselves again. Only that time, they had not gone so far away.

To construct these houses, Beacon of Light provided the foundation and the frame, erecting a good roof over it all, but the recipients of the homes put the walls up themselves. The construction crews tried to use the local people as much as possible. They were hired to build trusses in the supply yard, carry materials, and transport rock and sacks of cement on the backs of their donkeys. The crews asked the recipients of the houses to donate the beams from their old houses. They were nice, big beams, and BOL set

Reconstruction following the earthquake
in the Northwest Frontier Province of Pakistan.

up a band saw in Galoosh where they cut these beams into lumber to be used for studding. Men carried the beams into camp on their shoulders and were paid for their labor. In this way, everyone contributed.

The villagers appreciated this system, and it often worked well, but sometimes it was frustrating. No big problems occurred, but issues of time—the need to use every working hour and convincing the hired workers to appear at the same time every morning—along with management of the inventory got challenging at times. The volunteer crews from America were good-natured, but occasionally patience wore thin as it does any place where people try to work together.

"I quit," one of the volunteers announced one rainy day when the nails had not arrived with the other supplies for the third day in a row. "We can't build if we don't have nails. Even a Pakistani knows that. If they want a house, they can bring the nails or build the house themselves."

"Hey!" Darrell had come on site to look into the issue, and now he spoke up. "We don't want to be speaking down to the locals. They do things differently, but we're working in their country, not the other way around."

"Look!" the volunteer said, putting his hammer down. "We're the ones taking time out of our schedules and paying for a plane ticket to come halfway around the world to build these houses. If it wasn't for us, this program wouldn't work. If you're bringing in volunteers to do the work, then just let us take care of it. This messing around is for the birds."

Darrell took a deep breath and kept his voice even. He was as exasperated over the nail situation as anyone, and he was hoping this would not create a bigger problem. "Helping people in a crisis is good, but helping someone help themselves prepares them to care for their own needs in the future."

"So we're letting them help out. Let 'em act like it."

"Hey now." Jake, one of the other directors, had arrived in time to hear the last bit of the conversation. "Don't forget who left heaven to come to earth to help all of us. It cost Him a lot more than a plane ticket. You being a volunteer does not give you extra recognition, only extra responsibilities. Pull yourselves together, boys. I have a box of nails here that will hold until someone can get back from the yard with more."

That evening as Reuben and Darrell were walking down the hill into camp and darkness was creeping into the eastern sky, two boys, about eleven and fifteen, were walking down toward the yard also. They spotted the two men and raced over to join them. Darrell and Reuben had paused to look up at the sky and the birds chasing each other about in the deepening blue. Seeing the boys, they sat down wordlessly on some big boulders. The two boys climbed up beside them.

"Well, hello there," Reuben spoke to them, a grin broadening his face.

"Hello." A grin also split the younger boy's face. The older boy looked away from Reuben's friendly gaze.

"This is Salim and Alamin." Darrell put his hand first on the younger one's shoulder and then dropped a fond arm over the older boy's neck.

"I've seen you around," Reuben said. Salim's eyes sparkled, but Alamin studied the rock they were sitting on.

Salim placed his fingers on Reuben's prosthesis. "No leg?" he asked.

"Nope, no leg." Reuben rolled up his pant leg and detached the prosthesis. Salim's eyes widened, and he blurted something in Urdu. Alamin only looked over and went back to fingering the lichens growing on the side of a rock.

"I found them one day," Darrell explained, "when they showed up at camp as I was unloading crushed rock from the back of the jeep. They were cutting up, messing with the nails, and even pounding a few into a post. I told them to 'scoot,' and Salim replied, 'No go school.' It cracked me up that he misunderstood, and I laughed, which made him laugh too. One time I let them drive the jeep, and now we're buddies." Darrell reached out to punch Salim on the arm, and Salim smirked.

Reuben watched Alamin out of the corner of his eye. Alamin was studying the rock. He reached across the rock and touched a beetle that lay on its back, kicking its thin legs in the air. Alamin saw Reuben looking and pointed at the rock, the beetle's home. Rainwater from the afternoon storm was rushing past the rock. Reuben eased the beetle over onto its feet and set it on a dry rock, and Alamin smiled.

Salim and Alamin helped out on the building sites. Two other boys began working too, and the four became a crew of their own. None of them spoke great English, but Korim, the oldest, had a limited command of the language. He became the leader of the foursome. The American crew leaders went to him to explain what needed to be done. Korim always listened, his face impassive and his legs spread far apart, until the explanation ended, and then he moved ahead surely, barking orders to the other three. The boys usually got it right if they did it the way Korim told them.

The American crew leaders noticed Korim's capability and spent extra time with him, demonstrating how blueprints worked. Sometimes during lunch break Korim would take the blueprints aside and study them. Hasan, the fourth boy, knew no English, but that didn't keep him from trying. He jabbered a million questions as fast as he could, finally wheeling aside in disgust when no one understood. Korim always waited until the barrage had passed. Then he muttered an explanation and the sun came back out on Hasan's face. "Ah! Good, good!" he would say as he waved his hammer. "Understand!"

Alamin always retired off by himself at break, befriending all the dogs that slunk around the work sites. He fed them his American sandwiches. The dogs liked the bologna even if Alamin did not. Salim was a piece of work, a category all of his own. He was the clown, and one day he fell in love with a volunteer's mp3 player. He learned English songs much more quickly than any other English, and the crew learned more about the contents of that mp3 player than they had ever expected to. Salim wasn't old enough to be of much use, but the crew leaders left him on because they all liked him.

~~~~~~~~~~~~~~~~~~~~~~~~~~~~~~~~~~~~~

One day the man whose leg had been broken, who had never gotten his house, came into the camp. "Why aren't you building my house? I need my house. You said last month that you would build it in a week."

The discussion grew into a meeting, and the villagers flocked in to listen and add their input. Darrell and Jake sat in a circle with the men, and they all talked.

The villagers were unhappy. The original popularity of the foreigners was wearing away, and the strain of the arguments over PCA's actions and the misunderstandings were rankling again. The villagers were bitter over their losses suffered during the earthquake and flooding.

Sayyid was hunched over behind the others a little ways away, staring at the ground. He stood, his bright headdress silhouetted against the gray sky and the coming afternoon storm. He addressed the group in Urdu, and Wajid Sab interpreted. "We have experienced a very serious calamity here. This was an act of God. If we don't change our ways or acknowledge God, something even worse could happen."

He curled up in his corner again and clammed his mouth shut. Reuben waited for the village men to argue with Sayyid or even get angry enough to run him off. No one reacted. Reuben saw what sort of license the village granted Sayyid's shrewd old tongue.

The foreigners were not seeing what the Pakistanis saw. The group sat and observed each other for the space of a few seconds after Sayyid's speech. Finally the man with the broken leg who had begun the meeting blurted out, "But I paid rupees to have a house."

This news startled the crew leaders. "You did what?"

Examining the situation, they found what he said to be true. According to what they could sort out in the talk that followed, some of the villagers had paid to be on PCA's recipient list. Now they were not receiving houses since the crew leaders had abandoned PCA's list, and they were not happy.

The BOL personnel thought the situation over for a day or two and decided to continue as they had been. "There are greater needs," Darrell said as they discussed it. "There are people who have greater needs than the people on the list."

Chris agreed. "Let's work at it ethically as we have been. We've started working on our own list. We'll keep on with that, but with our eyes open. We'll only be here for a little more than a month."

The unrest compounded and spread after this decision, and rumors threatened from the village. Village men no longer came to the camp to visit or to listen to the English chatter.

There were houses to be built that were far away from camp, and BOL had placed a band saw in a remote area part way out to meet the beams coming in. The local men idolized that band saw, and as the time approached to finish the rebuilding project, a question arose among the villagers. *What will happen to the band saw after the foreigners leave? Who will get it?*

The Americans decided to sell the band saw, and competition sprouted over it.

Wajid Sab wanted the band saw. Coming to visit them one afternoon, he mentioned it to Reuben. "I would like to buy your band saw."

"Well," Reuben said, "there are some others who want it too."

Wajid Sab stopped Darrell on the path the next day. "Would you sell me your band saw?"

Wajid Sab wasn't the poorest man in Galoosh, and other men who needed the income more could use the band saw. The crew leaders sold it to another man two days later, and Wajid Sab stopped coming for tea. They missed his calming, reasoning influence with the villagers, for tension was growing. Vague rumors were drifting about.

The men talked it over and came to a decision. They went to Akram, a younger man from Lahore, the second largest city in Pakistan. He was a believer whom Darrell and Chris had met in Abbottabad. Akram had come to spend some time in Galoosh, so the crew leaders hired him to help around the stockyard and, primarily, to listen. He understood the local dialect spoken in Galoosh although the people of the village did not know this, and so Akram served as an ear for the team.

BOL had planned to build a hundred homes in Galoosh. There were enough materials to continue building for a while, but no one knew when the river would wash out a gully, making it impossible for the trucks to cross. The crew leaders arranged for several excavators to come to Galoosh and build a ford over the river. Once the ford was built, they contracted trucks to bring in all the materials for the last thirty houses. The inventory in the stockyard was now higher than it had been since the beginning of the project.

The grumblings in Galoosh grew and shaped into a shadow, a whisper chasing behind the backs of the foreigners. The workers in the yard balked over their instructions. They spoke the local dialect all the time now even as the crew leaders' fluency in Urdu grew. One day Alamin and Salim did not come to work. Korim did not remark on their absence, but the set of his mouth was grim.

The word from Akram was not good. "I do not know," he said, shrugging with a miserable expression one evening. "I hear them speaking of a riot again and again. I think they want to chase you all out."

The vague words spoke of a plot—a conspiracy. Rumor had it that there was going to be a riot, but no one knew for what. It lacked form. Was it real or was it just a threat?

One night as the crew lingered, hashing over the potential of it all, Reuben said, "We came here, understanding that it was dangerous. We committed ourselves to helping these people even though we knew we would be an open target for any threat that arose. We've walked with these folks and trusted them, and we continue to trust God and work as He leads."

One night Tony left camp without explanation. Khalid, the jeep driver, drove Tony away in his jeep. Everyone agreed that it was odd.

"We're going after them," Darrell said. He and Jake left, grim-faced, and followed at a distance in the BOL jeep. It was drizzling rain, and the gray sky roiled above the mountain tips. The ghostly fog drifted about, in and around the mountains, overtaking the jeep. Khalid's jeep had disappeared, and the two men wondered whether they had lost track of it. Wheeling around a corner, they suddenly came upon it. Khalid had pulled to the side of the road in a spot of dull light cast by an opened cloud above.

Jake stopped their jeep alongside Tony and Khalid. Trying to appear casual, he said, "Oh, hello, what are you doing?"

"Just looking at a new building site." Tony was equally noncommittal.

They exchanged a bit of talk on the location of the site. Rain was pelting them, stalling conversation. Darrell and Jake drove off slowly. They watched as Tony and Khalid roared off up the mountain. The PCA headquarters were up there. Darrell and Jake exchanged glances.

"Let's follow them," Darrell suggested.

"I don't like it," Jake said.

When Darrell and Jake stepped into the entryway of the PCA headquarters, the rain outside had halted, and a warm wind was blowing through the lower regions of the valley. Above, the mist swirled, and a little spot of clear sky peeked through the gloom. The entryway of the concrete PCA headquarters building was damp, and from inside, voices echoed out to them. There was a meeting.

Darrell eased against the wall and slid along it till he came to the doorjamb, peering into the room over the backs of the men seated there. Tony *was* there, and Khalid. Tony was speaking, and Darrell inched back from sight.

"We will take the boards, the metal, the trusses, and everything and then make sure that it is distributed to those we need to make happy. This is our chance to win back favor with the village. They are not happy because many of them have paid money to have a house. BOL will not build for all of the people on our list, and Wadoud, by the north end of the mountain, is not happy. He paid for a house, and he wants one."

"When do the Americans leave?" someone asked.

"They will go Tuesday morning," Tony answered.

Darrell and Jake exchanged glances. No one planned to leave for anywhere Tuesday morning.

"What do we do?" Jake whispered.

"We need to get out—or else go in there."

"Let's go in."

The two project leaders stepped into the room, squaring their shoulders. The conversation suspended, hanging in the air like the mist outside. Sitting around the room on the floor, the men stilled. Tony opened and closed his mouth like a fish gulping minnows.

"*Assalamu alaikum* (May peace be to you)," Darrell addressed them. His tone exuded mildness and good nature, but the pleasantry was awkward. "We were out looking around and heard voices, so we stopped in to say hello. Nice evening, isn't it?"

This remark was so smooth that the men gathered in the meeting began to doubt what had happened. They recollected their thoughts and regained their composure enough to make even replies. It was a nice evening, they all agreed.

"Yes, well, have a good night," Darrell called over his shoulder as the two departed. A collective sigh from the group behind scooted them on their way like a mischievous wind blowing errant leaves.

Jake and Darrell returned to the camp, but they had not been there long before Reuben and Mary Ann returned from an evening in Abbottabad. The couple was excited, breathing hard as they entered the ring around the fire.

"We saw a jeep down in the river!" Mary Ann cried. She shivered suddenly. "Darrell, run! Someone might be hurt!"

"I think it's Khalid's jeep," Reuben added.

All the men bolted. Reuben got some rope and a shovel, for what he wasn't sure, and followed as quickly as he could. By the time he arrived at the crash, the others were hauling a man out of the river. It was Khalid, thrown out of his jeep into the water. Tony was unconscious, still behind the steering wheel of the jeep.

No one ever clearly pieced together what had happened, but they gathered a few ideas. When Tony and Khalid had left the meeting, Tony had been driving Khalid's jeep. Tony, not an experienced driver, had missed a gear while shifting, and the jeep had freewheeled down the hill to a turn. At the turn, where the mountain dropped down two hundred feet to the river below, Tony had tried to miss a rock in the curve, and he'd lost control. The jeep had shot out over the drop-off and smashed down into the river.

Both men were still living but badly hurt. The BOL workers extricated the two and took them to a hospital north of Abbottabad, where two of the workers spent the night in the hospital with Tony and Khalid. Tony had sustained brain injuries, and it would be a long trek to recovery.

~~~~~~

A few days later, on a Sunday night, Reuben sat, resting his chin on one hand. Mary Ann sat mutely by his side, and they were both praying. Some of the BOL personnel were in Abbottabad at a Bible study. The new crew, just arrived, had gone to bed long ago, worn out by their afternoon journey to Galoosh. Few were still awake. Down in the stockyard, they could see the shadow of Faruq, the night watchman. Akram sat on the ground not far from Reuben and Mary Ann. Sayyid remained close to the couple, pacing.

Abruptly, Sayyid grasped the grate that Reuben had made with rebar and blocks of wood to grill hamburgers on and, ripping the blocks from the rebar, tossed the blocks into the fire.

Reuben got to his feet with an exclamation rising in his throat. "Sayyid!" Sayyid knew better.

"Oh, Sayyid!" Mary Ann cried, but Sayyid stalked away, shooting them an incomprehensible look and then facing the darkness. His back was rigid as he stood at the edge of camp.

Reuben sat back down and watched the blocks of wood, his little grill, burn. The grill, a cherished symbol of the American good life, glowed—soon to be ashes. With it burned Reuben's old ideas—the old outlook on life. His perspective on the world had been trashed by exposure to a place and a people that had lost everything. The village was fighting to get its old life back. They wanted their possessions again. They could have just accepted the gift of the foreigners, but they could not understand it. The villagers preferred to steal the gift away by force, to provide for themselves.

Reuben watched the blocks spark and knew that he would no longer need that grill. He stared into the fire for a long time. Mary Ann had gone to bed now, but Reuben wasn't about to sleep. The air was electric. Akram sat still too, on the other side. Reuben wished the crew leaders were back from Abbottabad.

Reuben's phone rang. It was Tony. "Is everything okay?" Tony was laid up from the accident, recovering at the hospital. A sick man like him should have been sleeping by then.

"Oh, yes," Reuben replied. "Everything is fine."

Reuben returned to the fire, reflecting. Akram looked inquiringly.

Tony called again. "Everything is okay?"

"Yes," Reuben said.

He called a third time. "Is everything okay?"

Reuben put down the phone. Only Akram was there with him. Sayyid had eventually strolled off into the darkness. Earlier that morning, in the middle of the Sunday service, Reuben had stepped outside for a moment. He had caught sight of a man climbing the mountain and carrying a gun. In all his time in Galoosh, he had not seen a gun. Reuben went back to the campfire, thinking of Christ in the garden, waiting for His captors to come and take Him away. Christ had come from a foreign country and spent His short time giving aid to the poor and destitute. The people had not been satisfied with what He gave them. They preferred the old way, the Law, and what they could do for themselves, as if saying, "Just give us the stuff and let us do it ourselves. We know better how to straighten our own lives out." So they had plotted to get rid of Christ, while Christ waited for them knowingly in the Garden of Gethsemane.

When Darrell and the others returned from Abbottabad late that night, Reuben told them of Tony's phone calls. The men listened with arms crossed. After he had finished, Darrell stepped forward, his brow lowered. "We know what's up. We're going to have to pack up and leave. Where's Faruq?"

Jake went down to the stockyard to collect the night watchman.

Darrell took charge. "Faruq," he said in Urdu, "what's happening?"

Deliberately, Faruq looked around at the gathered men and sat down on one of the stumps. He pressed his lips together and would not say a word.

The team leaders exchanged glances. "Sayyid. Where's Sayyid?"

Sayyid was there, not far off. With the question put to him, he only shook his head and said heavily, "Tonight need going. All Americans must go. Must go back to America."

They held a short counsel. It was about midnight. The men who had returned from Abbottabad had hired trucks, and soon the trucks arrived. "We need to get out of here by the first prayer call," they decided.

Mary Ann awoke to Darrell bending over her, a flashlight shining behind him. The urgent voices of the men reached her. "Mom. Mom. We're leaving. We need to pack up," he said.

All night, the team worked silently, quickly. The new crew was awakened. Their belongings were packed back into the suitcases and the bunks were taken down. Everything from the saws to the inventory was loaded into the trucks that loomed in the darkness while the drivers of the trucks paced. "We must be gone before the first prayer call, or the villagers will block the river," the truck drivers insisted. "You wouldn't let us bring our guns, so hurry!"

Sayyid watched, his chin quivering with some repressed emotion. Sometimes he lent a faltering hand. When he wasn't helping, he stood gloomily to the side or stamped around with a thundercloud on his brow. Reuben took him off to the side once. "Sayyid," he said, "Sayyid, it will be all right."

Sayyid shook his head and remarked, his tone morose, "American program not finished, but American program finished." His lip poked out.

At last the trucks were loaded. The first jeep was ready to go, but Reuben and Mary Ann lingered. Sayyid came down the hill to see them off. Reuben embraced his friend. "Goodbye, Sayyid, we will miss you."

Sayyid sat right down on the ground and began to bawl like a baby. Reuben felt awful. He knelt down beside him. There was nothing else to say.

Sayyid was not to be comforted, and at last Reuben climbed into the jeep. Just in time, the jeeps pulled away from the village. The first prayer call sounded, haunting the eastern sky with mournful notes. Mary Ann glanced behind them, half-expecting to see the villagers race after them. The building project was over.

Minnesota · Virginia · Pakistan · Ukraine · Afghanistan · Israel · Haiti · Bangladesh

Unfinished

IN ABBOTTABAD, THE INVENTORY WAS stored in the courtyard of the guesthouse where the team took refuge. The crew leaders had stayed behind that morning until seven o'clock when the Pakistani workers arrived for work. "The project is finished," they told the men. "The Americans are gone. You will all be paid if you come to Abbottabad. Thank you for everything."

By noon the team was together again in Abbottabad. They were all exhausted. The strain of the last weeks and the nighttime exodus had worn them down, but there was still business to do. The inventory had to be attended to and business relationships needed to be squared away, and they were all still tense. Was there still danger? Might the villagers follow them?

That first evening, Chris came in from the street. "Darrell, take a look out there. Isn't that the fellow who cooked for us in Galoosh?"

Darrell squinted out at the street into the fading light. "He looks familiar."

The man was leaning against a post, his face turned away. When he turned, a light came on in the house beside him, lighting the man's face. Too late, the man ducked. It was the man who had cooked their lunches at camp. Now the cook's eyes traveled upward to the guesthouse windows, and Darrell and Chris leaped back. The Pakistani had seen them, and gathering his gown about him, he ambled on. Glancing carelessly over his shoulder once, he paused but then continued over the rise.

Darrell made a move toward the door. "I'm going after him."

"He's gone," Reuben said from the window where he had gone to look. Darrell didn't follow. The guesthouse was guarded with an armed guard, and at any rate, it would have been difficult for someone to gain access to the inventory.

Several mornings after the exodus, the Pakistani workers from Galoosh appeared at the guesthouse to be paid as arranged. The crowd gathered outside the gate, and inside, Mary Ann walked from window to window. "Darrell, you be careful. God can save you from them, but don't do anything crazy."

"Oh, Mom," Darrell said and dodged out the door.

The crowd grew a little bigger. *Oh, dear.* Mary Ann peered out the window anxiously. *I wonder if all of them really worked for us. What if they are . . .* She drew herself up and put her hands together. *What am I thinking? The Lord will protect us.* She went into the bathroom and shut the door.

Outside, Darrell was saying, "Good morning, my friends. It's payday!" A mutter arose. The air was tense. Darrell stepped beyond the gate but kept his back to it. In the morning sunshine, the flowers nodded over the gate, and the breeze was warm, a friendly world in contrast to the animosity apparent on the faces before him.

The men were efficient about handing out the money, calling the names of the workers one by one. Each man came forward to receive his pay. They counted it over suspiciously and retreated.

At the end, the Pakistanis and the crew leaders eyed each other up. There was a minute of long silence, and Reuben wondered what the chances were that the men carried arms. Now, after they had their pay, would be the point of test. Khalid was there in the group, still looking damaged from his accident. He did not look Reuben in the eye. Tony was not there. Faruq, the night watchman, appeared grim.

The four boys who had worked on the construction sites were there. Korim was impassive as usual. Alamin looked as though he had a headache and wished he were home. Hasan's mouth worked explosively as though fifty things were coming to his head to say and all of them were being stopped just in time. Salim had accepted his pay with great dignity and now had his arms crossed belligerently, trying hard to keep his features twisted in a scowl. His heart tugging, Reuben watched them, asking himself what would come of the relationship with the boys.

Behind the group, a man barked something under his breath, and quietly the group moved away. "Goodbye," said the Americans.

"Goodbye," came the reply.

Hasan looked back, and his mouth finally opened. "Goodbye," he called. "Goodbye, Darrell. Goodbye, Chris, Reuben. Goodbye, goodbye!"

Salim, too, looked over his shoulder. Suddenly he galloped back, throwing himself at Darrell. He wrapped his arms around Reuben for just a second and then raced back.

～～～～～～～～～～～～～～～～～～～～～～～

The team spoke together often about what had taken place. What had happened exactly? Where had things gone wrong? What would have happened if they had stayed? Would the villagers actually have attacked them?

With the questions came the uncomfortable reassessment of their decisions, and they asked each other if they should have stayed. What would have been the most compelling witness for Christ? There had been more to do in Galoosh, but sometimes life was like that. Unfinished things weren't always meant to be finished.

Before long they were asking each other again. "But what do you think would have happened? Was it cowardly to leave?"

Reuben asked, "Why did we leave? Were we afraid for our lives? Yes, perhaps. But were we too concerned about saving our inventory? Suppose we had stayed to face the music and let them have what they wanted, taking joyfully the spoiling of our goods. Would they actually have harmed us if we had trusted ourselves to God and let them do with us what they wanted?"

It was done, and they would never know. At least they were comforted that no lives were lost.

Yet this seemed little comfort in the face of the unfinished work. The team leaders especially were depressed. The work had been abandoned. There were a few unfinished houses they had started, now worth very little. The villagers worried them too. How about the unfinished work of souls? They wondered about the recovery of Tony and Khalid.

Two weeks later Darrell, Chris, and Jake decided to return to Galoosh for a surprise visit. The road to Galoosh was filled with memories of their hasty escape. The sunshine and blue and green mountains again belied all the drama that had occurred among their crevices and ledges. They parked the jeep where the stockyard had been. On the mountainside, the scars of where the tents had been were still visible.

"I hear—" Chris stopped, and the other two turned with him. A familiar sound had caught their ear.

Exchanging looks, the three walked around the path to the location of the sound—the noise of hammers. As they rounded the mountain, one of their old work sites broke into view, a place where a kit had been delivered but then abandoned over their abrupt departure. The case was one that had bothered the crew leaders. The house had been for a widow, a poor one, who should have been on PCA's original list and had been added tardily by BOL.

The studding was up! Next, they saw figures crouched upon the boards. Two hammers were pounding. Hasan and Alamin hammered away. Below stood Korim, looking over the boards. Salim was waiting with one of the boards to hand it up to the two on top, and he was bellowing, "Hurry up! My neck's hurting."

Hasan turned his head to reach for the board, but he dropped it again. "Jake!" He had seen the visitors. Korim wheeled, and Alamin looked up. Only Salim did not turn. He was hollering because the board had dropped onto his toe.

The three crew leaders strode up, and Korim stepped forward, beaming proudly. Hasan and Alamin swung down from the rafters, and Salim finally turned. His face lit up, and he exclaimed, "They're back! Now Korim can't drive us like slaves anymore!"

The four young men who finished the house for the widow after BOL left.

Several days later, the team was grouped around their luggage in the Islamabad airport.

"This cane just won't go in," Mary Ann told her husband, looking reproachfully at the stick from where she was kneeling by an open suitcase. It was the cane that had been given to Reuben at the wedding in Galoosh.

Reuben was perplexed. "I am *not* leaving it here."

"We'll have to carry it then." Mary Ann pushed a wisp of hair out of her eyes. "I'll carry it. For all they know, I need it."

She limped through the check-in line, leaning on the cane. At the security check, there were strong objections. "You simply cannot take a stick on the plane!"

"I know," Mary Ann nodded sympathetically. "These days you never can tell. But you don't think I would actually hit someone with it, do you?"

"Well . . ." The security guard looked down his long nose at her. He paused there.

Mary Ann leaned forward. "I tell you what. As soon as we get inside the plane and can sit down, my husband will put it in the overhead storage bin. That way it won't be handy for me to grab."

Within the hour, they were in flight, cane and all. Reuben leaned back, thinking of Sayyid and of those four boys. He missed them already. What was ahead for them? Why hadn't they just stolen the kit materials and sold them for money? Had they found that there was more to life than looking out for their own welfare?

Reuben thought of himself. What was ahead for him and Mary Ann? After their first taste of foreign soil, he was ready for more. Tired as he was, he knew there had to be more for them.

CHAPTER 12

Ukraine

Israel

Virginia   Pakistan

Afghanistan

Haiti   Bangladesh

Minnesota

Seedtime and Harvest

IT WAS JANUARY 2007. REUBEN and Mary Ann had been home from Pakistan since September. Christmas had come and gone, and now they had just set foot in Ukraine. They had come to be house parents to the seed team organized by Beacon of Light and Master's International Ministries.

Reuben and Mary Ann were exhausted as they stepped into the chilly world of the Ukrainian winter. *Jet lag never gets any easier,* Reuben thought as he tried to manipulate their luggage. Their flight to Ukraine had two layovers, one in Zurich, Switzerland, and another in Frankfurt, Germany. Reuben had looked over his itinerary during the long flight over the Atlantic.

"Mary Ann, we have a problem," he had said.

Their layover in Frankfurt was much too short, and they would need to change airlines. So in Zurich, they had gone up to the ticket counter and explained the problem to an attendant. "It's too short of a layover. I am an amputee. I can't run."

"Give me just a minute." The icy blonde attendant pursed her lips, ghastly with cherry-red lipstick. "This shouldn't be a problem." She printed out a ticket. "Someone will be at the gate to assist you when you land."

"Oh, thank you," Mary Ann said, giving the lady her most winning smile, and the attendant smiled back.

When they disembarked in Germany, a lady with a wheelchair had been waiting at the terminal, a big yellow X marked on the back of her jacket.

Reuben addressed her in German, and the lady had been delighted. She gushed German back at him, indicating that he should get into the wheelchair.

"You're kidding," Reuben said softly, but it was for him. After he settled in and set his briefcase on his lap, they sped away. The lady was a marathon wheelchair-pusher, and Mary Ann had to scramble to keep up. They took a network of routes, going through doors marked for employees only and onto elevators that descended into distant basement sections, up and down and around. When it seemed that they must be at the end of the maze, the lady swiped a card and they went through yet another inaccessible spot.

Finally, a minivan had met them outside the airport. In the minivan, they had zipped around and back into the airport. They had arrived with a few minutes to spare, saying goodbye in German to the helpful lady.

Reuben grinned now, remembering it all. He was glad to have finally made it to Ukraine.

Ukraine had some of the best and deepest topsoil in the world. When the Soviet Union had controlled all of Eastern Europe, the farming community had disintegrated. Land had been confiscated, and no one bothered much with what remained. There was no use farming, since the government took their entire yield away; the crops were commandeered for the benefit of the nation while the country became poor. Once a bustling agricultural economy, the people of Ukraine had nearly quit cultivating their land.

By the time the Soviet Union dissolved in the 1990s, a new generation had grown up, a generation that knew nothing about farming. They did not know how to utilize the resources of their soil, though they now had access to some plots of land. Their parents knew, but they were old now, disillusioned by the years of oppression. No longer did they have a will to work.

Master's International Ministries had observed this and wanted to remedy the problem. Part of their solution was to organize teams of youth to go to Ukraine for six weeks at a time to assemble seed packages. The mission, based in Kiev, Ukraine, worked with BOL on the details of the seed project.

Reuben and Mary Ann loved working with young people, which was fortunate since they had ten of them to look after. In Ukraine, they went everywhere with the group: to work, to church, to socialize. The youth on the team spent a great deal of time interacting with the local youth, especially believers. Mary Ann cooked for the group, and Reuben spent his days in the seed house. The seeds were purchased by BOL from Holland in bulk. In the seed house, the team used wooden dispensers to fill small paper packets, each packet holding enough seeds to plant a garden for a household. Next, they assembled packets of twelve kinds of seeds into a family package and added literature to each bundle.

The first weeks, they filled packet after packet of seeds all day long. It felt as though they had filled hundreds of thousands. At night Reuben dreamed about seeds rolling out of the dispensers.

"Verily, verily, I say unto you, Except a corn of wheat fall into the ground and die, it abideth alone: but if it die, it bringeth forth much fruit" (John 12:24).

One night Reuben came in from a day of packing seeds, rubbing his hands. It had been cold all day in that seed house. His fingers had felt as if they were going to form around the seed packet. *All for what?* Reuben asked himself, sitting down on the bed to ease off his wooden leg. Standing up all day had made his stump sore. He found himself weary of the seed packing. Normally he liked working behind the scenes, but tonight, he didn't want to ever see another seed. *Is there more I could be doing? Is there more?*

Mary Ann discovered him in the room, and she was tired too. Joining him, she said, "The whole team is going over to the pastor's house after supper to be with the church youth."

"That's nice."

Mary Ann sighed. "I shouldn't complain, but I get so tired of cooking when I want to be out and about. I want to go meet people and talk to them and interact with them. Isn't that what we came for? Isn't there more we could do?" It was a common struggle of Mary Ann's. She loved people, and she loved reaching out to them. Sometimes cooking seemed like being enclosed in a big wire cage full of nice smells and calories.

Reuben stretched out on the bed. "I know. All those seeds are still rolling down the chute. It feels like they're in my ear, pouring, pouring. Is supper ready?"

"Uh huh."

The two of them got up and went out to the supper table; both stayed behind to clean up when the team left for the pastor's house. Outside it was snowing, an endless drift of snowflakes. The cold crept in around the windows. Reuben dried dishes slowly, thinking.

"You know," he said at last, "we're new at this foreign ministry thing, and we want to be out and about witnessing and interacting, but the work behind the scenes still needs to be done. Without that, ministry can never happen. Someone has to pack the seeds, and it's just as important."

Mary Ann frowned at a pan rimmed with dried food. "I suppose so. But I feel like my gift is with people, not cooking."

Reuben thought it over. "That casserole you made tonight was good."

"Oh, that." Mary Ann flicked her hand. "That was one of the girls' recipes.

I told her I liked her recipe."

"I suppose," Reuben said, "in a way, we're planting seeds. That's a very important part of ministry. It's not the most glamorous part. It often involves a lot of just plain work. It doesn't really feel as if you're using your gifts, and you can't walk away and add up the converts. But with so many seeds, there will be a harvest."

"I hope so," Mary Ann replied, swirling the suds and wringing out her dishrag. "There are millions of seeds in those packages."

Reuben smiled. "Spiritual seeds, dear. Spiritual seeds."

~~~~~~

Eventually the team had packaged all the seeds, and they traveled to numerous villages, holding meetings and passing out the family packages. The team sang songs, and a pastor traveled with them to preach in the Ukrainian language. The meetings were all about seeds—seeds for gardening and seeds for salvation. There was a strategy in all this that Reuben enjoyed. Under the umbrella of gardening, they could introduce the Gospel. Planting seeds, Reuben reminded himself, was what evangelism was all about.

Master's International Ministries arranged the seed meetings with the leaders of the villages, who got them places to meet, usually an old concrete building of some type, with no heat whatsoever.

At one meeting a pastor came to Reuben during the gardening orientation. They had not yet begun the preaching. "You need to close this meeting *now*. These people will freeze."

They probably will, Reuben thought grimly. *The people holding the meetings might be in some danger of that themselves. And by the way, does Ukraine even have a growing season?*

The group quickly sang a song in Ukrainian. The team had been spending their mornings in language class and had learned a couple of Ukrainian songs to sing at the seed meetings. Of course, no one had thought it would be so cold that their breath would freeze on their faces. Reuben moved his arms to get his blood running. It was odd, but it was even colder in these old buildings than it was outside.

The pastor was hastily finishing, explaining to the attending audience that they had been introduced to two kinds of seeds. The one would produce fruit from their gardens if they planted and cared for them. The other would take root in their hearts and bring forth fruit for eternal life if they allowed it. Food for their bodies was important, but food for their souls was even more important. "Would anyone like a Bible?" He always asked this at the end of the service.

Hands went up all over the building filled with little old people wrapped to their noses in scarves, big silent men, and thin pale children. They all looked cold. The round, weathered faces of the women squinted up at the Bibles as they were passed out. "I want one," their faces seemed to say. Almost everybody took a Bible.

Sowing the incorruptible seed, God's Word.

Because of the cold, the team skipped the testimonies that the group usually gave and dismissed the meeting. Reuben found it incredible that anyone even came. The local pastor had told him that many of the people had walked several miles to attend. Reuben hoped they wouldn't freeze on their way home. At the door, while people filed out, the team handed out the seed packages.

Everyone received a seed package—maybe more than one. The team had tried various systems to make sure each family got only one package, but it was hard. The people all looked alike when they were bundled up in such big coats, their faces covered up to their eyes. How was anyone to know who had given seeds to which family? A little old lady would stand there, her pixie face brilliant with blue eyes blazing up at a person, smiling in innocence and hope. Who wouldn't give her a package? The coats were so voluminous that any number of packages could have vanished inside them.

Reuben gathered the team at the door after most of the people had left. Not many had hung around to chat. A Mennonite lady who lived in Kiev and had come to witness one of the seed meetings was still talking to Mary Ann. Reuben moved up behind his wife. Mary Ann's skin was blue, and her teeth were chattering. "Oh, yes," she was saying, "we're heading to Afghanistan this spring."

"You're crazy!" The lady's voice was flat. "Those people in Afghanistan are crazy. You're crazy to go there."

Crazy? Crazy! It's crazy to be holding meetings in sub-zero temperatures with no heat in the building! Reuben thought as he put his hand on Mary Ann's shoulder. "Are you ready to go?"

"I th-think s-so," Mary Ann replied, smiling up at him.

Mary Ann's friend frowned at Reuben. "You shouldn't make your wife go to Afghanistan. It's dangerous. You're crazy."

"Maybe so." Reuben wasn't inclined to disagree at this point. He just wanted to get Mary Ann beside a heater.

"Oh, no!" Mary Ann exclaimed, waving her hands. "We're not crazy. You see, God wants us to go. He's calling us to help those people. Too many people are too scared, but someone has to help. God said to go and teach all nations, and—"

"Mary Ann . . ." Reuben tugged at her arm.

Mary Ann frowned at him. "Well, it's true."

"You're cold," he told her. "Let's go warm up."

"I'm not anymore," she said, but then gave in. "Goodbye!" she called over her shoulder to the woman.

Late that night as they lay in bed, drowsiness overtaking them, Mary Ann sat up suddenly. "Dear, I asked the Lord if we were crazy, and immediately He gave me this verse: 'For God hath not given us the spirit of fear; but of power, and of love, and of a sound mind,' " she said.

"What?" Reuben was almost asleep.

"2 Timothy 1:7," Mary Ann told him. "Love is the most important part."

"You forgot the sound mind," Reuben laughed.

"Well, that's what I wish I would have quoted to that woman today," said Mary Ann, lying back down.

The time to leave Ukraine came soon. In no time, it seemed, they were packing up and driving to the Kiev airport early one morning. At security, they ran into difficulties. The team had a lot of leftover yogurt, and Mary Ann had packed some, intending for them to eat it as a sort of airport breakfast.

Security didn't like it. "No yogurt goes through," they said.

"No problem," Reuben said. "No problem. How about we take it through in our stomachs?"

Since no one else was in line, they opened the cartons and drank the yogurt. The security officer watched them, surprised. He was young, not hardened by years of dealing with passengers, and the longer he watched them, the more he struggled to be stern. A grin wobbled through. Finally he burst out laughing and drew near.

"What were you doing in Ukraine?" he asked, now friendly.

Reuben explained about the seed project.

"Ah," said the officer. Then he got excited. "Are you Mennonite?"

"Well, yes," Reuben replied.

"I have a brother in Canada who received a house during a disaster project. Some Mennonites built it for him."

"Really!" Reuben was interested. "What sort of organization do you suppose it was?"

The man tried to remember. "It started with *m*. Maybe MDS?"

"I see," Reuben said. "That stands for Mennonite Disaster Service. I've heard of it."

The security officer considered them. "Yes, it was Mennonite all right. I really, really appreciate how you people go out of your way to help others."

"Ah," Reuben said, "it's not about the Mennonites. It's about God and people who love Him and serve others because of what He has done for them. It's about planting seeds."

Mary Ann downed the last of her yogurt and tossed the plastic container, looking to the security officer. "All done. Now, what's next?"

CHAPTER 13

Ukraine
Virginia Pakistan Israel
Afghanistan Haiti Bangladesh
Minnesota

Life-Giving Water

WINDOWS HAD BEEN SHOT OUT, buildings had been bombed, and bullet shells lay strewn about in the brown dust. Twisted metal and wreckage from combat rattled in the alleys when a man tried to walk through them. The first night, Afghanistan rang in Reuben's ears. He stretched on the bed, trying not to kick the bedclothes. Mary Ann, bless her, had fallen asleep. She lay now with one hand tucked under her pillow, and Reuben marveled at her.

She had forgotten all about the heat of the black airport where they had shuffled through the heaped luggage, digging for their bags. Airport security had tossed them there. Flashlights of travelers had bobbed about all over as they had all hunted for their baggage. The electricity had been out. Crying for a job, porters had howled at their elbows.

What are we doing here? Reuben asked the black square of the ceiling. *What are we thinking? Kabul, Kabul, Kabul.* The name of the city marched around in his head. They, and Darrell who was with them, had not even been able to fly into the country directly from the United States. Their passports could not show that they had come directly from the United States, so they had spent two days in Dubai, meandering around the oil riches of that country. In April 2007, indoor ski slopes in the shopping malls were the newest engineering marvel in Dubai. Out on the streets, though, if they had stumbled off the main drag, little huts lined the alleys, selling a scoop of flour here, a little rice there—all the poor could afford to take home with them.

Just that night, they had flown into Kabul and were trying to sleep in the Operation Mercy guesthouse. The name of the charity sounded so odd in this war-torn country. "Operation Mercy." Reuben tried the name out. He made an effort to draw some inspiration from the words. That was what he and Mary Ann were doing here, an operation of mercy. In the same breath he addressed the Lord. "Exactly what are we doing here? Just what do you plan to do with an amputee and his wife?" Reuben had learned a long time before to be honest with the Lord. He figured the Lord could handle his true feelings better than anyone else. Thinking, waiting, he listened. He'd had enough of these talks with God to know he should listen. When he talked to God alone, God often had something to say on the subject.

I didn't send you here because you knew the language. I didn't send you here because you know the culture. I sent you here to be used as a vessel. You work because you love me, Reuben. Keep quiet, and let me do the talking.

Just being who I am, who Christ is, is so much more important than what I could say or do. Reuben thought this over again. It wasn't a new idea to him, but he decided the point needed refreshing. *Fine, God. But since I've built my life trying to become like you, you'll even have to BE for me. If I'm going to BE for you, you'll have to be there to BE for me.*

Reuben suspected that the Lord chuckled. There were a lot of BEs, but he pressed on. *It all kind of comes back to you, Lord, I guess. Maybe what I do or think isn't actually that important. It doesn't affect the course of things all that much when you've already mapped out our lives. If I make a mistake, it doesn't keep your work from happening, because your work isn't happening because of me. When I do something right, well, it doesn't make your work happen either. It's not my work. Maybe the only thing that makes a difference in how I work for you is how connected I am to you. Maybe I need to glory more in my infirmities, because when I am weak, then am I strong. When I am nothing, then you can be everything.*

It was all pretty cliché. Reuben had the distinct impression that he had been taught those ideas in primary Sunday school class, but it wore him out trying to think through it all now. *I do this because I love you, God, not because I have it figured out.* He fell asleep, smiling, drawn on by jet lag.

Evidence of Afghanistan's violent decades fighting with the Soviets, then Western powers, was on display the next morning as Reuben, Mary Ann, Darrell, and their guide wandered through the city, kicking up the dust in Kabul's back streets. Imploded buildings, walls splattered by bullets, and gaping windows and doors all served to relay the impression of a ghost town. People lurked about. Most of Kabul's population had pulled a life together out of the crumbled city.

Women in blue burqas, curtaining off their souls, contributed to the mysterious feel of the city. Withered men, girded in robes, wearing pointy beards, and topped off by white turbans, added an odd twist to the scenery. Exploded missiles and abandoned tanks were scattered through fields that men plowed with oxen, a bleak testimony to the modern world that had blazed in—and then left again. Afterward, the men of Afghanistan had picked themselves up and gone about their lives again, using the ancient methods, as before. Not much had changed.

Missiles don't build, they destroy.

Darrell stopped to take a picture. Mary Ann was reassured by his presence. After all, it was because of him that she and Reuben had come. Darrell had wanted to visit Afghanistan to investigate a water project, but BOL had been reluctant to send him alone. They'd had no one to send with him, and BOL preferred to send international crisis workers out in pairs. They had double-checked with Reuben about sending Darrell by himself. "Of course, if you would offer to go with him, then the problem would be solved," they had said. It had worked out well. The Lord had led them, and here they were. Together they would go out into this place and see what the Lord had for them in Afghanistan.

Darrell pointed out an old army truck full of bullet holes. "I heard that they filled those with people and shot them up with machine guns during the war."

They made their way back in the direction they had come, scooting their toes through the dust to unearth old rifle shells. A little motorcycle roared up behind them as they threaded their way through a narrow, quieter street lined with what appeared to be residences, and they stepped aside for it. The cycle turned in at a house and stopped just as they walked up. The motorcycle driver took off his helmet and looked back in their direction. The man didn't look like an Afghan, his sweeping beard and longer hair cut in a bowl shape now appearing from under the helmet.

Reuben was interested in this man who looked like a Mennonite. Walking up, they paused to speak with him.

The motorcycle driver said, "My name is Al Geiser."

Reuben offered his hand. "Reuben Yoder."

In the conversation that followed, they learned that Al Geiser, an engineer, lived in the house they were standing in front of. Originally from Kidron, Ohio, he and his wife lived in Afghanistan. Al worked with the United States Army Corps of Engineers in an effort to design and build hydroelectric turbines to provide electricity to remote villages. Reuben was intrigued. He loved ingenuity, and this project caught his attention.

"Do you work mainly with foreigners or Afghans?"

Al Geiser surveyed the Yoders and hooked his thumbs in his belt loops.

"Come on in for supper. We'll talk."

It became clear that the surface of Geiser's work was engineering and construction, but the heart of his interest in Afghan development was providing employment for Christian believers who had been ostracized for their beliefs. Reuben discovered in this man a like interest in strategic ministry, and he was delighted. Encouraged by the man's vision, Reuben felt greater excitement about their own time in Afghanistan. They had come to accomplish similar work.

~~~~~~

The following year, after Reuben and Mary Ann would be home in Virginia, news would come of a man in Afghanistan, captured while returning from a funeral. The story was vague. Foreign Affairs blamed the Taliban, but it was all supposition. The man was Al Geiser, the engineer.

Six days into his capture, his kidnappers executed what they told him was a "last rite" over his bound body. The weather blew cold about them in the mountains. Al thought he might freeze to death. His captors told him not to worry, that the next night he would be "in a place of immense warmth." Al assumed they meant death.

"I faced death, and that was okay," he told his family later, "but it was the unknown and the waiting that was hard."

To the curiosity of his guards, Al prayed often. "Why do you pray so much? Your fate is not in God's hands; it's in ours," they said. For fifty-six days, he was held, blindfolded and starved. He refused to pay ransom. He told his captors that they could kill him, and he would only go to heaven.

After about a month and a half, Al's captors misunderstood that someone was paying Al's ransom and moved him down out of the mountains. Once they discovered their mistake, they holed up in a house to spend the winter. One night someone knocked at the door, and Al heard English voices. A U.S. Special Operations unit forced entry and rescued him, a rare recovery of a captive from the hands of the Taliban.

Reuben waited till he supposed Al would be home in Kidron, Ohio, and dialed Al's phone number. "So you have escaped with your life and are back with your wife?" he asked his old acquaintance.

"Yes."

Reuben continued, "With all that has happened to you, you will probably not return to Afghanistan."

There was no response from the other end of the line for a moment before Al answered, "I think we will return; there is so much unfinished work."

Then Reuben knew that Al was truly committed to the cause.

Several years passed. One day Reuben was sitting at his desk studying when a new email popped in. "Do you know this man?" it asked.

Al Geiser had returned to Afghanistan to continue his work. This time, he and several workers with whom he was traveling had been shot and killed by the Taliban.

~~~~~~

Up in the high mountains of Afghanistan, to the northwest of Kabul, the Yoder three took the bus to Taloqan, a seven-and-a-half-hour ride. The stunning peaks of the region floored the couple as they watched the passing landscape. Poppy seeds in thousands of acres, donkeys hauling salt from the mines, mud brown huts with goats on the roofs, wizened men, and little children sucking their thumbs drifted past the cracked bus windows. These scenes met their eyes, wearying them in the glare of the sun and clarity of the sky. Brown sandy dust rose to settle in the crinkles at the corners of their eyes. Up, up, up they went.

Afghanistan housed a different kind of poverty than they were used to. The travelers had seen and would see the poor in many places—the handicapped, the bereaved, the abused—but here they saw what primitive poverty looked like. Here the Taliban had swooped down to destroy and lay waste these villages under one pretext or another. These regions were gripped in Islamic terror, but out of fear, the mountain people embraced the very culture that produced these terrors, mutely submitting to the horrors of righteous butchers.

Out in those mountains, plastic was a novelty, electricity a phenomenon. Television and cell phones had not yet drowned out the outlying places with their noise. The people subsisted in mud huts, and cleanliness was a luxury. Water trickled out in distant spots, and the homes of the poor sprang up in the desert. Small children spent their days trudging to distant water holes. With their donkeys, they loaded containers of water to pack home over the miles.

Children spent their days carrying water for the family.

This was the reason BOL had sent the trio to Afghanistan. They could not change every village in northwest Afghanistan, but they could impact a few. These villages needed better access to water.

As they traveled beyond Taloqan in an old army jeep, a military checkpoint harassed them about their day's journey. A commander came out, razor in hand and without his uniform, to look at their papers. The younger officers, waving rifles in the proximity of the driver's and Reuben's shoulders, backed off to give room to their superior. However, they hung about the perimeter to see the fun. Reuben averted his eyes from their swinging guns as the barrels undulated about abdomen level. *They are awfully careless!*

The commander tossed aside the papers, uninterested in extensive document investigation. But the present predicament of three gallivanting foreigners pricked his concern. "Where are you going? Why? Are you a part of the American military?"

Reuben thought the last question ridiculous. Two old people and their son, unarmed, jouncing around like popcorn in the back of an old army jeep on sunny Afghan roads full of potholes did not seem like much of a military platoon. Reuben refocused his attention on the argument the interpreter and the driver were having with the commander, on whose face a trickle of lather had dribbled beneath his sideburns. One of the younger soldiers used the end of his rifle to scratch his head.

After a lot of gesticulation from the driver and worried wrinkling of the commander's nose, they were told to wait. The young soldiers drew in again, pulling a tight guard around the jeep. They were disposed to be friendly, and Reuben and Darrell spent the next five minutes exchanging smiles with them. Reuben used the interpreter to ask them a few questions, to which the soldiers shrugged and grinned.

After a bit, a man arrayed like Saul's armor bearer strode out of the base and jumped into the jeep with them. The soldiers stepped back, and the jeep continued on its merry way. They were to have a guard with them.

From there the roads disappeared, and they followed the tracks behind poppy fields and bounced over rough terrain until they arrived at their destination.

Rolling into that first village, the impracticality of what they proposed to do dawned on Reuben. They had suspected that it would take a lot of pipeline to get water into the villages, but the miles of rock and sand and peaks and sparse pastureland stretched indomitable. *What are the chances of even finding water to be piped in?* Reuben stopped himself. That was ridiculous, of course. *There has to be water somewhere. This isn't Mars— people live here.* He shook the thoughts away as he and Darrell climbed from the jeep, their hired interpreter and an Afghan engineer at their side.

From the huts, people began to filter forth. They all seemed small, withered by the arid climate, their faces puckered in the bright sunlight. The tribesmen gathered around.

The interpreter looked to Reuben and Darrell, and both men looked at each other. Where should they go? What should they do? *Be.* The word breathed in Reuben's ear. *Wait. See what happens. Something will happen. Don't force it.*

The tribesmen exchanged glances, and one, presumably some head of the village, began to speak.

Guttural mountain talk rushed from his mouth. Reuben wondered if there were words to what he was saying. It all sounded as one long syllable, like water rolling over rocks, with no pause for breath. The man stopped, his voice suspended in the air, and whatever the man had said proved to everyone's satisfaction that the foreigners were as deaf as doorposts. The gathered villagers sprung their attentions on the interpreter, who grew flustered. Eyes popping, he turned to Reuben and Darrell.

"They want to know if the military sent you."

"Tell them no, we come of our own accord from far away. We have a plan we want to talk to them about."

The interpreter said that the village elders had agreed to hear them out, and they all gathered under a tree at the edge of the village. Reuben cast a wary glance to Mary Ann, and she patted the seat of the jeep to indicate that she would stay there.

Reuben looked about him as they reached the village tree to where they had been escorted. The men had seated themselves in a circle, and Reuben found himself in a familiar predicament. He could not sit Indian-style with his wooden leg on. He despised the attention that removing his leg drew, but he could not see any way around it. He felt the gazes fix on him as he took off his leg.

Two old men put their heads together, and the heads of the other men collectively swiveled toward Reuben. The interpreter, who had taken off his eyeglasses to polish them, nearly dropped them. And from the windows

A typical village constructed of bamboo and mud in the remote mountainous regions of Afghanistan. In the distance are other villages that also asked for good water.

of the huts, Reuben felt a hundred stares. The two old men nodded to a younger man who rose and produced a stool.

"Oh, no, no," Reuben protested, embarrassed. But they insisted.

The interpreter leaned in with a flourish of politeness. "They said that if you need to take anything else off, you should do so."

"Oh, no that's all."

"Are you sure?"

"Yes, I am sure."

The same young man who had brought the stool now served them tea. The men drank it solemnly. It was bitter tea, but pieces of hard candy were passed around to put between their teeth, and as the black tea washed over the candy, a little sweetness came away with it.

"My dentist would have a fit," Darrell murmured.

The tea and pleasantries disposed of, they were invited to speak, and they mapped out their plan.

"Water is important," Darrell began.

Everyone nodded. It was a profound thought, though not original.

"From water comes life," Darrell added.

That was true too, everyone agreed.

"We want to help you get water more easily. Your children spend many hours fetching water for your homes when they should be in school."

Brows creased. *Well, yes, of course they do. Children are supposed to fetch water. How else would we survive?*

"This is hard on your children," Darrell continued.

Maybe.

"And your donkeys."

The foreigners have a point.

"So we would like to help you. We could build a tank here in the village that everyone could tap out of and lay pipe to it from the nearest water source."

The tribesmen thought about this.

"Then you could have plenty of water to drink, cook with, and bathe in."

Bathe in? They looked at each other in surprise.

"The water should be clean water. Today when we came from Taloqan, we saw children playing in the gutters. They washed themselves and cupped the water to their mouths. Often this makes children so sick that they die. Do you want this to happen to your children?"

The elders scratched their heads and stroked their beards. "What would it take?"

"What do you have here to build a tank with and lay pipe?" Darrell asked them.

At this, free discussion broke out among the men. Reuben leaned back and watched. Darrell grinned. "I wonder," he said to no one in particular, "what one of our fellowship meals would sound like to someone who didn't know English?"

It took some doing, but after a while they came back with an answer. "We have men who can dig ditches to lay pipe, but we have no pipe. We

Water to bathe *with*, not *in*.

have rocks to build a tank, but no concrete."

"Ah," Reuben said. "Well, we have concrete and pipe, but no men. What if we all work together?"

So the project began. In the initial meeting, getting everyone to agree seemed a small enough matter, but there was a lot more to village politics than all that. The villagers were not lacking in opinions. They gave all the details and decisions quite a lot of time and attention.

A location for the tank needed to be chosen because the site needed to be on someone's land. Someone mentioned that the person on whose land it was would control the water, so a paper was drawn up and signed, saying that whoever had the tank on his land would be generous about letting the rest of the village access it as much as they needed. For whatever value this would hold, the document was drawn up with great ceremony.

After the meeting, Reuben discovered Mary Ann back at the jeep, her

Coming to an agreement on a location for the tank.

sandaled feet dangling out over the floorboard, prattling away to the children who had gathered about. The armed guard, observing her hilarious attempts at communication, tried to help out with his limited English vocabulary.

Working on the project became part of their daily routine, making the trip into the highlands above Taloqan. At the military checkpoint, an armed guard always jaunted up and claimed a spot in the jeep. They stopped there as a matter of rote to pick him up, and no one at the military camp ever bothered to check their papers anymore. In fact, the young soldiers who sprawled about told them that to be allowed American duty was a scrapped-over honor.

The armed guards always followed the proceedings in the villages with great dignity and amusement. They did not find it necessary to get themselves dirty helping, but occasionally they felt it incumbent to make suggestions.

The pipelines took days of work. First they used a laser transit to mark the line of the ditch. After it was laid out, the village men lined up with their mattocks and made the sandy soil fly. It became a great party for all involved.

Digging a trench for the two-kilometer water line. "No problem," the men said. "Give us three days."

Afghanistan had the second-highest rate of childbirth mortality in the world. The value of women was reckoned according to their ability to bear children, and young girls were married off to deliver babies to men three times their age.

The generation of girls who were becoming young mothers the year Reuben and Mary Ann were in Afghanistan had grown up under Taliban rule—a time when women were not allowed out of the house, not even to go to school.

These girls knew nothing of health and hygiene. In horror, they conceived, and in ignorance, they brought forth. The Afghans reasoned that since childbirth is a dirty process, the dirtier the environment for birth the better. They brought in dirt from the barn to spread around, and there in the filth, women sprawled to bring forth their young.

The youngest mothers were often not sufficiently developed to give birth. Hemorrhaging haunted births like a vulture, waiting to tear life from the young women. One in seven women died in childbirth. Because of these circumstances, the silent terror of their fate grew and spread through young girls like cancer. Some, when old enough to be married, committed suicide.

Babies who survived the ordeal of being brought into the world had yet to traverse a perilous environment. Sometimes the families disposed of baby girls. Swaddling the little ones up in clothes for the first year, mothers fed their babies poppy drugs—opium. As toddlers, children bathed in water and then drank out of it. One in four children died before the age of five.

Nadia, a nurse from Taloqan hired by Operation Mercy to give health classes in the villages, traveled into the mountains with the Yoders sometimes. She had a daughter who liked to ride along also. The trips taxed the endurance of all three women. On some of the steep places, the driver gunned the jeep up the incline. Sometimes they rolled back and tried again, and then the driver would hold the brakes while someone crawled out to place rocks behind the wheels to keep the jeep from rolling backward over the drop-off. The hairpin curves on the trail-like roads, carved into the face of the mountain, provided an even greater terror for Mary Ann, determined as she was not to mention it.

Nadia evidenced less patience on these trips than Mary Ann. She clung to the door and rolled her eyes, muttering. After one horrendous trek, she called one morning as they were preparing for another trip. Her daughter Tabita would go along instead.

"Why, Nadia, what is wrong?" Mary Ann crossed her eyebrows at the phone. The voice at the other end faded. "I so, so ill. Obviously, I not today go."

Disappointed, Mary Ann thought it over. *If Nadia doesn't go, then I'll only be in the way of the men.*

"My daughter she want to go."

"Ah," said Mary Ann, "but Tabita isn't a nurse."

"I teash her. I teash her many thing. She go."

There was no use stalling. "Okay!" Mary Ann agreed. "It is sad that you cannot go today. The guard says the roads are much better today."

"Better?" Nadia's voice was loaded with doubt.

"Oh, yes. Much better. The guard said so."

The roads were better, although Tabita squealed plenty. Mary Ann, watching with glimmering eye, thought her shrieks a bit excessive. Reuben and Darrell ignored Tabita's apparent distress, and Mary Ann tried to.

After one little shriek from Tabita, Aamir, the guard they had picked up, turned to her. He had been with them on trips before, and he rattled off to Tabita, who had flipped back the face of her headdress. She turned luminous eyes on him, which widened till they were as round as balloons. Tabita scowled, and she turned back to the window, pressing her lips together.

Curiosity burned in Mary Ann. She knew Reuben and Darrell would not ask, so she addressed Abdul, the interpreter. "What did Aamir say?"

"He said that American women are courageous even though they are Christians. He said American women have spunk."

"Oh, they do," Reuben agreed.

"Oh, my!" Mary Ann flashed her eyes at her husband. "We're pretty regular people. Tabita is just scared. Aamir doesn't need to pick on her." From being annoyed with Tabita herself, she now thought the men were being mean.

"I don't think you're regular at all," Reuben replied, grinning down at her. Mary Ann snapped her eyes at him, and then she, too, faced the window, pressing her lips together, her expression matching Tabita's.

The next time Nadia went with them, she abandoned the normal procedure of sitting in an empty room to wait while a few women dribbled in over the space of a day. She and Mary Ann marched to one of the houses where Nadia knew someone. A wedding was in progress. Mary Ann found herself seated on the floor in a mud hut, surrounded by more women than she could breathe through. Nadia stood up and began teaching her class on hygiene and childbirth, though Mary Ann felt that it was hardly the time. The women, however, piled around to listen, so the nurse broke them up in three classes and taught all morning. The wedding was postponed until the seminar had finished.

～～～～～～～～～～～～～～～～～～～～～～～

Throughout the world, rumors and newspaper headlines told the story of Taliban oppression. And the conditions in Taloqan confirmed it. Authorities exiled a man for giving a Bible to a student who had requested one. Another Christian girl walking the sidewalk died from a bullet fired from a man passing on a motorcycle.

Darrell was out with friends one night. Curfew had come and gone. It was foolhardy to be out after that imposed deadline, but Darrell was. Wearing a headlamp, he scuffled along in the dark. The friends lingered behind a bit, but Darrell was ready to get home. He was forging ahead when a string of foreign phrases broke into the night from in front of him. Darrell looked up, moving closer to see who it was.

"Stop, Darrell." He could hear his friend's agonized whisper. Again the friend hissed, "Stop!"

He hesitated.

"Darrell! They said to stop or they'll shoot."

Darrell froze. He thought of the headlamp, marking his forehead. He eased his hands up, flicking the light off. No one said anything more, and after a couple of minutes, the group slipped down a side alley to their homes.

Reuben tried to shake off the worry, but Darrell's story shook him up more than he cared to admit. *Lord? Are you here? Do you hear the cries of fear and oppression from these people?*

Mary Ann was not happy with Darrell for being out after curfew when she heard the story. "Darrell, the Lord took care of you. But don't let it happen again."

Darrell only grinned.

Minnesota   Virginia   Pakistan   Ukraine   Afghanistan   Israel   Haiti   Bangladesh

Celebration

REUBEN, MARY ANN, AND DARRELL were making the long, hot drive up to one of the villages. Everyone was in high spirits, for that day they were finishing the pipeline. Reuben and Darrell planned to stay up for the night to attend the big celebration. Darrell was whistling as he pulled out his mp3 player, and Mary Ann stuck her head out the window and let the wind rip at her hair until the driver complained. She pulled it back in again.

Abdul, the interpreter, was also cheerful that day. On some days, he would develop attitudes where he tried to tell everyone everything and run around causing trouble. He dressed very conservatively, portrayed his lifestyle even more conservatively, and in general tried to paint a picture of himself in sainthood to his fellows. His occasional snits only made this tendency more ridiculous. When things did not go his way, Abdul grew religious and prolonged meetings, blaming all the things he took issue with on the Christian faith of the foreigners. He felt that Reuben and his wife and son were excellent people with a few blind spots, particularly when payday arrived. His English was by no means stellar, but Reuben thought they should keep Abdul in spite of his idiosyncrasies. Interpreters did not bloom on trees.

On this day, Abdul scooted over to Darrell and put his ear close to Darrell's ear. He strained to hear above the roar of the jeep, and after a bit he said, "What are you listening to?"

Darrell had been raised to share, but he didn't suppose that Abdul would like what he was listening to. He ignored the question. Abdul poked his ears close again and repeated, "What are you listening to?"

Seeing no other way out, Darrell removed his earbuds and surveyed the man. "A Christian man is preaching." He thought that would turn Abdul away, but Abdul asked to listen.

Darrell gave him an earbud, and he plugged it in his ear.

After a bit, Abdul pulled his earbud out. Darrell punched the pause button and looked at him questioningly.

"This is good," Abdul said. "It's all good, but they don't talk about Mohammed."

"Well," Darrell said, "it doesn't talk about Mohammed in the Bible."

"But Islam is the only true religion, and Mohammed is its prophet."

"This man doesn't believe that. He believes in Jesus now. He became a Christian."

Abdul frowned. He motioned as if he was about to put his earbud back but pulled it away again. "Antonio Inoki became a Muslim."

"Antonio Inoki?"

"He is a wrestler."

"Oh," said Darrell, pressing the play button, "that's why. Christianity forbids violence. Antonio needed a religion that would allow him to wrestle."

They listened in silence. Then Abdul pulled out his earbud again. "Forgiveness? What is forgiveness?"

Darrell thought a bit. "It's like, okay, say I did something bad to you, maybe I stole your goat. You think about it and say, 'It's okay, Darrell, you can have my goat. I forgive you.'"

Abdul frowned again. "I don't understand."

"Well, it's like this," Darrell tried again. "When we sin, God does not like it, right? Okay, so when we do wrong, we go to God and say, 'Please forgive me for doing this sin.' God forgives us. He doesn't remember our sin anymore."

"He doesn't?"

"If we accept Jesus's blood to cover our sins, He doesn't."

"But if someone takes my goat, I take his. That's fair."

"Wouldn't it be nice if you could say, 'That's okay, you may have my goat'?"

Abdul rubbed his eyes and laughed. "Yes, of course, if I had taken the goat. Or if I were rich like you, I could share all my goats and not have to worry. That would be nice."

"No, no." Darrell sat sideways on the seat. "Forgiveness comes at a cost to us. When God forgave us, it cost Him Jesus, His own Son."

Abdul put his earbud to his ear, scowling.

When they arrived at the village, all the men were standing around the water tank that they were planning to finish. Abdul bounced out of the jeep and ran up to them, chattering. They stood together, bright spots of color against the brown of the landscape and the gray of the overcast sky, their weathered faces squinting. When Reuben and Darrell reached his side, he asked Darrell for the mp3 player and displayed it to the villagers while they listened to him. At first their expressions were bland, but they began to warm up as Abdul's speech progressed. A few replied, and one time the whole group laughed. Reuben wished he could understand what they were saying.

"What are you talking about?" Darrell asked Abdul.

"I am telling them about this forgiveness," Abdul explained. "We've never heard such an idea. The men think it is funny that forgiveness lets people have goats that are not theirs. Everyone knows that stealing is wrong. We all want to live in a place like that where people just let you have their goats. I don't even know a good word in our language for this idea, to let someone else just have your goats. Are you sure this is not communism?"

That day the finishing details on the water tank were completed. The pipe had already been laid. Clear water began to fill up in the tank, and the little children grouped around it, turning the spigots to see the water come out and then turning them back off before too much water was wasted. They knew the cost of spilled water.

A celebration was planned for the evening. Some of the people from

The crew finishes up as the underground spring begins to trickle into the tank. Water overflow will fall into the front trough for donkeys and goats.

Operation Mercy had come along to arrange the program with the village. They had packed a generator, a projector, and equipment to view the film *Treasures of the Snow,* which had been translated into Dari, the language of the province. They could not use the projector until after dark, and if the group from Taloqan could not return before dark, they had to stay in the village. It was too dangerous to travel after dark.

Reuben arranged to stay for the night, but Mary Ann went back with the jeep at their normal departure time.

The folks from Operation Mercy set up the screen on a hill outside the village. The villagers cooked a big meal, and they ate as darkness was falling. The villagers slipped out to the knoll and stretched out. Just as the film was to begin, the wind slammed a gust into the screen, nearly toppling it, and rain sprayed over them all. A storm was just around the hill. The people scrambled for a hut, and the Operation Mercy men hunted through the dark for their cords and equipment, grabbing and running. The group congregated in the hut where the projector was reassembled. Villagers layered themselves into the room, and in spite of the storm, more gathered at the windows. They were entranced by the projector and the moving pictures on the big screen.

The mountains on the film blossomed in green, and the blueness of the sky reached off the pictures. The water seemed unlimited. In the story, little children squabbled. Lucien dropped the kitten into the ravine, and the little boy, Dani, broke his leg trying to rescue his kitten. Dani's leg did not heal right, and he walked with crutches. Dani's big sister Annette drove Lucien away. She told everyone what an awful boy Lucien was. No one liked Lucien any more. Lonely, sad, and bitter, Lucien ran off to the old man up on the mountain.

Watching his friends' faces, Reuben asked himself what they were thinking. *Lord, let this explain forgiveness to them. Let it reach their hearts.*

Lucien carved Noah's ark with all the little animals for Dani, who still could not walk right. He crossed the mountain pass in the middle of a ferocious snowstorm to ask the famous doctor traveling through to come and heal Dani's leg. Lucien nearly froze to death, but he made it in time to catch the doctor. The doctor looked at Dani's leg, and through surgery was able to fix it. Annette and Lucien both learned to forgive.

As the film ended, the people drifted away, for bedtime came early in the mountains. When the light left, day was done, and now it was two hours since darkness had fallen. Reuben found himself in the mud hut with his military companion, the interpreter, Darrell, and the Operation Mercy team, trying to arrange their sleeping quarters. Reuben assigned spots; he himself would sleep at the guard's feet. They spread their thin mats, and the guard removed his uniform and stuck his rifle under his pillow. Sleep came to their eyes soon in that dark place.

In the middle of the night, hooves cut sharply into Reuben's calf, jerking him from slumber. He got up so quickly that his vision spun. "What—"

Mumbles and grunts burst from the other men. *"Phhhthybtt!"* the guard spluttered, sitting up. Abdul only moaned and turned over on his mat.

"Goats!" Reuben exclaimed. One pranced in front of him. He could see the shadow.

The guard yelled. The goats were thrashing a bag in the corner. *Rip. Squeal!* The guard leaped to his feet in the dark, sprawling at the corner of his mat. A goat bleated from underneath. Mumbling, the guard picked himself up and threw himself at the corner again. Shadows danced, and the racket rose. More squeals and bleats, sounding almost human, flooded the air. The guard kicked at them, and the goats capered about, protesting.

Reuben turned on his flashlight, startling them all with the bright flash. The door was open. Abdul came straight up off his mat, blurting Dari.

"*Mmhphthplit!*" Abdul scrubbed sleep out of his eyes, glaring about. "Goats!" he added in English, the word dying away as he realized he was behind times. "Stupid goats. They want candy."

The candy! Reuben remembered how the engineer had been feeding the caprine population earlier with the hard candy the Afghans used to flavor their tea. "Well, give it to them and get them out!"

"It's all gone!" the guard wailed. Abdul interpreted this for Reuben's benefit.

Reuben got to his feet to help. They corralled the animals, working them toward the door. When the goats were gone and the door was secured, Reuben lay awake, thinking. *If goats could come in so easily, what or who else could also enter? Lord, this is crazy!*

～～～～～～～～～～～～～～～～～～～～～～～～～～～

When the jeep had pulled away from the village, Mary Ann had only been thankful that she did not have to sleep on the hard dirt floor that night, and she pitied Reuben. There was a day when she would have felt she was missing out on all the fun, but her sense of adventure was waning these days.

Mary Ann forgot this a minute later, absorbed in her alternate fate. *This driver does not have much experience,* she thought. She termed him a "wicked driver" and supposed that her bones would either be all in place or else all out of place till she arrived back in Taloqan. The trail was pretty steep, and the driver pretty bad. She gasped as they jolted over something unexpected. He blew his horn at nothing. They jounced over rocks and under them—for rocks hung over the cliffs like impending doom—down an incredible grade. Mary Ann closed her eyes and thought they would flip end over end. She prayed hard. The dirt floor with Reuben was beginning to appeal more and more. Down they went, on down, around a corner . . . *kaput! Put, put, put.* The engine died.

"Oh! Lord!" Mary Ann gave the still landscape one horrified look and hid her face. Nadia put her hand to her mouth and whimpered.

They sat for a bit while the driver smoked a cigarette. When the cigarette was finished, he stubbed the glow out, tossed it on the rocks, and bailed out to have a look. Up came the hood in a horrible squall, and the driver buried himself behind it. *I wonder if he'd know a battery from a piston,* Mary Ann thought. *Not that I would know myself. And did he have to smoke that cigarette?*

With a roar like a wounded animal, the engine sprang to life, leaping forward. The driver galloped around and jumped into the driver's seat and away they rolled. On down, down, down till the road had long disappeared and they were driving though a dry riverbed.

They rattled over the rocks for a spell. *Vr-rroom-uh-uh-uh-uh* . . . The engine sputtered to silence. Mary Ann sat. The driver sat. Nadia slept. Around them the golden light of sunset lit the world till all was blinding. The shadows grew longer and darker . . . and longer. Mary Ann thought of the apostles in the dungeon who sang, and she hummed and then squeaked out a timid note. The driver swiveled his head and needled her with a glance. She would have tried for the second note, feeling braver, but a sound caught her ear. Another motor rumbled in the distance.

It was an old truck lumbering along the riverbed that served the countryside well, sparing people the bother of overland routes. Mary Ann thanked the Lord for the old truck. Help was on the way. Closer and closer the wheels crunched on the gravel, now parallel to them, and then spinning on past. The rust glistened in the sun before it all disappeared in the haze.

Time always passed like eternity for Mary Ann when she couldn't see a clock, and so she was shocked when she found out how late it actually was. Darkness rimmed the eastern sky. Another truck approached. This time the jeep driver got out and waved. The truck stopped. Mary Ann thanked the Lord again, this time for Samaritans in a land of priests and Levites. The men from the truck and the driver got the motor working in short order.

This time the jeep crawled over quite a distance, and darkness had nearly blanketed the land when the jeep stalled a third time. Confident that the Lord would send someone to help them along, Mary Ann nonetheless reminded God of a concern. *It isn't safe to travel here at night, Lord. People do strange things to foreigners.*

In the darkness they saw a light, which meant that a village lay nearby. The driver got out and drifted ahead on the path. Nadia slept on. Mary Ann began to nod herself, awakening to a hubbub. This time God had sent a whole village to fix the jeep. Men peered in at her, and Nadia stirred to pull her burqa about her more closely. Mary Ann set her chin to ignore them and prayed for their souls. The poor men had families somewhere, and maybe God would enrich their lives for being obedient to her need. She hoped so.

Mary Ann was weary when she finally reached the Operation Mercy compound. The guard, a jack-of-all-trades, opened the gate for her. "Lock your door to your rooms, Auntie. I will bring some hot water up for a bath."

Mary Ann took the hot bath and fell into bed. Outside, a terrible thunderstorm was lighting up. Glad that she was not stranded in a dry riverbed somewhere, she closed her eyes and fell asleep.

Reuben awoke early the next morning. The cacophony of goats outside reminded him of the incidents of the past night. "Goats!" He stood, slipping on his wooden leg and trying to brush wrinkles out of his clothes. The latrine available was just a hole between two walls, and he was sure Mary Ann would be glad she had returned to Taloqan. Washing his face with a handful of water from a bottle, he walked to a rise to look over the village in the early Afghan morning. The business of the day awaited him, and after that was finished, he intended to get back to Mary Ann as soon as possible.

Abdul had indicated to Reuben that there were already problems brewing among the elders of the village in relation to the water project. Out under the tree, drinking tea, he observed the old men to determine the extent of their peevishness. He wished to speak to them about something, but was unsure of how to go about it or how far he should go.

"Tawab, sir," Reuben spoke to the old man on his right, with Abdul interpreting, "how do you like the water?"

Tawab sneered when this was interpreted. "It's great water. But—"

"But what?"

Ibrahim, younger, but a respected figure, lunged to his feet. "Ah, Reuben, sir, you cannot understand. Unfortunately, this is a village problem, and there will always be village problems. This is politics—as old as these mountains. You need not concern yourself. We are very grateful for the water. Go back to your sweet wife and enjoy her smiles."

"I wish to know the problem," Reuben insisted.

Ibrahim was not so reluctant to share gossip as he had appeared. "Latif, sir. He is angry because no one made provisions for the water to be piped to his garden."

"But it's not piped to anyone's garden!" Reuben was scandalized.

"Yes, sir, but Latif is our chief."

It tempted Reuben to snap, "Ridiculous," but he folded his arms and bowed his head. "Ah, brothers, I have something to speak to you about."

"Please." Ibrahim inclined his head and sat. The others perked up.

"Remember how we spoke of water giving life? Water truly gives life, doesn't it? We must have it to stay alive. We need more than just water to drink. We need it to keep clean."

Patience spread over the village men's faces as Abdul interpreted his speech.

Of course we must keep clean. We know that.

"There is water that is more important to our lives than this water coming through the pipe. This is the water for our souls. Just as our bodies need water to survive, so our souls must also have this water to live. This water is the love of God for our fellow men. Have you forgotten the film so soon? Forgive and give, my brothers. Do this, and God will bless you long in this land with different kinds of water."

They sure listened! Reuben's mind spun. *I also know that my message fell on hardened ears. Not only that, their ears have never before heard such things. Will they understand? Only time will tell.*

Reuben and his cohort got up to go. The village would have to work out the politics of the water themselves. If they wished to pipe it into their chief's garden, they would have to do so themselves.

Aamir, the guard, had been impressed by the whole experience. On the drive down the mountain, he wanted to talk. Making Abdul earn his wages, Reuben and Darrell and Aamir talked.

"Forgiveness," Aamir said over and over again. "What is forgiveness?"

Reuben was quiet as they drove on after dropping Aamir off at the military barracks. The irony of the story of love and forgiveness being played in the humble hut in the northwest province of Afghanistan was not lost on him. He remembered in vivid detail the small room surrounded with men who leaned on their rifles and watched as children learned about forgiveness. These men cared so little about life. What could it possibly mean to them? Reuben knew Mary Ann had been praying, and he would continue to pray himself.

Some plants need only a sprinkling of water to grow, Reuben figured. *Especially those that spring up in the desert.*

Minnesota Virginia Pakistan Ukraine Afghanistan Israel Haiti Bangladesh

The Khyber Pass

THE SNOWCAPS OF THE KHYBER Pass rose above them. Reuben, Mary Ann, and Darrell were departing Afghanistan nearly three months after their arrival in Kabul. They were leaving through the Khyber Pass, part of the Spin Ghar mountain range which stood between Afghanistan and Pakistan. They were returning to Pakistan.

Mary Ann pressed her face against the window. The little Toyota Corolla taxi they had hired had been climbing through the rugged terrain for hours. Before she came to Afghanistan, she had not known about the Khyber Pass, but Reuben had told her that it was one of the oldest mountain passes still used in modern travel and had been a vital link on the ancient Silk Road. Mary Ann hadn't been clear on what the Silk Road was either. Reuben explained that it was an important trade route dating back to the Middle Ages that connected Europe with Central and South Asia.

"How do you know all this?" Mary Ann wanted to know.

Reuben grinned. She swatted at him. "Look, there's the crossing."

As they approached the wide, dusty stretch of no-man's land, the border between Afghanistan and Pakistan, the Corolla taxi lurched suddenly, throwing Mary Ann and Reuben forward.

"What!" Mary Ann caught herself lightly like a cat landing on its feet, and she braced on the seat in front. Through the settling dust, out of no-where, men thronged the taxi, shouting and trying to open the door. The

165

taxi driver hollered something over his shoulder.

"What did he say?" Reuben called above the clamor.

Darrell relayed over his shoulder, "He said they make cars stop this far from the customs office because of bomb threats. Let's get out."

The din increased when the three Americans crawled out of the taxi and stretched to their full height. "What do they want?" Mary Ann was amazed.

"I think they're porters," Reuben said, placing himself in front of one of the doors. "No, no," he said to the face at his elbow. "No. No, thank you. That's fine then. No, we don't need porters." The mob ebbed back and forth in front of him, crying for their bags. Mary Ann ducked behind his back and peeked under his arm.

Darrell pointed out a uniformed man at the edge of the crowd. "Police," he said. Reuben muscled away from the taxi, towing Mary Ann and trying to get back to the trunk that was tied down over their load of luggage and accumulated tools from the water project. One of the would-be porters was yanking on a bag.

The porters did not realize that a policeman had stepped up to the crowd, and one of them slapped the face of the policeman, shoving him back with the tide of porters. In an effort to bring order, the policeman seized a piece of pipe. Drawing near to the taxi, he cracked the offender first across the shoulder and then landed a good blow to his backside. The policeman brushed the porters away and said in English, "Get in and drive over to that building." He waved at the customs building. They rode the taxi up to the entrance strung around with high barbed wire.

"Why are you going to Pakistan?" The customs official frowned as they showed him their papers. "Why?"

"We have friends there we want to go back and see," Reuben explained.

The official opened their passports on the table and placed the heels of his palms on their open pages. "No." He shook his head. "No. You're crazy. You should not go to Pakistan."

Reuben thought of pointing out that they were coming from Afghanistan, but he didn't. Darrell tried to explain what they had formerly been doing in Pakistan while Mary Ann looked out the windows almost obscured in sandy dust. The sun beat down on the pavement outside, and the customs building on the Pakistani side looked far away. The brilliant color of the pass had faded here in the dust.

"Okay, okay," the official agreed. "You be very, very careful." He stamped their passports and waved them out the door. "Walk. Over there."

"What about the car?" Mary Ann cried. "And all our stuff!"

"No car," the official said behind them.

"What about you?" Mary Ann whispered to Reuben. "Will you be able to walk the whole way over there okay?"

Reuben was just about to hush her, embarrassed, when the taxi driver blurted something they did not understand, and the official looked sharply at Reuben's leg. He barked an order, and the taxi driver said, "They bring cart."

Soon they brought a cart, and the officers piled all the luggage onto the cart. Reuben became part of the baggage too, on their demand, and they set him on top of it all. *The cherry on the cone,* Reuben thought.

Armed escorts marched them across. The sun beat down on them as they ambled across the border lined with razor wire. Reuben's legs dangled over a suitcase, and he hoped his wooden leg would stay on. "How did they know I'm an amputee, anyway?" he asked his wife sheepishly.

"You had your leg off in the taxi, remember?" Mary Ann reminded him, traipsing along over the baked concrete beside him. The blazing sunshine was giving her a headache. "Is there any water left?"

Reuben handed her the water bottle, and she drank. Then she wished she hadn't. On the Pakistani side, she would need a rest stop. She hoped there was such a thing there.

At the customs office, Darrell went to check in first while Reuben guarded their stuff. A guard motioned for Mary Ann to follow him.

"Powder room," the guard said impatiently when Mary Ann only looked at him. "Fresh?"

"What's a powder room?" Reuben asked, wrinkling his forehead.

"A restroom," Mary Ann told him. "Should I go with him?"

Reuben had to stay with the luggage, and Darrell was busy. Mary Ann followed at a distance. *Oh, Lord,* she was thinking, *protect me! This man might be trying to kidnap me.*

They walked on in silence, the guard's heels clipping ahead on the concrete, around the long building and beyond it on more hot concrete infested with weeds growing through the cracks. Mary Ann grew flustered as the walk continued. It was embarrassing—not to mention dangerous. She wished she had waited until Reuben could have come along. What should she do? Mary Ann's habit of talking to God took over again. *Lord, I guess if you provided the restrooms, you can provide safety. Please don't let him kidnap me. Maybe he works for the terrorists.*

They found the restrooms eventually at a separate building. The guard waited outside for her, and together they made the trek back, ending in the room with the customs officials.

Reuben was glad to see her back. "I guess there are different ways to be martyred," he said, "but having you kidnapped while finding a restroom was not what I had hoped the Lord had planned for this trip. Next time I will go along."

"You're funny," Mary Ann said, forgetting all about her fright and propping her elbows on the counter to watch the customs official examine their passports. "The Lord took care of me. What was there to worry about, after all?"

It took them several hours after leaving the border to reach Peshawar, where they had arranged to spend the night in a guesthouse. The border patrol sent an armed guard with them the whole way to Peshawar to "protect them," as the command official had said. The three Americans didn't ask what they were being protected from, but they hadn't been on the road very long before they pulled over again to watch as security guards around them took their posts, lining the road. An American general was moving his convoy through the Khyber Pass.

"You know, we could have taken a plane from Kabul to Peshawar," Darrell said as they watched the tanks roll past.

"Oh, I'm glad we didn't!" Mary Ann exclaimed.

Reuben, watching the rocks high up on the peaks, didn't say anything, but he was also glad that they had gotten to cross the Khyber Pass in a taxi. It was the most beautiful scenery he had ever seen, and he had a sort of fascination with the idea that these were Osama bin Laden's stomping grounds. He looked at the rocks and wondered if bin Laden was there somewhere. *I should find the terrorist leader and tell him about Christ,* he thought.

~~~~~~~~~~~~~~~~~~~~~~~~~~~~~~~~~~~~~~

Beacon of Light had sent Reuben and Mary Ann with Darrell back to Pakistan to look for ministry opportunities in the absence of humanitarian aid. During a rebuilding project, such as the one in Galoosh the year before, it was difficult to discover the true spiritual interest when the hands of the people were in the pocket of the relief worker. They also wanted to finish up some business regarding the rebuilding project in Galoosh and heal the relationships from the abrupt departure the year before.

The guesthouse in Abbottabad was right beside the Pakistan Military Academy, a huge cadet corps the size of a square mile. From Mary Ann's window, she could see the wall of the academy enclosure and listen to the shouted commands as the military platoons completed their exercises. From anywhere in the building, they could hear the bands that played for hours over the loudspeakers.

Unknown to Reuben and Mary Ann, about a mile beyond the military institution there lay a compound where a man and his family were in hiding. Being the most wanted man in the world, he had lived in extreme secrecy in that compound for two years. Four years after Reuben and Mary Ann were in Pakistan, U.S. Navy Seal Team Six carried out the deadly raid which killed Osama bin Laden, the founder of Al Qaeda and the target of the U.S. occupation of Afghanistan and War on Terror.

Reuben and Mary Ann set up housekeeping in Abbottabad at the apartment that Beacon of Light had rented the year before during the rebuilding project, and it seemed they were busy immediately. First, the three of them packed up and went for a two-week tour of schools and hospitals and orphanages in Pakistan.

They visited a Christian school in Muree that had suffered a shooting at the hand of the Taliban three years before. The Taliban had swooped down upon the school, storming it and killing six men. The outlaws hunted for the children to shoot them also, but never found them. The young students had taken refuge in the chapel on the school grounds, and the Taliban warriors had strutted right past the doors of the chapel, never supposing that the children would be inside.

When the Yoders arrived at the school at noon one day, they found the place under heavy security. Their contact, a man called Karl, came to meet them at the guardhouse, and he gave them a tour of the place. Many of the children who attended the Muree School lived there under the care of house parents because their parents were involved in some sort of mission work in other parts of the country, or even other countries. The students of Muree were preparing for a graduation ceremony on the following day, so the three Americans watched the preparations while eating lunch with the proprietors of the school. At three in the afternoon, eight youth from the school were baptized.

Reuben listened as the young people gave their testimonies and answered questions. He so wished he could understand the language. The young people were baptized in an old water trough. Beyond the school, a military encampment spread over the terrain. During the baptisms, military trucks roared by the wall behind the school, doing a series of gun demonstrations that made Reuben's ears ring. He watched, astonished at the incongruity of it all. Just over the wall, the military played with their weapons, oblivious to the little exercises of faith happening on the other side. The people inside the wall, however, were fully aware of what was happening outside the wall. They understood the danger. They knew those guns were not friendly to their cause, but they did not care. They had a battle to fight too, just like the Pakistani military.

While on the tour of schools, the three spent a night in Lahore, the second biggest city in Pakistan. They had gone to visit Akram, their spy in the Galoosh stockyard the year before. The July weather in Pakistan was almost unbearable, and temperatures soared into the 120s the night they slept at Akram's house. They had planned to stay at a hotel, but Akram's family had arranged for the foreigners to stay with them.

"Come," Akram said as the evening grew late. "We have a place for you to stay." Mary Ann gulped and smiled brightly at this announcement. *Where?* Fifteen people lived in the two small rooms in Akram's house. Where would they put the three new people? It was already hot enough to roast a goose in those rooms. She opened her mouth to protest.

"Why, thank you," Reuben was saying. Mary Ann closed her mouth.

Akram led them up the narrow stairs by the light of a quivering lamp flame. The electricity had gone out, but as they walked out under the night sky onto the roof of the house, lights flickered on around them.

"Good," Akram said. "Now the fan will work for you." He switched on an ancient fan browned with age and the grime of the countryside. The fan began to rattle, hacking at the wire cage over the blades. Akram slammed his fist into it, and the blades settled away from the cage. The *rck-rck-rck* ceased. Akram spread a mat for them and one for Darrell. "Sleep well."

"Oh, dear," Mary Ann whispered as he left them. "How do we undress out here?"

Reuben glanced around at the houses beside them. "You may not want to." There were people on those roofs also, some sleeping, some talking, some smoking or talking on their phones, a few just looking at the stars, but all dim outlines in the shadows.

So they went to sleep on the mats, but first Reuben turned the fan off. It felt more like a heater than a fan. The sweat trickled down their necks, and they tossed and turned all night long. In the morning, as they rose under a red dawn, the temperature was already climbing. It had cooled down to 110 degrees overnight.

～～～～～～～～～～～～～～～～～～～～～～～～～～

After a few weeks in Pakistan, the Yoders arranged to travel to Galoosh. By then, Mary Ann had acquired a personal interpreter, a young woman by the name of Tamseela. Tamseela was a fine Christian girl who grew up in a Christian family. She lived by a Presbyterian church the Yoders visited sometimes.

On the day they were to go to Galoosh, the threesome swung by the church. Mary Ann got out of the taxi to meet Tamseela and made her way through the churchyard. Tamseela raced out of her house, a lean-to attached to the church, light-footed as a deer, her arms open wide. Mary Ann ran forward to meet her. She hugged Tamseela and decided to adopt her on the spot.

"It will be so nice to have an interpreter," Mary Ann said, holding the girl at arm's length and looking into her dark eyes. "No one ever understands my Urdu."

The two women laughed and went to the vehicle to join the others.

"Tamseela," Mary Ann said as they drove away, "I thought your family lived in the church basement. Isn't your father an elder?"

"He is an elder," Tamseela said, leaning back in her seat and beaming out the window. She straightened and explained, "During the earthquake, the foundation of the church building was damaged, so we are living in the lean-to until repairs can be made."

"I see." Mary Ann felt a pang. Some people put up with so much inconvenience. It made her feel guilty to think of the nice home she had in America.

It was only midday when they reached Galoosh. The group of five, including the driver who also attended the Presbyterian church, had talked the whole way. They grew silent as they climbed up the last hill, approaching Galoosh.

Time had been kind to the scars brought by the earthquake and the flooding. Fresh growth covered the shifted slabs of dirt, but remarkably little had been done in general reconstruction of bridges and roads. The landslides had been cleared away from the roads, however, and this made driving much easier than before.

They parked the taxi near the old campsite and started up to the village. As they climbed the path, Mary Ann scoured the mountainside with her

Mountainous Galoosh.

eyes, excited to see familiar landmarks. Here the landscape had changed too. The bare spots where the tents had been were now grown up in grass. The cook shack was still there, and an old potholder of Mary Ann's still hung from the nail. A rusty can or two, still sitting on the shelf, had melded into the wood, sticking a little when she lifted them to look at the labels.

"Come," Reuben called as he exited the cook shack, "let's go on to the village." Beyond was the destroyed girls' school. A man stood above it on the mountain kneeling on some rotted timbers. A jeep was parked beside him on the path. The man looked now, shading his eyes, and Reuben waved. The man leaped from the timbers and ran down the path. Reuben met him with open arms. "Khalid!" It was Khalid, the one who had been in the jeep accident.

Khalid pulled back from the embrace and looked straight into Reuben's eyes. "You're coming to my house."

A happy Khalid and his sons.

"Is that the same jeep?" Darrell asked.

"Same," Khalid replied, grinning.

The jeep had been restored. They all walked down the path to Khalid's house. Khalid's wife had had no warning to prepare for guests, and they sat down to wait while she cooked a meal. She caught the chicken and plucked it, cooking it along with some rice. Mary Ann watched her while the men talked. Word of their arrival spread throughout the village, and soon others drifted by to say hello.

"I want you to know," Khalid said as they sat on the mat, "I was very angry when you left, but you have done me no wrong. You people treated me right."

Hours later, as they left Khalid's house, they spotted another man crossing the river toward them. This man was whistling and carrying a sack of vegetables. The figure looked up suddenly and stopped in his tracks, wavering on the plank. "Wajid Sab!" Reuben exclaimed.

Wajid Sab advanced on them. "You are coming to my house," he said without bothering about preliminaries. "I am very glad to see you."

"Ah, but Wajid Sab," Reuben said, "it is already late, and we must go back to Abbottabad for the night."

"Then you must come tomorrow. I have many things to tell you."

The jeep scurried back to Abbottabad since the driver needed to make a trip to yet another city that evening. The driver dropped Reuben, Mary Ann, Darrell, and Tamseela off at a restaurant where they ate supper and talked and laughed. The visit to Galoosh had put them all in high spirits.

The next morning they returned to Galoosh, driving back up the mountains, and this time they spent their time with Wajid Sab. At the time when the building project was in progress, Wajid Sab and Reuben had many discussions about faith, values, and life. Now they easily fell back into their old patterns of conversation.

"The village doesn't know how to thank you," Wajid Sab said. "When your team came to Galoosh, the heart of the people was so low. We all said, 'What can we do? How can we begin again? What's the use?' You people helped us begin to rebuild our homes, yes, but also our lives." He concluded by saying, just like Khalid, "You treated me right and owe me nothing."

Reuben and Darrell received this thanks with gladness. It was good to be back and be friends. "But what about Sayyid?" Reuben wondered. They still had not met Sayyid.

"Ah, Sayyid," Wajid Sab shook his head. "We do not know."

"What do you mean you don't know?" Reuben felt a pang of fear.

Wajid Sab chose his words carefully. "After you left Galoosh, Sayyid burned all of your tents. He didn't want the villagers to get your things. He spent a great deal of time alone after you left. There was a problem. Sayyid did not stay at his house with his wife. She lived in town in Sayyid's house with Sayyid's two sons. Sayyid lived with his goats. While Sayyid was gone, it was said in the village that a neighbor man was friendly with Sayyid's wife. One day, it was said, the neighbor man took Sayyid fishing. Sayyid never came back."

"Sayyid!" Mary Ann cried. "He never came back?"

"No."

"No way . . . " Reuben shook his head.

Mary Ann mourned for Sayyid. "He seemed so close. With more teaching, he might have seen the light. Oh, poor Sayyid."

"Well, he was a funny old man." Wajid Sab shrugged and spread his hands.

"That's awful!" Mary Ann said reproachfully to Wajid Sab, and she pressed her nose into Reuben's sleeve. Reuben put his hand on her shoulder, but his mind was not quiet, thinking of his good old friend Sayyid. He, too, grieved at the memories that Wajid Sab's story had stirred.

On the ride down the mountains that night into the deepening shadow of the valley, scenes of Galoosh played before Reuben's eyes. He had wondered about the wisdom of leaving Galoosh the night of the exodus, but somehow, in spite of it, God had worked in the lives of the villagers.

Finally he said to Mary Ann, "You know, our work is rather immaterial to God. He just uses it. He doesn't wait to see if we did a good enough job to work through us. Actually, sometimes it doesn't seem to really matter how good a job we did, or if we failed. Maybe it has more to do with why we did what we did. At any rate, God seems to have used our building project in Galoosh."

"You're right," Darrell said from up front. "Isn't it incredible how God works? If all of that mess there hadn't happened, it's possible that Khalid and Wajid Sab would be no different men than they ever were." He glanced at Tamseela, and she smiled at him.

No one responded for a minute, and Tamseela looked out the window at the sunset floating in orange and purple. "God loves us all very much," she said softly.

CHAPTER 16

Minnesota — Virginia — Pakistan — Ukraine — Afghanistan — Israel — Haiti — Bangladesh

Being in the Way

NIGHT HAD FALLEN ON DARRELL at a cafe where he was writing an email. He lingered, taking the time to word the email carefully. He supposed that he ought to care more about getting back to the apartment, but it was taking him a while to find the right word.

"Excuse me," a husky voice said at his side.

Darrell looked up to see that a young man had joined him. He wore western clothes with his shirt tucked in and his cuffs rolled up. A jacket hung on the young man's shoulders, swinging as he moved his arms. His curls were oiled, and his face smooth from a recent shave, but his black eyes were bleary and bloodshot. Darrell could see tumult behind his tidy appearance, and he set his email aside, interested in this person. "Can I help you?"

"I wanted to talk to you. I don't see many foreigners here. My name is Ehson."

Ehson's English was polished. Something was different about Ehson, and Darrell tried to put his finger on it as he collected his things. The two men stepped outside into the warm night air to talk. They stood under the cafe's neon signs while the moths fluttered and the bugs crawled on the lights. After several minutes of conversation, the only thing that Darrell could discern as different was that Ehson asked none of the standard questions that people asked when they stopped a foreigner to talk.

177

Instead, Ehson talked about himself. "I am at the top of my class in college. I get very good grades . . ." Ehson paused to look about restlessly. He plunged on with his story. "But I started friendships with bad people. With them I have done things that are not good. They will destroy me if I do not get away from them. I left my home. Now I face depression all day long, so this morning I set my alarm for five o'clock because I planned to drive to Balacot and jump off the bridge . . ." Again Ehson's voice trailed away.

Darrell listened in shock. Ehson's manner was not melodramatic. Instead, he seemed almost absent-minded, as though he drifted on the tide of his thoughts. He acted as though there were nothing strange at all about telling a stranger these things at their first meeting.

"But when my alarm clock went off this morning, something held me back. I didn't go. I lay around in my house all day, and now I am out for a walk."

Darrell sighed at the weight the man was carrying. "Listen, Ehson. You have a problem. Do you want a solution?"

Ehson was staring at his hands, the fine nails and the even color of the skin. He turned them over and sighed as Darrell had done. "Yes."

Darrell took out a little New Testament he carried in his pocket. "This book has answers in it, Ehson. Here. Keep it. Have you ever heard of Jesus?"

"He's the son of the Christians' God?" Ehson looked at the cover of the New Testament.

"Yes. It's like this, Ehson. In the beginning God made people to serve Him. He created them and put them in the Garden of Eden where everything was perfect. But the people God created chose to sin, and God could no longer have a relationship with those people or their children. Now they were in an awful mess. Men started to kill each other and do all sorts of awful things."

Ehson looked Darrell in the eyes as Darrell continued his narrative. The compelling story of God's salvation plan seemed to pull Ehson out of the haziness with which he had described his struggles. Encouraged, Darrell told the old story with all of his energy, speaking with emotion as he told how God had saved him from a life of sin. "See, Ehson. Sin brings death. When you or I or any person sins, that sin is a debt that has to go somewhere. God can't just overlook it. The cost has to be absorbed. Jesus absorbed the cost of our sins on the cross. He did that to offer us forgiveness. He can forgive any sinner."

Ehson stared at Darrell. "What about the car and the motorcycle I stole?"

"He can forgive that too! But you need to accept that forgiveness. You need to allow Christ to take away your sins, Ehson."

Four men sprung from the shadows at the corner of the cafe. Their faces were dark like their clothes. Two of them had hairy faces. Ehson threw his head back, glancing over his shoulder. His eyes flew open, bulging in a terror that Darrell had never seen on a man's face before. Ehson opened his mouth, but one of the men smacked his hand over Ehson's mouth. The four dark men grasped Ehson and dragged him around the corner.

"Ehson!" Darrell called. "Hey, wait!" His voice quavered. He called again, desperately, "Ehson? Ehson looked back once before he disappeared into the darkness, gripped by his attackers.

Horrified, Darrell stood under the lights of the cafe for a few seconds. His gut clenched. He had half a thought of going after Ehson or waiting to see if he came back, but then he thought better of it. Moving quickly, Darrell turned from the cafe and began jogging for the guesthouse. He jogged a block before he remembered Ehson had the New Testament in his pocket. Realizing the danger of his own situation, he burst into a run.

Darrell's face was wild when he burst into the apartment and told his story. Wherever Ehson had gone, God had wanted him to talk to Darrell first. Darrell had been at the right place at the right time, and God had used him.

~~~~~~~~~~~~~~~~~~~~~~~~~~~~~~~~~~~~~

The heat continued through the month of July. The Yoders were still at the guesthouse in Abbottabad, and each breath they took felt like it came out of a hot oven. At night they tossed and turned, rising early in the morning, still bleary-eyed but ready to escape the added warmth of the mattress. Darrell left for the States at the end of July. Reuben and Mary Ann missed him, for they had leaned heavily on Darrell's companionship. The little apartment seemed empty without him at first, but soon their days filled, events swirling in around the hole of his absence like rushing waters that carried them along on their currents.

Reuben walked the streets day after day, visiting the market and stopping by the cafe where he checked his email. He liked to walk and did not often take public transportation, and along the way, he took extra time to stop and talk to people. Often he made a special effort to speak with the students carrying books on their way to and from universities. He discovered that many of them spoke good English and were quicker to get involved in deep discussions.

"See, Mary Ann," he explained one day as they were shopping. Mary Ann had not questioned him about his long walks, but he told her anyway. "It's like Christ when He met the woman at the well. He could have foreseen immediately that she had no cup to draw from the well and gone on His way. But He took His time and waited, and He met the woman who came to the well. We're in too much of a hurry, Mary Ann. If we take time to stand about, people assume we have time to talk to them."

Mary Ann smiled up at him. "Let's go look for more fabric then. I want to buy some for Connie, and who knows who we might meet."

Reuben followed his wife, but he continued to mull the ideas over in his head. *I like the verse in Genesis that says: "I being in the way, the Lord led me." Of course, that was referring to finding a wife for Isaac. But it can also apply to me in Pakistan.* Reuben grinned.

"Young people think they need to get married so quickly. They don't want to go serve someplace, thinking they will get married if they stay at home," he said to Mary Ann, forgetting that she hadn't been listening to him think. "But if they'd go to service, the Lord might lead them to the well where Rebekah comes."

Mary Ann quirked an eyebrow at him. "What?"

"The verse in Genesis that talks about being in the way and the Lord leading you . . . when Abraham's servant was hunting for a wife for Isaac."

"And?"

"I just thought it was funny."

"That's not funny." Mary Ann frowned. "It's true."

Reuben started to laugh, and Mary Ann joined him. Then she sobered and added, "Look at Darrell. He met Tamseela while he was serving."

"True," Reuben agreed.

The night before Darrell had left, he had sat down with his parents and told them that he needed to do something about Tamseela. He liked her too well to forget about her, and he felt the Lord directing him toward a friendship with her. Darrell didn't have the least idea how to go about expressing interest in a Pakistani girl, but he had asked Reuben to talk to Tamseela's father.

Reuben prayed momentarily about the meeting he needed to have with Tamseela's father, but then pushed it out of his mind, going back to the verse from Genesis. Reuben had meant what he had said about "being in the way." Being in the way applied to a lot more than wife hunting, though.

As Reuben was returning from the market a few days later, he was limping, though he tried to disguise it. The heat had made the stump of his leg sweaty, and the sweat made the sock liner in the prosthesis chafe the skin. Carrying his bag of tomatoes, he was hurrying as fast as he could when a red car slowed beside him. Reuben looked over and waved.

"Is there a problem with your foot?" A man leaned out of the red car's window, laying a hand on the sill. The rings on his hand sparkled in the sunshine.

"No." Reuben gave a half-laugh, half-sigh. It bothered him to have people notice his limp. He worked hard to conceal it. "There's no problem with my foot. I don't have one."

The gears of the car chattered as the man parked, and Reuben looked over in surprise. The man leaned across his center console, throwing the passenger's door open. "Get in."

Startled, Reuben did as the man had said, wondering if he was doing something dangerous. Accepting a ride from an unknown man in Pakistan was hardly smart. In the back of his mind, he could still hear his mother saying, "Never take candy from a stranger or get into his car with him."

"Where's your apartment?" the man asked as they drove on. "My name is Rajah."

"And my name is Reuben," replied Reuben, wondering how he could accept a ride from Rajah without giving his address.

Let go, a silent voice prompted him. *Tell him where you live.*

"Thank you, Lord," Reuben breathed. Turning to Rajah, he answered, "My house is by the south wall of the military academy. I will show you. Thanks for offering me a ride!"

"Why did you say you didn't have a foot?" Rajah asked after a moment.

"It was cut off." Reuben pulled up his pant leg and showed it to Rajah. "I used to be a farmer, and it got caught in a machine."

Rajah looked the prosthesis over from his seat before reaching to turn the vehicle's air conditioner on. "How long ago did that happen?"

The drive took almost as long as walking would have. Afternoon traffic slowed the activity on the streets to a crawl as Reuben explained his accident. They inched along while horns around them blew and Rajah asked questions. "What country are you from?"

"United States," Reuben replied.

"I see." Rajah raised his right brow in surprise. "I thought maybe you were European or Turkish."

"Turkish!" It was Reuben's turn to be surprised. "But you spoke to me in English."

"It's the only foreign language I know." Rajah shrugged and smiled. "I didn't think you spoke Urdu."

"I don't," Reuben answered, but his mind was not on languages. He was trying to guess what was behind Rajah's gesture of kindness.

"Never mind," Rajah said. "Are you a Muslim?"

"No," Reuben answered. "I am a follower of Jesus. Do you know who Jesus is?"

"Yes." Rajah frowned. "Do you support the war on terrorism?"

"No, we do not." Reuben's tone firmed. "We . . ."

"We?" Rajah was curious. "Are there more of you?"

"My wife and I." Reuben retreated from the point, wishing for a moment that he had chosen a different pronoun. He did not know this man. Taking a deep breath, he plunged in again. "We do not believe in war and fighting. We follow Christ's teaching to love and help people, not hate and kill them."

"So what is your message?" Rajah inquired.

Reuben thought this over.

He was still trying to think of a good answer when Rajah asked, "A message of love?"

Reuben leaned to look into the man's eyes. "Rajah, my friend, you are exactly right."

They had reached the guesthouse by then. Reuben got out, pausing to say thank you.

Rajah offered his hand. "Should we meet again?"

"That would be good." Reuben walked around to the driver's side and looked in the window, considering. "Do you have any free time tomorrow? We can meet for tea at the place where you picked me up today, or you could just come to our apartment."

Rajah thought it over. "My wife is out of the country, caring for our daughter who is sick. Suppose you come to my house? It's only two blocks behind your apartment."

The two men agreed on a time, and the next day Reuben walked to Rajah's apartment. Reuben found Rajah making tea and setting out biscuits when he arrived. He liked Rajah's apartment on sight, open and roomy with big windows open to views of the city. Most apartments in Abbottabad were small and cramped, closed off to the outside world.

The men sat in wooden chairs covered with hard cushions and drank tea together. As the two warmed to each other, they found much to talk about. Rajah often mentioned his country's politics. Naturally, this led to American politics.

"I hate George Bush," Rajah said on one occasion.

Reuben opened his mouth to say something like "you shouldn't hate" or "God put him in power." Then he closed it again, figuring those arguments wouldn't work in Pakistan. "Why?" he asked instead. The setting sun cast a flickering shadow on the wall.

"He kills Muslims," Rajah said, his mouth twisting. "He hunts down Muslim men, and he kills many innocent people because he hates Muslims. He wants to make the whole world Christian."

Silenced, Reuben mulled it over, sipping the tea. He crunched a biscuit, tempted to point out that Rajah's perception of Bush's foreign policy was inaccurate. He felt like telling him the people Bush was after were terrorists who had gone to the United States to murder thousands. He also thought about saying that Bush wasn't necessarily a follower of Jesus and probably wasn't that interested in whether Muslims became Christians or not, but he realized that to Rajah Christianity was a culture, not a faith.

"Well," Reuben said at last, "aren't there radical men in your country who bomb people and places and kill many people?"

His good nature disappearing, Rajah glared over Reuben's comment. Looping his arm over the back of his chair, he scowled. "They are Muslims."

"But you're a Muslim and do not kill and bomb people."

"They are Muslims." The scowl eased, and Rajah considered the ceiling for a moment. "They are Muslims, but they are radical. They are not true Muslims. True Muslims are the people you see walking to the bazaar in the morning to buy a chicken to feed their families, the men who go to the mosque and pray. True Muslims do not blow people up."

"I see." Reuben rubbed his stump, searching for words. "You see, in your country you have the Taliban that do these things. You do not believe they should be doing this. You say they are not true Muslims. In my country there are men like Bush—men who come to fight the Taliban and other terrorists and kill people. But like you, I do not support my countrymen. I do not believe they should do this. They are not true Christians. Tell you what, Rajah, I have a book somewhere, and in this book are many writings that say what true Christians believe and how they act. In this book it says that people who truly follow Jesus should not kill."

"Are you talking about the Bible?" Rajah asked, looking past Reuben.

"Yes, would you like to read one?" Reuben tried to conceal his excitement.

"Yes." Rajah stood. "Sometime. Excuse me one minute." Rajah set his tea aside, walking into the other room. Reuben heard him on the phone. Reuben waited and waited. When Rajah finally came back, the mood surrounding their serious conversation had fled.

"I should go," Reuben said, standing up. Rajah walked him downstairs, and they did not talk about the Bible anymore.

Later that week they spoke on the phone. Reuben invited Rajah to come over that evening. "No . . ." Rajah said. "I cannot come to your house. Another time."

Another week or so passed, and Reuben did not hear from Rajah. "I want him to have that Bible," Reuben said to Mary Ann one morning, fidgeting. "He needs to read it. I feel this strong burden."

"Relax," Mary Ann suggested. They were eating plums and toast for their breakfast, and the morning sunlight of another hot day in Abbottabad streamed in around them. From over the military academy wall, they could hear the barked commands of the officers drilling the cadets. They could also hear the hawkers in the alleys, calling out their wares. Mary Ann considered her piece of toast before taking a bite. "Pray about it," she said, brushing away the crumbs. "If God wants you to give him a Bible, it will happen."

"I've got to go to the bazaar before we go to Tamseela's place for lunch," Reuben said, rising abruptly. He was fretting about the Bible and did not want to sit there worrying. "You're right, of course," he added.

"I'll go with you." Mary Ann stood too.

The two walked through the early heat to the market. They minced single file past the meat markets, treading carefully around the entrails and feathers. The smell rose, potent, off the refuse piles under the blazing sun. Farther down, cabbage leaves and tomatoes and peelings and scraps lay in another heap. Mary Ann held her nose, and they stopped at a nearby stand to get some cucumbers.

"Come this way." Reuben gestured with the sack of vegetables. "It doesn't stink so badly here."

They turned off their usual path and walked down the narrow street between looming buildings. As they came around a corner, the shouts of children and the hoarser yells of adults hollering back at them came from over a high wall.

"It's a madrasah," Reuben said. Mary Ann shielded her eyes to look up at the minaret of the Islamic religious school. Reuben took her arm as a rickshaw rattled by, steering her to the side of the road by a wall. While the rickshaw was passing, Mary Ann felt something poking between her shoulder blades. Turning, she fingered carved iron bars in an opening of the wall, and she stooped to peek through.

"Look, Reuben." She tugged at his sleeve. He bent at the waist to look. Inside the compound, rows of little boys in their white gowns and prayer caps had lined up in remarkably straight rows graduating from the shortest to the tallest. They raised their fists to the level of the person's shoulder in front of them, their feet pounding rhythmically. Left, right, left, right. A man up front led the exercises. The little boys watched him closely, repeating each move.

As they continued watching, the children swiveled their arms out, bent at the elbow, fists in the air, chanting English words. "We hate A-me-ri-ca! We hate A-me-ri-ca! We hate A-me-ri-ca." The arms slid forward again. Left, right, left, right. They swiveled their arms out again. "We hate A-me-ri-ca. We hate A-me-ri-ca." *Stomp, stomp.* They executed an about-face and repeated the chant while facing the other direction.

"Oh, Lord," Mary Ann breathed. She looked up into her husband's eyes. "That's terrible."

He nodded, and after a moment they strolled on down the alley. Reuben's brow creased in thought, and he did not speak for the entire walk. Mary Ann, too, was absorbed in her thoughts, praying for the chanting little boys. When they reached the apartment, Reuben got out his cell phone to make a call. Mary Ann slipped to his side to listen.

"Rajah? How . . . yes, yes . . . how are you? No, that's fine. I just wanted to ask about the gift you and I spoke of. Do you want it?"

After Reuben had ended the call, Mary Ann waited for him to explain. Reuben turned to her with an exultant look, but he barely seemed to see her. "We need to be bold, Mary Ann. There's so much hate. We have to fight with a message of love. We need to be 'in the way.' "

"I agree." Mary Ann nodded.

"Rajah's going to meet me. Where's that Bible?"

Mary Ann got him the Bible, and they wrapped it for Reuben to take with him. Back on the streets the city was already beginning to slow for the heat of the day, but Reuben hurried. Down one street and up the next he went, not stopping to look around. After about ten minutes, he reached the corner where Rajah had picked him up a few weeks earlier. He had just stopped, wiping his brow, when the red car appeared beside him again. This time Reuben went straight over to the open window and handed Rajah his package. "Here is what we talked about," he said.

"Thank you," Rajah replied, slipping it under his seat. Reuben stepped back, and the red car pulled away from the curb much more quickly than it had the previous time.

It was late one afternoon a week later when Reuben went to check his email. The afternoon sun dangled like a red pendulum low in the west, and breezes stole across the sweaty crowds of the late Abbottabad traffic. That day had been cooler, and it was easier to concentrate than on the days that sweltered, making every action seem like too great an effort. By the time the emailing was finished, it was getting close to evening when Reuben stepped outside the cafe where the taxis rolled through the streets, collecting passengers. Reuben watched the passing crowds, trying to think how Christ would have viewed such a hodge-podge of lives.

A man jumped from the back of a taxi, landing nimbly on his toes. Tucking a briefcase under his arm, the man glanced about brightly. Reuben suspected the man had spotted him, but the man dug a mobile phone out of his pocket and spoke into it for a minute. He stood near Reuben, giving Reuben time to observe him. He was a scholar of some sort, apparently, wearing a distinguished Islamic cap, undergirded by an iron-gray beard that accented the scholarliness.

Putting the phone away, the man approached Reuben. "Hello, how are you?"

Reuben responded with all the polite responses, but inside he was thinking rapidly. He wanted to make this conversation last longer than the standard exchanges of a foreigner with a Pakistani. The alertness in the stranger's manner had struck Reuben, and he wanted to find out more about this man. "My name is Reuben," he added.

"Where are you from?"

"I am from America," Reuben told him.

"I thought maybe so." The man clapped his hands together with glee. "I would enjoy speaking English with you. Why are you in Pakistan?"

Reuben scratched his head. "That question has a long answer. Would you like some tea?"

"All right." Reuben's new friend did not stop to consider. The two ambled off to find a teashop, talking.

"Last year I came to Pakistan to help rebuild houses after the earthquake. The organization that built those houses sent me back to finish up some business."

Faqir accepted that explanation without question and asked, "Are you a Christian?"

"I am a follower of Jesus Christ." Reuben sipped his tea and set it aside to wipe his mouth.

"I am a scholar of religion," Faqir told Reuben. "You must tell me about this Christianity. I have heard some things about it that I do not understand."

"Like what?" Reuben asked.

Faqir regarded him shrewdly. "Come to my house to talk."

"Where is your house?" Reuben wanted to know.

"It is far away," Faqir admitted.

"I will need to talk it over with my wife," Reuben said.

"Where is your wife?" Faqir asked immediately.

"She's at my apartment," Reuben explained. "Suppose we meet for tea again tomorrow? I must go now."

Faqir agreed, and they parted ways. Faqir looked pleased with himself as he walked away. Reuben wondered about it. He remembered warnings about kidnappings of foreigners, all from sources he had dismissed as fear-mongers. He did recall hearing that the area Faqir had said he lived in was dangerous. Still the urge to find out more about Faqir wouldn't go away.

The next afternoon as the sun dropped nearer to the western horizon, Reuben again waited on the corner by the taxi stop. Faqir arrived direct-ly, much as he had the day before. He hopped out of the back of a taxi, striding up to Reuben with a smile. That day they talked for two hours in the teashop. By the time their third cup of tea had grown cold at their elbows, Faqir had again invited Reuben to his house.

"Come for supper," he urged.

"I don't know where you live," Reuben said.

"Well, it's like this." Faqir scratched his head and traced a map on the table with his finger. "Take the bus from the mosque in the main bazaar toward Rawalpindi. Get off at the third stop, and if you walk down the street maybe one block, you can get a taxi on the corner to—"

"Now hold on," Reuben interrupted. "How about you just come and get us? I don't think I can find it on my own. We'll meet you at our corner at four o'clock tomorrow evening."

So it was arranged. When Reuben told Mary Ann, she said, "I will want an interpreter," and called Tamseela.

Tamseela did not react favorably. "Are you crazy?" she asked. "You should not go with that man. You do not know him. He could be anyone. He could harm you."

"But Reuben said we would go," Mary Ann objected.

"Reuben is too trusting," Tamseela said flatly. "Don't go."

After that, it didn't seem to be quite the thing to ask Tamseela to go with Mary Ann, so the two went alone to the appointed street corner the next evening. Faqir was already waiting for them. Warm and enthusiastic, Faqir whisked them onto a bus for a long ride.

Mary Ann stared out the window and wondered if Tamseela was right. It was beginning to get dark. "God," she prayed, "don't let Tamseela be right, and if she is, take care of your foolish children. Unless you want us to be martyrs, Lord." Mary Ann paused to think about it. "Then it would be okay. Just give us the strength to suffer for you."

It was getting dark by the time Faqir finally led them into his home an hour distant from that street corner. The women of the household immediately absorbed Mary Ann into their midst and carried her off into a side room. The Pakistani custom of women and men eating separately sometimes unnerved Mary Ann. She would have preferred to stay with Reuben, but she faced the women with a bright smile. Faqir's home was nicer than most. The ladies seated Mary Ann in a wooden chair with fancy carvings on the winged armrests. The carving dug into Mary Ann's elbows. The room was painted a smoky blue, and in the bright light of a single bare bulb, the air appeared hazy in the evening warmth.

Conversation died after the first couple of minutes. No one spoke any English in that room, so Mary Ann clung to the arms of her chair, wishing for Tamseela and smiling as hard as she could. Two older ladies had come in to sit on the bed and stare at Mary Ann, one of them looking ill. After some time, Faqir brushed aside the curtain in the doorway and shouldered into the room.

"These women came to me for help," Faqir explained to Mary Ann, gesturing to the ill-looking one. "She has high blood pressure."

"Are you a doctor?" Mary Ann asked respectfully.

"No, I am an imam. Allah has granted his imams special powers." Faqir turned away and faced the old lady. He began to mumble in Urdu over the bowed head of the woman. Mary Ann held her breath.

After a minute or so, Faqir's mumbling ceased. He breathed three puffs of air into the woman's face, and then it was over. The two women rose from the bed, thanking Faqir, who nodded and left the room. The two women followed.

Mary Ann wanted Reuben. She wished she dared follow Faqir and find her husband.

The evening lengthened and grew late. Reuben made a motion to go, but Faqir did not seem interested. Reuben insisted that they needed to leave, and finally Faqir agreed they could leave. They all walked toward the bus station.

"We can go by ourselves," Reuben said. "Can you give me directions about which buses to take?"

Faqir seemed relieved by this idea and supplied the instructions. He got on the bus with them to make sure they had good seats and said goodbye, stopping to wave before he disappeared down out of the bus. Mary Ann fell asleep soon after the bus started to move, but Reuben remained alert, not wanting to miss their stop. It had begun to rain. By the time they had reached the corner where they had first met Faqir, it was pouring. They walked home with the dark wetness pouring down their faces.

Early the next morning Faqir called Reuben's cell phone. "Reuben, brother, I am so sorry that I did not make sure you got home safely last evening. It was my responsibility to make sure you were safe, and I did not."

"It's okay," Reuben replied, wondering at the sudden concern. "We made it all right. It was not a problem. What are you doing now?"

"I am going to work."

"Ah. And what is that?"

"I am a computer technician for the military base close to where we meet for tea."

"The military base?" Reuben was surprised. "I live right beside that."

"Really!" Faqir sounded excited. "You must come see me at my office. Perhaps I can show you the military base. I'll need to clear it with my commander."

The next time Reuben saw him, Faqir shrugged when the visit was brought up. "My commander says foreigners aren't allowed to visit. I'm sorry we can't meet there. But I wish to talk with you more about religion."

"Come to my house after your job is done," Reuben suggested. "It is just down the street. Not far away at all."

"Tell me how to understand the Scriptures," Faqir said immediately upon his arrival the afternoon he showed up at Reuben's place. "I have a Bible at my house. I am studying it some, comparing it with the Qur'an, but it is so hard for me to understand."

"Well, it's good that you are studying," Reuben said, pleased. He got an Urdu Bible, asking the Lord how he should open up a topic like this. He picked up his English Bible, and it fell open at John 4. "Are you familiar with the Gospel of John?"

Faqir wasn't, so Reuben helped him turn there, and they read the passage about the woman at the well together. "This book is the living water, Faqir, and as you thirst for it like this woman did, your thirst will be satisfied and you will understand the truth."

Faqir listened well, and their friendship deepened. It grew common for Faqir to drop by after work to talk and drink tea. Reuben prayed that the seed sown in Faqir's heart would bring a harvest sometime. Harvest or not, Reuben knew that friendship was one of the most powerful tools to spread the Gospel of Christ.

CHAPTER 17

Proposal

THE LONG, HOT DAYS TURNED from June to July. The haze of heat hung over the valley of Abbottabad. On a day that seemed hazier than the rest, Reuben was to have a meeting with Tamseela's father. Darrell had urged him to do this, and Reuben wondered for the fiftieth time how he was to go about proposing a relationship between his son and a Pakistani Christian's daughter.

When Reuben stopped by the internet cafe that afternoon, he found an email from Dr. Mueller back home in Virginia. Dr. Mueller was asking about the Bible covers. Reuben and Mary Ann had met Mueller at a conference after their first trip to Pakistan. A Christian doctor, Mueller had served in Pakistan for several years, and he was highly interested in Reuben and Mary Ann's experiences. He had suggested that they make cloth covers for the Bibles that they would give away. The covers made the Bibles look more like a gift and safer to carry in public. One evening before their second trip to Pakistan, the youth girls from their home church in Virginia had gotten together to help Mary Ann make them.

Just the day before, Reuben had given away one of these Bible covers with a Bible in it. He had met a student named Sefullah on the street a week or so earlier. During their conversation, the two had exchanged phone numbers. Sefullah had come by for some tea at the apartment. Mary Ann had set up a little table between the chairs in their living space and had set out cookies and tea. Reuben habitually kept a Bible there on the table, encased in one of the cloth covers.

Sefullah had eyed the book upon entering the room and continued to glance at it. Finally he had asked, "Is there a holy book in there?"

Ministry is sowing one seed at a time.

Reuben had handed it to him, and Sefullah had walked out of their apartment carrying a Bible.

Reuben finished a reply to Dr. Mueller, telling him the little story, cheering over it himself. He was fond of creative channels to spread the Gospel, and his email was warm with enthusiasm. Reuben rose from the booth in the cafe. That was enough of that. He needed to go to Tamseela's house and talk to her father. He wished for some camels to be with him as they had been with Eliezer at the well.

Tamseela's father was waiting for him by the church gate. A guard guarded the walled church, and both the guard and Tamseela's father were sitting under an outcropping of gnarled vines that grew like unruly hair over the wall. The leaves were dry—dying. Tamseela's father said something to the guard as Reuben trudged up. They laughed, and Reuben smiled with them. He wondered if Tamseela's father had made any guesses about the nature of this meeting. Tamseela's father patted the bench beside him, and Reuben sat, easing off his wooden leg. He was fine with the silence, fine with just sitting there. He did not want tea, and formality would have made him nervous. A bird twittered, and Tamseela's father began to talk small talk.

"How's Darrell?" he asked, a glow deepening in his eyes.

Reuben swallowed. "Have you noticed any interest between my son and your daughter?" he asked, not bothering to answer the polite question. The man's smile paused for a beat; Reuben waited, trying not to be anxious. He hoped Darrell wouldn't have his heart broken. Darrell hadn't said much, but Reuben knew that Darrell's feelings ran deep.

"Yes." Tamseela's father tucked his mouth in, but his eyes still smiled. "I have noticed. They like each other, don't they? I think this is good," he added.

Reuben described to him the relationship that Darrell wanted to have with his daughter, and Tamseela's father said he must talk to Tamseela's uncles. "I need the agreement of my family. Marriage is an important thing."

Marriage! Reuben had forgotten temporarily what culture he was in. Since Tamseela's family was Christian, it seemed the cultural gap shouldn't be so wide, but they were still Pakistani. Darrell wasn't asking Tamseela to go out for ice cream. These arrangements would be final.

Reuben and Tamseela's father sat for a time, talking. "You know," Reuben said in the course of the conversation, "that we have different cultures, and that we do things different ways. If Tamseela leaves Pakistan, she will become more like American Christians, like my wife. Are you all right with these changes?"

Tamseela's father agreed with this, but he was adamant about one thing. "Tamseela will not leave the country until after she is married." He rose then and ambled off to get tea. Reuben, watching him go, thought the stoop of the man's shoulders made him look older. Letting go of a daughter would not be easy for him.

They drank the tea, but the talk faltered. In the face of what they had been discussing, small talk would be annoying, and there didn't seem to be much more to be said on the subject. They had agreed that it could happen; they had agreed that there were differences to work through. Being men, they were done talking about it. After the tea, Reuben left for the guesthouse. When he arrived, Mary Ann was fidgeting with some embroidery. She dropped it when Reuben entered.

"Well?"

"It seems he likes it. But he wants to ask his family first."

Mary Ann clapped her hands together. Reuben shrugged, but looking into his wife's shining eyes, he had to admit that it was sort of exciting. Darrell would be happy.

That evening Reuben and Mary Ann headed out to Bach Christian Hospital, nestled at the foot of the Himalayan Mountains at the edge of Abbottabad. The hospital was staffed by Christian doctors, many of them from other countries. Patients came and went, receiving general surgeries and care. Even though it was Christian, the Pakistani people benefited much from its presence, and the Pakistani government left them alone. BCH offered most of its services free of charge.

The place had its enemies and was heavily guarded, though Reuben and Mary Ann were let in through the gate without questions. The doctors must have informed the guards that they were coming. Reuben liked the place. Entering the grounds, he looked around at the rolling hills about the hospital, the nurtured green. Bach was in the city of Abbottabad, but it didn't feel like it, being up on the ridge.

Mark, one of Reuben's doctor friends, strode toward them now, his white hair standing in shocks over his head. They immediately fell into conversation.

"Come see the little shop over here." Dr. Mark tugged them aside. "We're just starting to do prosthetics."

"Seriously!" Reuben was delighted. Prostheses were close to his heart. He looked the shop over with avid interest. Mary Ann tagged behind, listening to the two men hash over the equipment in the shop. "Where's your transfer jig?" Reuben wanted to know.

"My what?" Dr. Mark said, pulling down his glasses to look over them at Reuben.

"Your transfer jig . . . you know, to align the plate and arm assembly."

"Never heard of it," Dr. Mark said promptly.

"Never heard of it?" Reuben echoed, scandalized. He pulled out a stool and sat down to demonstrate what he was talking about. Reuben concentrated on his description, sure that Dr. Mark would say, "Oh, that."

Dr. Mark didn't, though. He watched Reuben in amazement while Reuben explained. "If you don't have one, I could build you one."

Dr. Mark shook his head. "No, come here and work. You build that transfer jig, and you'll have a job. We need someone who knows what he's doing to make prostheses."

Reuben's face lit up at the suggestion. "I would love to! Look! What better place for ministry would there be than sitting at a person's foot fitting them with a prosthesis? Oh, I would love to!"

"Come," Dr. Mark said simply.

Reuben looked at his friend, longing to accept on the spot.

Later as he and Mary Ann walked down the ridge under the sparkling stars to catch a taxi, he was quiet, thinking it over. He sighed once, and Mary Ann said, "Yes?"

"I would love to, but we just can't manage it."

"You mean what Dr. Mark was talking about?"

"Yeah, there are too many other things we're already trying to do. And I know God led us into what we are doing. We can't just walk away, can we?"

"No, probably not," Mary Ann agreed. She wasn't as passionate about prosthetics as Reuben was, but she wished he could work in it. She knew how much he would have enjoyed it. "Of course, if there were someone else to do what we're doing . . ."

"There are never enough people to go around," Reuben remarked, dejectedly. "Where is everyone? There's so much to do."

"I expect that's how Jesus felt," Mary Ann said.

"I suppose that's how He still feels." Reuben's tone was bitter.

"There are people working," Mary Ann reminded him. "Plenty of people. It's just that there should be more. But God will fill the needs."

"You're right," Reuben sighed. "I don't think people understand, though, just how much there is that could be done."

"You don't know until you step out," Mary Ann said. "When we were at Faith Mission, we never thought about someone needing to work at Bach Christian Hospital in Pakistan to make prostheses."

"That's why people should get involved." Reuben wasn't in the mood to allow excuses. "If folks would just look around them, they'd see. But they're too wrapped up in their own lives."

"Makes me wonder what we're missing," Mary Ann suggested.

Reuben walked on swiftly for a moment, crunching the stones under his shoes. "Okay, yes, I see what you mean. We're all blind somewhere. I need to be patient. God was patient with us."

Reuben took her hand in the darkness, and they walked the rest of the way to the corner in silence.

The next evening Reuben and Mary Ann planned to go to Faqir's house for supper again.

"I wish I had an interpreter to go there," Mary Ann said at about four o'clock.

"Well, ask Tamseela," Reuben said.

Mary Ann did. Tamseela agreed to go if her father would allow her.

"Her father is really protective of his girls," Mary Ann said, closing the phone and folding it in her hands in her lap. "Really protective. Tamseela told me she and her sisters are not allowed to go out alone."

"They've not had a very secure life, if you think about it," Reuben said. "They're Christians in Pakistan, and they live inside a walled church compound with a guard. This is not America."

"I guess," Mary Ann agreed.

Tamseela called back. "Dad said I may go. He wasn't sure, but he wanted me to be able to help you out."

So the three set out for Faqir's place together. At Faqir's, the arrangements were much the same as before. The atmosphere of the place was never warm. Faqir and Reuben were in a separate room, talking. Mary Ann supposed they were enjoying themselves. She was so thankful she had Tamseela along this time to do some talking and for moral support. Once again the ladies gathered, but this time Tamseela chattered with them, relaying their questions to Mary Ann.

"They want to know why you don't wear jewelry," she said.

"Oh, my," Mary Ann said, "they always ask that one."

Jewelry held huge cultural implications in Pakistan. It indicated status and other personal information. Carefully, Mary Ann tried to explain. She didn't want to anger anyone.

"Tell them that God said in the Bible that women were not to make themselves beautiful and showy with gold and ornaments, but to make their character beautiful by following Him." Mary Ann stopped and tried to think. "See, I once was not a nice person at all. It was only after the Lord started speaking to me and I let Him work in my heart that I started to become beautiful inside. And after that happened, I didn't care about the outer look so much."

Tamseela repeated this rapidly in Urdu, waving her hands as she talked. *What a girl,* Mary Ann thought as she watched her. She had the feeling that Tamseela was enlarging a bit on her testimony, explaining things. The women listened to Tamseela without remark, staring in turn at Mary Ann. Their black eyes glowed like sparks, some surrounded with the loose, wrinkled skin of age, others wreathed with thick, dark lashes.

The evening drew to a close, this time earlier than before, because Reuben was not anxious to repeat the late departure.

As they were gathering to go, Faqir mentioned that a small child in the household was ill. "He hurt his leg," Faqir said. "Such a small boy to bear pain."

"Oh, my!" Mary Ann clucked her tongue. "How old is he?"

"He is just one year old."

Tamseela got up from her chair. "Where is he?" she asked.

"Do you want to see him?" Faqir asked, surprised, but he led the way.

Apparently the leg was sprained at the knee. It was swollen, and the child lay still, sleeping, his damp curls spread on the quilt. Tears had dried on his cheeks, and one hand tucked itself under his jaw.

Tamseela knelt by his side. "He's beautiful," she said in English. "What's his name?"

"Hussein," Faqir replied.

Tamseela laid her hand on the baby and started to pray out loud. "Lord, heal this child." She switched to Urdu then, but Mary Ann held her breath, thinking it was the most touching sight she had ever seen. Faqir paused in the doorway, his hand holding the curtain up. He watched over his shoulder, listening as Tamseela prayed. The music of her voice ran on. When she stopped at last, Faqir only smiled with his usual poise and drew them all away. "Leave the child to sleep now."

As they rode the bus homeward through the dark, Mary Ann wondered what Faqir had thought. Tamseela was silent beside her, and Reuben rubbed his aching stump as the three grew absorbed in their own thoughts. The lights of town sparkled in the windows as they drove on, and the bus windows rattled as the motor roared. The driver gunned the vehicle down the highway, swerving to miss a few rickshaws out with late passengers.

In the dark Tamseela said, "I don't want to go back there. I didn't like it."

"But the baby," Mary Ann said. "Surely you are glad you could pray for the baby."

Tamseela did not reply right away, and then she sighed ever so slightly. "Yes," she said, "I wanted to pray for the baby."

Reuben heard the exchange and wondered. He remembered Tamseela's opposition to their first visit. He didn't know why she had objected, and she did not seem about to explain herself. Faqir seemed to hold some renown with miraculous healing powers as a religious leader. *Is that why Tamseela dislikes the place?*

Reuben knew Tamseela had a far better instinct about her own people. He thought of asking her more, but instead, only said, "We have to plant the seed, Tamseela." He stared out the window at the lights of the houses they were passing. "It's hard, though, when we do not see much fruit. We have to go back to the U.S. soon, and only God knows what will become of these people—our friends . . ." He let his voice drift off.

CHAPTER 18

Minnesota Virginia Pakistan Ukraine Israel Afghanistan Haiti Bangladesh

The Siege

THE DAY IN EARLY JULY was gray and hot. As the sun disappeared behind the encroaching clouds early in the morning, the heat rose in waves from the concrete of the city. The leaves of the few trees hung limply from their branches. The clouds rolled in low, and the traffic in the city crept. All of Pakistan was creeping those days as the tension between the Lal Masjid, or the Red Mosque, and the government worsened.

The Red Mosque and its joint madrasah in Islamabad were manned by two Islamic militant brothers. The doctrine they spread among their supporters promoted the reign of Sharia law and the overthrow of the Pakistani government. For the past eighteen months, the Red Mosque faction had scrapped with the government, setting fire to buildings, kidnapping officials, and attacking peacekeeping forces.

On the evening of July 3, 2007, a friend phoned Reuben and Mary Ann. "Stay put. There's trouble in Islamabad." A riot had erupted when some Red Mosque students had stolen weapons and radio sets from the Pakistan Rangers, the internal security force. Riot police had fired tear gas to disperse the students. From there, approximately 150 students had gathered to burn the Ministry of Environment building and clashed with the rangers guarding it. The army was pouring into the area as it was shut down for a crisis response. The G-6 sector of Islamabad had been cordoned off, and the hospitals of Islamabad had declared an emergency.

A second person called to inform Reuben and Mary Ann about the fighting, and Mary Ann called Tamseela in turn. Tamseela had told them earlier that she was planning to be in Islamabad that day. Tamseela answered the call on the first ring. "Hello?" Her voice sounded like she had caught a terrible cold.

"Tamseela!" Mary Ann was both relieved and alarmed. "Are you okay?"

"Yes," Tamseela croaked. "I am fine. I was at a bazaar near the first riot, and the tear gas got me."

"Oh, Tamseela!" Mary Ann cried. "Praise the Lord you aren't hurt!"

"No, I'm fine. Only my eyes feel funny. They burn underneath."

Nine people had been killed, and about 150 hurt. The students retreated into the Red Mosque while the Pakistani troops laid siege outside. The G-6 sector, the city of Islamabad, and the country all settled down to wait. A week passed as the government handed down ultimatums.

During that week, not all was on hold in Reuben and Mary Ann's life. Reuben taxied to the Presbyterian church one afternoon to meet with Tamseela's father for the second time. This time they sat down inside on mats on the floor. One of the younger children brought Reuben a glass of 7UP.

"I talked to Tamseela's uncles about Darrell's love for her," Tamseela's father reported, "and they all said, 'Of course, why not?' So I say yes."

Reuben smiled, wishing Mary Ann would have been there to share the moment. He could picture her excitement, for Tamseela was beginning to matter a great deal to them. Just then, Tamseela peeked around the corner. Her eyes bright and her face innocent, she slipped to her father's side, and he took her hand.

"Tamseela—" Reuben began, but her father broke in.

"I told her."

"Oh!" Reuben said.

Tamseela nodded. She was almost scowling in an effort to keep her face straight, but a smile shone through.

"You know," Tamseela's father said, "Tamseela has an older sister. In our culture, it is customary to marry the oldest first." He didn't say anything more on the subject, but Reuben wondered why he had said it. *Darrell had better check under the veil before he says any wedding vows.*

Later, as the two of them talked, Tamseela admitted, close to tears. "I didn't know what to do. I prayed and prayed, but I would always see Darrell's face. I was angry with myself and confessed it to God. He told me to be at peace and rest because my love for Darrell was from Him."

"I can't wait till Darrell knows!" Mary Ann cried when Reuben reached home. "Oh, Tamseela! I wish I could just give her a great big hug right now."

"You'll see her tomorrow," Reuben told his wife. He sniffed the air. "What did you fix for supper?" All the fervor was beginning to wear him out.

Mary Ann shook her spoon at him, opening her mouth for another question, but then stopped and shrieked, "The spaghetti!" She vanished, and Reuben followed, hungry and hoping the spaghetti wasn't burned.

The next day dawned, and Mary Ann awoke early. Her back was paining her. She rose, stiff in the joints, to see if moving around would ease the ache. The birds twittered outside. *Just like home,* Mary Ann thought. It brought the old homestead back to her mind. Inching to the window, she leaned out to look at the town. The dust and haze had settled over the night, and now the morning sky lowered itself over the city to the east. In the west all was clear except for two billowing white thunderheads that rode high in the sky. All around them, the sky was as blue as a child's eye.

Mary Ann buried her nose in the pitiful flowers that grew in the window box. They never perked up, no matter how much she watered them. Still she soaked up what cheeriness they did have, trying to forget her back. She recalled all of the plants she had cultivated when they lived at Faith Mission. She loved plants, but she had needed to give them all away.

As Mary Ann stumbled back to bed, she groaned. It was no use. Reuben had stirred, and presently he went about the business of getting awake and dressed. Mary Ann told him that her back hurt.

"Stay in bed," Reuben said. "There's no need to get up."

She did so for a while, but toward the middle of the day, Mary Ann got up. Her back didn't hurt so much, but she knew she shouldn't do anything strenuous. Reuben hired a rickshaw for them to go to a cafe. They drank tea and checked their email.

The emails were glum. Darlene had sent an email with before and after pictures of Mary Ann's flowerbeds.

"The weeds are awful!" Mary Ann wailed.

"Looks like the enemy has been sowing the tares," Reuben observed cheerfully. His cheerfulness didn't make Mary Ann feel any better.

Connie had emailed. She was having problems with her throat again and had an appointment with a specialist. At the age of nineteen, Connie had suffered thyroid cancer.

"Poor girl," Mary Ann said. "She needs a mom."

Lily, Mary Ann's sister, had emailed also. "Mom isn't doing well," she had written. "She's not eating much and seems to be in discomfort. Dad is distressed for her sake."

After the emails, Reuben and Mary Ann made their way back to the apartment. Mary Ann sat limply on the rickshaw as it rattled down the street. It was turning into an awful day.

"I wonder," Reuben remarked to no one in particular, "what is happening in Islamabad."

That morning the government had moved the ultimatum. Aziz, one of the leaders, had been captured trying to escape the mosque clad in a burqa. After his arrest, about twelve hundred students had surrendered. While the rangers were under orders to shoot anyone leaving with weapons, the government was offering money and free education to anyone who left the Red Mosque unarmed. Women and children were promised safety to return to their homes. Still, authorities were estimating that there were three to four hundred women and children in the mosque and about as many students who were not considered threats. Deadlines had come and gone. The news drifted about that the army had begun to storm the mosque.

Mary Ann sighed. "All those poor women and children. I wonder how God is watching out for them."

Reuben looked her over. "Would you like to go see Tamseela later today?"

"Yes," she said, "I would like that."

First, they returned to their apartment. The noise was bad. A family had moved in to share the floor of their apartment a few days earlier. There was

Students of Lal Masjid surrender following the warning by the government in Islamabad, Wednesday. — Naveed Akram

Used by permission of *The News International.*

only a thin division between the two sections, and most of their privacy had fled. Mary Ann stood by her bed, packing her bag with some things to take to Tamseela, when the door creaked. Alarmed, she glanced up.

"Well, hello," she said to the little boy who had walked in.

He was one of the newcomers' children. Looking Mary Ann's possessions over, he strolled around the room. Mary Ann closed her bag with a snap. It was almost too much.

"Come," she said.

The boy only looked at her with liquid brown eyes.

"Oh, right. You don't know English," Mary Ann said to him. "Well, there's one language little boys speak." She called to Reuben. "Dear, can you bring a cookie?"

"A cookie?" Mary Ann could hear Reuben's muffled voice from the other room. "Hold on."

After a minute Reuben appeared with the cookie. The boy was still staring at Mary Ann's things, and Mary Ann was staring at him, trying not to be cross. "Give him that cookie, and see if you can get him to leave."

"Okay." Reuben studied the boy. He tried offering the cookie, but the boy did not reach for it. "Come." Reuben tried again. At last he put his hand on the child's shoulder and nudged. "You must come."

"Look, Reuben has a cookie for you," Mary Ann coaxed. The boy's eyes grew larger and larger, and suddenly he ran from the room and disappeared.

"Reuben, our stuff . . ." Mary Ann began fretting.

"Leave it for now," Reuben told her. "Are you ready to go?"

"But he was in our room, looking at our stuff!" Mary Ann tripped off to get a bag of the cookies.

She told Tamseela about it later as they sat out on some rocks in the churchyard. Mary Ann had been taking some pictures of Tamseela, which she secretly planned to send to Darrell. Now the two women were sitting, talking.

"I used to be at the top of my class when I was in college," Tamseela said suddenly. She did not offer any comment on the connection between this and Mary Ann's story, but Mary Ann accepted the change of subject. "I was even elected the class president." Tamseela's slim brown fingers scratched at the lichens on the rock.

"You were?"

"Yes. There were maybe seventy or eighty students in my class. One day my teacher talked for a long time about how she hated Christians. I prayed quickly that God would give me wisdom, and then I asked her why she hated Christians. I told her that I am one. My teacher replied, 'Why would you want to be a Christian? You're so sweet.' I told her that I was a needy person, that Christ came to my heart and filled it, and that I never want to go back to being that empty person again. I told her how Jesus is love, and now my heart is filled with love. Even though she would hate me, still I would not hate her. I would love her . . ." Tamseela's voice trailed off.

"I suppose," Mary Ann answered, "that little boy saw that we loved him." The surmise fell on thin air.

Later that afternoon, they heard the situation in Islamabad was not getting better. The soldiers were fighting an uphill battle. There had been a battle in the main courtyard of the mosque and an ambush from beneath the stairwell. A militant had detonated a suicide jacket as the Pakistani forces arrived at a room that contained half a dozen of the rebels.

The militants had stored ammunition and fortified the mosque for months. Areas of the madrasah were booby-trapped. Eighty percent of the complex was reported clear, but all of the militants had retreated into the basements and were using women and children as human shields.

"Oh, it's awful," Mary Ann said as Reuben and Tamseela's father discussed the bloodbath. "It's absolutely awful! We're so blessed with safety. Why those poor people? Why not one of us?"

No one answered because no one knew the answer.

~~~~~~

The next week as Reuben and Mary Ann stood outside a cafe on the street corner where the taxis came and went, their phone rang. It was Mary Ann's dad. "It's all over. Mom died."

"Mom died!" Mary Ann could barely hear above the noise of the afternoon traffic. Her father was crying.

"She's gone, Mary Ann. She's gone." It was all Mary Ann could hear. Finally she closed the phone, her cheeks wet with tears.

"Poor dad. I wish I were with him."

"We'll have to fly home early," Reuben said, taking her hand. She leaned close in spite of the public. They stood together, taking strength for a moment.

There was much to do the rest of the day, random business to finish up and arrangements to make. Reuben and Mary Ann met Tamseela at a restaurant. Darrell and Tamseela were talking frequently on the phone now. Their relationship was well underway. Darrell was making plans to return to Pakistan soon, but Tamseela had brought packages for them to take to him. While Reuben used the phone, the two women sat on a bench outside the restaurant and wept. Their precious days together were over.

"I'll be lonely," Tamseela said, leaning against Mary Ann's shoulder.

"Darrell will be back soon," Mary Ann assured her. Tamseela smiled through her tears.

As they packed late that night, a friend and his family brought food. It was already past midnight, and at one-thirty they had to take the bus for Islamabad. The American couple and the Pakistani family sat around to share one last meal, and after a while, it was over. They had to catch the bus.

Reuben and Mary Ann spent the night on the bus, arriving at the airport early in the morning. The burdens of the past day or so weighed on them. Their time in Pakistan was over. As they neared the airport in Islamabad, soldiers lined the road on both sides. Sandbags were piled high, and the Pakistan Rangers crouched behind them. Islamabad was still waiting for the end of the siege of the Red Mosque. Mary Ann shivered as she looked out the bus windows. Reuben looked over her shoulder as the ghostly faces passed, one after the other.

An army truck passing by a bunker on a G-6 road in Islamabad on Wednesday. — Naveed Akram

Used by permission of *The News International*.

On the plane, Mary Ann fell asleep immediately. She woke after an hour to find that they were in the air. Reuben looked up from his book to her questioning eyes.

"It's over, isn't it?" she wondered.

"Pakistan, you mean?"

"Yes. Was it worth it? There were no converts, no churches started. We had to leave early. Our work for BOL just suddenly ended. *Poof.*"

Reuben closed his book. "You mean that if we had stayed home we could have been there for Mom's death?"

"I suppose."

"Mary Ann, there's no guarantee that we would have been there even if we had stayed in America. We live in Virginia. Your parents live in Lancaster. Wanda said she wasn't there for your mother's death, and she

"Not everything that can be counted counts,
and not everything that counts can be counted."

lives ten minutes down the road. Your other sister is coming from halfway across the United States. She won't be there much before we are."

Mary Ann twisted her fingers in her lap, staring at them. "You don't think I was neglecting Mom to be in Pakistan?"

"Remember what Christ said about following Him? About the foxes having holes and birds having nests, but He not having a place to lay His head? And then He said to let the dead bury the dead. That's harsh, but I think Christ meant it. And as far as what we got accomplished in Pakistan, think of all the relationships we built—all the seed that was sown. Faqir, Sefullah, Ehson, Rajah, and everyone . . . and there's Tamseela."

"Yes, there's Tamseela." A worn smile quivered on Mary Ann's lips.

"In these few months we don't have a long list of converts, but what we are doing can't be counted," Reuben said. "We have to trust in God to grow the plants. We've done our part, but if it's God's work, He knows why things ended up the way they did. Jesus said He would build His church. Kingdom work takes place one person at a time."

Minnesota Virginia Pakistan Ukraine Afghanistan Israel Haiti Bangladesh

Land of the Bible

THE EARLY MORNING AIR LAPPED around Reuben in waves of warmth. Down on the cobblestones, coolness crept about the ankles of the pedestrians, but currents flowed down, introducing the heat of the approaching day. The sounds of morning in Jerusalem warned and beckoned hawkers and passing traffic. Music played from one of the little shops. Reuben listened with a certain pleasure.

The word "Israel" was a fascinating one. Reuben thought of it as he trudged up the winding ridges of the Mount of Olives, looking out over the city. Israel intrigued him, and as he looked across Jerusalem, a bold mosaic of the old stories leapt to his mind. This was the land of the Bible, the land of Abraham's walk of faith, where the Israelites marched to conquer the Canaanites, and Jericho toppled. Where Samson broke pillars, killing hundreds of his enemies, where David slew Goliath, and where the Assyrians captured the Jews and carried them away. Here Christ was born and welcomed by angels, and He lived to heal thousands and feed multitudes before His death ended in life. The sites of the Biblical accounts were still there. They were markedly changed, perhaps, but they were still there.

~~~~~~~~~~~~~~~~~~~~~~~~~~~~~~~

Nearly a year had passed since Reuben and Mary Ann had returned to

Virginia from Pakistan. They had again gone back to Pakistan for Darrell and Tamseela's wedding, and from there had traveled to Israel. It was May 2008, and Beacon of Light had asked them to be house parents at a new base they were just beginning in Israel. Reuben and Mary Ann had agreed to go on a short-term basis since they did not feel they could be away from responsibilities at home for a longer period of time.

Reuben and Mary Ann were the first to reach the country, joined a little later by various team members. They rented an apartment in Jerusalem, right in the heart of history, and as Reuben looked out his window or strode through the narrow streets, he turned many things over in his head, thinking about the country he had heard about since childhood.

In a way, actually seeing the country that had only existed in his imagination was disappointing to Reuben. The angels had left the skies of Bethlehem. No rich plainsmen wandered over the dry land with multitudes of animals, servants, and children looking for oases. The tourist economy had taken the place of the old relics, and vendors shrieked from all corners of the city, filling their pockets on foreigners' penchant for souvenirs.

Religion was everywhere, in the swinging side locks of the Jews, the black-clad women of Islam, and the crosses around the necks of tourists. But the power of Pentecost had melted away like frost in the noon sun. On his first visit to the Mount of Olives, the emptiness of the historical sites struck Reuben. There where the Lord sweat blood, praying, olive trees still grew. Many folks still looked down on Jerusalem from the brow of the hill, but Reuben wondered if any of them understood the burden of the Saviour who had stood there weeping.

Every year on Palm Sunday, a reenactment of Christ's triumphal entry occurred, and he and Mary Ann joined the celebration. The crowd gathered on the Mount of Olives and, crossing the Kidron Valley, poured into Jerusalem. It was a joyful throng, waving branches and singing. It was a hot day, not a skiff of cloud was in sight, and the crowd thronged along the road.

As they came to the place where Christ had cried over Jerusalem, Reuben said aloud, "If Jesus were here today, I wonder what He would say or do?"

A drop of water splattered on his glasses. Startled, they looked up. A few more drops splashed on them. "It's raining!" Reuben exclaimed, startled.

"But there aren't any clouds! The sky is clear," Mary Ann exclaimed.

"If thou hadst known, even thou, at least in this thy day, the things which belong unto thy peace! but now they are hid from thine eyes" (Luke 19:42).

As fast as it had come, the rain stopped.

Reuben sank deep into thought as they trudged on. *I think I have it. If Christ were here today, He would weep again because the people are still blind.*

A year later, on another stay in Jerusalem, Reuben and Mary Ann again went to the Palm Sunday Celebration on the Mount of Olives. There was no shade, and the sun beat down on the celebration. Mary Ann used her palm to shield her eyes from the sun as they waited, for the crowd was late. When the procession did begin, they were at the front of it. Late for the evening service, they began the descent, hurrying. As they crested over the slight terrace where Christ had stood weeping, drops of water burst on them.

"It's raining again!"

Reuben shook his head. "And the people are still blind. The Jews have missed it. So have the Arabs. But what about us? Have we missed it?"

Christ had known then, and the world had since witnessed what a scene of discord Jerusalem had become, as three religions grappled for its control. Abraham's son had been sacrificed at this place, allegedly, and the Jews had built a temple there. From the start of Islam, Jerusalem had been designated a holy city, and Mohammad was said to have made a miraculous journey there by night. Christians staked their claim to the place because it housed so many sites associated with the life of Christ.

"See!" Lonnie, one of the single team members, exclaimed one evening as the team sat about, grappling with world questions. "You can argue either side." The team members, trickling in from the United States, were crowded into the cramped apartment. The intimate living cost them their privacy but generated a lot of what's-it-all-for discussions. "If you stick up for the Jews because we started out at the same place and believe that they have a historic right to the land, you alienate the Arabs. And the Jews have done some horrendous things to the Arabs. Western Christians are known for taking the side of the Jews. No wonder a lot of the Muslim Arabs hate Christians! How do you walk out on the street and tell anyone that you are a Christian, an American one, and not immediately make enemies with the Arabs? But then, on the other hand, there is no lack of stories about the ugly things that Muslims have done to the Jews. Politics run so deep here that you almost have to tumble in on one side or the other.

"The people have long memories too. They point to the Crusades and modern history and . . ." Lonnie's voice trailed away.

"But I don't understand," said Mary Ann. "Haven't the Jews been here since Bible times? How did all the Arabs get here?"

Lonnie continued, "In 70 A.D. the Roman Emperor Titus massacred many of the Jews and scattered them to the winds. Then in 138 A.D., they were barred from living in Jerusalem. People who moved into this region from the surrounding areas and descendants of other ethnic and religious groups are the people now known as Arabs. A few centuries after the Jews left, the Emperor Constantine declared this area Christian, and "Christian" it was until the Muslims rolled in at the end of the millennium. Then Christians came brawling in with their Crusades, determined to win the Holy Land back, and forever ruining their reputation with the Muslims. They failed to ever really establish long-term control here. But instead of leaving the land strictly Islamic, the Ottoman Turks let the Jews filter back in during the 1500s. And a lot more has happened since, but suffice it to say that this city, and country too, is still being claimed by three religions. No wonder it's been blasted with suicide bombers and the political turmoil keeps everyone up at night."

"I had an interesting experience the other day," Reuben piped up. "I stopped at a man's shop when I was out looking for a place to check my email, and the man, Ibrahim, wanted to know my nationality. He thought I was probably from America and asked if I was a Christian. I asked him, 'Christian? What's that?'"

"Ibrahim said, 'Well, you're from America, aren't you?'"

"I asked him, 'Are you saying that Christians and Americans are the same thing?'"

"Ibrahim said to me, 'They are, aren't they?'"

"So what should have I said? I told him, 'Not necessarily. There are Christians in America, but America isn't Christian. Not truly. There are people who call themselves Christians, and then there are people who live like Christians.'

" 'Oh, yeah, the born-again kind,' he shrugged. 'I've heard of them. What are they anyway?' That was an open door, but I'm not sure how well I answered his question."

Reuben's story silenced the clamorous discussion for a moment.

Ryan broke in. "See, that's classic. You probably handled that as well as could be, Reuben. But where do we need to come out on all of this? How do we relate to political fanatics?"

Lonnie raised his chin from where it had sunk onto his chest. "So how much do these politics actually matter to us? They shouldn't, should they? If we go into a place cheering for one side or another, we'll destroy our own message of peace for all men."

"Well," Reuben said mildly, "Anabaptist Christians don't take part in politics, do they? There shouldn't be any problem there. We aren't concerned with the governments of this world."

"That's all great," Lonnie agreed, "until you get to Israel. Anabaptists don't care a bit about which political party is in power in, say, Tanzania, but when it comes to Israel, then all sorts of opinions come out of the woodwork.

"I've heard our own people discussing Israel's military power. The general assumption is that God blesses the Israeli military and that's why they are strong." Lonnie grinned. "I once heard a preacher preach about God blowing one of Hamas's missiles that had been fired at Israel out to sea."

"That must have been one fierce wind to blow a missile out to sea!" Ryan chuckled.

"Now there you are!" Lonnie was hounding his point again. "Suppose it had been one of the missiles Israel had launched at Hamas? Why are followers of Christ cheering on a missile that's going to kill people, no matter *who* it's launched at! If that's the way we look at the Israeli-Palestine conflict, you're going to have to tell an Arab to come to a Christ that is empowering his enemy to launch missiles at him. There's no love and forgiveness in that. And if you lose that, you lose the power of the whole Gospel."

It was into this bed of antagonism that Reuben and Mary Ann walked. Among this kind of racial hatred and oppression, they attempted to live.

What could be done against such deeply rooted prejudices of ethnicity and religion?

Reuben thought, remembering his upbringing, that there was a kind misconception about Israel in every child's mind. Perhaps a picture of David, knee-high in alfalfa, sweeping languid fingers over a harp in a succession of plaintive notes while the sheep gathered around, listening with human expressions on their faces. Everyone knew that if the bad lion or bear came, it would be dispatched rapidly with the little slingshot. Israel was a land where ravens fed hungry men and iron ax heads floated on water, where spies carried bunches of grapes the size of basketballs back to the weary children of Israel, and even the donkeys saw angels.

But reality was different. The hungry man who was fed by the ravens was being hunted by a hardheaded, debauched nation led by an evil queen, and the spies carried those grapes back to a horde of whiners. The donkey who saw the angel had to hurt the leg of the Amorite man upon his back to get him to understand God was angry with him. The places where the sheep fed in Israel were desert. Every night a mist rode in from the sea, and in the morning, sheep traipsed along crooked paths, tearing off the tender little shoots that had just shot up and would soon wilt. Barren and baked, the deserts were spread under a cruel sun.

Reuben saw, at the Wailing Wall and at the sites around the holy city, that when the Law of Moses was read, the veil was still drawn on the hearts of the Jews. They still pursued things that could not save them. They spent their time and energy and passion fighting their archenemy, the Palestinians, and did not understand that the real enemy had captured their souls. The stories of the Bible were stories of the work of a holy and merciful God among a sin-entrenched nation, the way He worked among all men at all points in history.

Reuben, roving around the streets of Jerusalem and on his trips around the countryside, watched the harassment of the Arab people by the Israeli military, which was admittedly a power machine. The power and glory of Israel on the streets and at the checkpoints represented no righteousness.

The Arabs antagonized the Jews also, of course. Hamas fired away at

Jerusalem daily from Gaza, but no one was accusing them of establishing the kingdom of the Lord. Reuben was saddened by it all. Both sides were caught in bondage—eternal strife—and there would be no peace until they all bowed their knees before the Prince of Peace.

CHAPTER 20

Discouraged

THE POTTER'S RECTANGULAR FACE TILTED upward under his turban, and his eyes slanted downward over his nose, over his wired rimmed glasses to the mud in his fingers. His long fingers were nervous and sensitive, and he worked with lethargic precision that said, "Never hurry. Never hurry. What matters will be there in the end." Gently, he put the clay aside and tapped his fingers together, gazing at the top of the doorway.

Reuben, also methodical, lifted piece after piece of pottery. Pottery fascinated him. He admired handmade crafts, and the symbolism of a potter's work had drawn him to this shop in the first place. He had seen more elaborate pottery, but the simplicity of these pieces did not bother him. Mere artisanship was no mean thing.

"None of your pots are painted." Reuben pivoted, speculating to his host.

"No." The tapping ceased.

A flurry down the street made Reuben look up, and he moved to the door, crossing the threshold. "My bus is here. Thank you."

The cloth bound head inclined, and the tapping began again. "Thank you."

~~~~~~

Reuben and Mary Ann were back in Israel the second time. They had left Israel in September 2008 and had returned to the States to take care of some family and personal business. Now it was February 2009, and the effects of a war in nearby Gaza were still in the air. Even though a ceasefire had been declared in January, Gaza Strip militants were still launching shells into Israel.

By the time Reuben and Mary Ann returned, Beacon of Light was developing different programs in Israel. They taught English classes to students from all walks of life, from university students to mothers to businessmen, and even one policeman. Mary Ann taught a group of ladies and became good friends with them, one young woman in particular. One day Mary Ann had asked them to write their life stories, but the young woman had put her paper aside, sadness in her eyes. "I can't write it; my story is too painful." Mary Ann went to her house to visit, and the two women became good enough friends that the young woman told her story to Mary Ann, a story fraught with desertion and divorce and abuse. These stories broke Mary Ann's heart, and she tried harder to be a friend to the girl.

Some days, Reuben and Mary Ann went to the park and grilled hot dogs to feed hungry Sudanese refugees who were arriving daily in Tel-Aviv. The refugees were fleeing war, trekking across Egypt into Israel. It was a grueling journey, and they told horrible stories of oppression, abuse, desertion, starvation, and organ theft. The refugees were dumped in the city parks with no place to go and no one to turn to. Israel allowed them to enter but did not offer provisions of any kind.

BOL was also starting several self-help programs, outfitting one man to make olivewood pens to be sold in the United States. Some families were given sheep to raise for market. One widow received a sewing machine.

In spite of the affluence in the land of the Bible, the poor and the handicapped still tucked themselves away in apartment buildings and cellars. The halt, the maimed, and the blind had not disappeared. Particularly on the other side of the wall from Jerusalem, the West Bank barred many poor, keeping them from the eyes of the international community who flocked to the Holy Land as tourists. Reuben and Mary Ann turned the majority of their time and attention to the handicapped people of the West Bank.

Reuben and Mary Ann were visiting a Palestinian home with Yusef, the interpreter. Reuben shifted his feet as they stood outside the small house. A few flowers nodded from behind a stack of broken pots and pieces of wire. The flowers had wilted, but their faded colors were brave against the brown around them. A little boy had come to the door, Asif's brother.

"Asif doesn't want to see you," the child insisted. He was handsome in a cloudy, dark way, his jaw set in belligerence. "He said no one could come today."

Yusef turned to Reuben, interpreting. "He doesn't want to see us."

Mary Ann's face fell. "Why? What's the problem?"

Reuben clasped at his leg. Without turning, Mary Ann put her hand out to touch his arm.

"Can you ask why he doesn't want to see us?" Reuben inquired after a moment. His face was white, and beads of sweat sparkled on his forehead. He waited a second, and the iron lines on his face eased a bit. "Tell him to tell Asif that it's the people who gave him the wheelchair."

The brother was hanging around, waiting to see how well he had discouraged them. A triumphant little smile rose on the child's face.

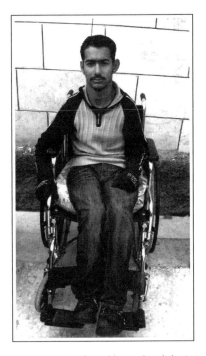

Asif and his wheelchair.

"He thinks we're just going to go away," Reuben murmured to Mary Ann.

Yusef explained, and the little boy hesitated, his eyes falling on Reuben. Worry flickered before he bit his lip and nodded, scampering off.

"Asif's been so discouraged and depressed," Mary Ann remarked. "The last time we were here he barely wanted to talk, and he kept his face turned to the wall."

Reuben said nothing. For no reason he could figure, the phantom pains of his amputation had set in that day in force. With little to help the unreasonable sensations, the pain was costing him dearly. The dreary winter rain had rolled in around them, and he adjured silently of the universe about him. *Why?*

The universe echoed back, *Why?*

The little boy arrived back at the open door. "He says you may come in."

Out of a drab world into a drab room they went. The place darkened as they entered it, blocking the light from the doorway. Asif looked up languidly from the wheelchair they had given him and only nodded. He had drawn his chair up to the cluttered table, and a little frame of an airplane on the table absorbed his attention. Its motor purred as Asif stared at it.

Reuben forgot the phantom pain, delighted. "Where did you get this?"

"I made it myself." Asif demonstrated the trappings of the small craft to his guest, and the two men lost themselves in a fascination. Uninterested in the plane after she had realized it couldn't really fly, Mary Ann took time to watch her husband with the boy and pray.

At twenty-two years old, Asif should have been in school or the military, absorbed in girls and cars, worrying about a career. Instead, he was incarcerated in his wheelchair. A vaccination with the wrong vaccine had affected his nervous system when he had been only a year old. He would never walk on his own.

Abruptly, Asif pushed the airplane away, startling Reuben. A minute before, he had been showing off the wonders of his machine. Now he sighed, drifting away into silence. They waited. Reuben sat back in his chair and rubbed his cheekbones. What could they do for this boy? Was there anything that would cheer him up? He needed purpose in life. At twenty-two, everyone needed a reason to be, something to do. Here he was, stuck in this dingy room.

"He needs a Bible," Mary Ann whispered.

Reuben stilled her with his hand. "Yes, of course, but . . ."

They left after a couple of minutes, Reuben still mulling it over in his head. The gray, damp world outside enveloped them again, and the cold air burned their nostrils.

"Wait a minute. I am going back." Reuben departed the way they had come. Mary Ann looked after him and then followed.

Asif had not roused from his slump, but the sudden return of his guests made him raise his head ever so slightly. "It's okay," Reuben assured him. "We just want to look at your room." Asif waved them in with an indifferent gesture.

Reuben scanned the room, calculating. Mary Ann licked her finger and swiped at the wall, frowning at the grime that came away. "Reuben, it's dirty."

Reuben was busy examining the rough walls and the flaky ceiling.

Asif's mother came to the doorway, wiping her hands. She looked questioningly at Reuben and Mary Ann.

"Yusef," Reuben said, "Yusef, where are you? Yusef, ask Asif's mother if we may paint this room for him." He was glowing with excitement.

Yusef did, and Asif's mother agreed to the idea. Asif barely lifted his eyes.

"We'll be back," Reuben told Asif.

"That's good," Asif murmured.

A week later, Reuben and Mary Ann were dragging buckets of paint and brushes onto the public bus and through the border into the West Bank. They were waiting for their connecting bus when Reuben recollected his potter friend. He drifted down the street and entered the shop, raising his hand to the proprietor. Busy this time, the potter spun his wheel faster, ignoring his visitor. Not until the pot had risen straight out of the damp clay did he pause to look over his eyeglasses at Reuben.

"I don't have much time today." It was all Reuben could think of to say.

The potter adjusted his glasses, smoothed his turban, and eased the pot off the wheel. Both men looked at it. The wet clay gleamed.

"You could have the pot if you would want it."

"Well, thank you!" Reuben said. He eased the damp pot into his hands.

"It needs to be baked," the potter remarked.

"No problem." Intrigued, Reuben turned the pot. "I can bake it. We have an oven at my house."

"Ah," said the potter, and he smiled at the spider web on the wall.

Reuben arranged to pick up the clay pot later that evening so that it wouldn't get broken during their travels, and he went on his way.

At Asif's house, Asif's mother welcomed them, smiling. She touched the pail of paint. "I wonder if I could have what's left," she murmured. Mary Ann resolved that whatever was left would go to the woman. Asif's mother was still a young woman, aged by the care of a son who should have been able to care for her by now.

They worked hard all day. First, they cleared the room of all its belongings and spackled the rough places, managing to add two coats of paint before the long day had ended. By the time they stopped for a bit of lunch, Reuben found himself exhausted. He had been working on the ceiling. The strain on his neck and the effort it required to balance on his wooden leg were wearing him out. After lunch, he switched to working on the walls, ignoring the growing discomfort of his prosthesis.

Mary Ann was chirpy as they finished late in the afternoon. Being a woman, she found the clean white room smelling of paint even more satisfying than Reuben did. Gloating, she swiped her finger on the wall as she had when she had checked for dust. She rubbed it then, trying to get rid of the paint before anyone noticed. "Let's sing for them!" she suggested, balling up her fingers to hide the paint.

So they did, and Reuben just happened to locate a Bible story book in his pack. "Here, young man," he said, drawing up a chair beside Asif. "This is a book to cheer you up. There are a lot of truths in this book. You read it and see what you think." Asif's younger siblings gathered around Asif, crowding in to get a look at the new book.

"Okay," Asif replied, shaking his shaggy hair down over his eyes. His eyes had gained a slight sparkle throughout the morning, but the excitement of all the hustle had worn him down. His mother entered, taking her place behind Asif's chair. Speaking apologetically to them, she stroked the hair back out of Asif's eyes. "He is tired; he will appreciate it more in the morning." Her eyes thanked them.

Reuben looked around at the other children. "I think . . ." he said and dug in his backpack again. He had more Bible story books, and he gave each of them a copy.

Asif wasn't the only one who was tired. Reuben staggered once as they boarded the bus to go home, and Mary Ann plopped into her seat with a sigh. "I am so glad we could do that for the poor boy."

"Yes," Reuben said, "I'm praying that he saw the hands of Jesus." Christ had spent His days around hopeless needs like this one. Reuben sighed, thinking of the paint on the walls. He had been excited about the project, but now it felt worthless. *Paint on the walls*, he scoffed to himself. *What if I couldn't walk and someone came and painted my walls?* It felt pretty ridiculous. What was the point? Reuben was so frustrated that he jerked the zipper on his backpack, making it split. *What is the answer to all this suffering?*

"Those walls looked so nice," Mary Ann said by his side. Reuben looked at her and then at the zipper on his backpack. She hadn't noticed it. He set the bag between his legs and worked on it patiently.

It was getting late by the time they reached the station where they had to switch buses. Reuben remembered the clay pot. Barely able to keep from limping, he made his way to the potter's shop to fetch it. The clay pot was still sitting on the windowsill, drying from the afternoon sun. The potter did not speak as Reuben picked it up, tapping his fingers together from where he reclined, but as Reuben left the shop again, he looked up and wished him well. The chafing of Reuben's prosthesis sock was rubbing his stump sore. It was time to change the sweaty sock. As Reuben found Mary Ann again, he searched for a place nearby to sit down and change it. Across the road, an old building with a porch on the front of it squatted by the wayside. Two chairs stood mutely to the side of the porch. They sat down on these, and Reuben removed his wooden leg and tucked it behind his chair while they waited for the liner to dry.

Mary Ann leaned toward Reuben. "Look at those men over there."

Reuben had seen them. A group of men stood at the other end of the porch. They were talking among themselves, and Reuben was struck by their air. Self-confident and alert, they carried themselves like trained men, their shoulders raised in muscles. Their clothes were good quality, but unremarkable and plain rather than showy. A short growth of beard, not much more than stubble, showed on their faces. One of them cupped his hand to his hip as though unconsciously holding something. Reuben couldn't see because of the long jacket, but he suspected the man was armed. He glanced away as the men looked in their direction. Leaning back, he let the air flow over the stump of his leg.

Another man was approaching. Reluctantly, Reuben sat up. This man was slender, swarthy-skinned, and wearing sunglasses. He walked up to where they were sitting. "I am security here. Are you okay? Do you need any help? Maybe a wheelchair?"

"No." Reuben gestured to Mary Ann. "She helps me, and actually, I can walk just fine. Right now, I have my prosthesis off to rest my leg and give it some air."

"I see," the man nodded. He squatted in front of them. "What happened to your leg? Where are you from?"

Reuben recited their story. The man listened, but during Reuben's explanation, his gaze wandered all around at their surroundings. The group of men had gathered in a tight huddle. Two were talking with their heads turned in the direction of Reuben and Mary Ann. The third regarded them openly, his arms crossed on his chest.

The security guard asked a few questions about the things Reuben had told him before he changed the subject. "Do you see those men over there? They are dangerous. They are Hamas."

Surprised at this turn of conversation, their eyes followed his motion. The three men looked away. "There might be problems," the guard continued. "I wish you would get your prosthesis on. You should get out of here soon."

Reuben and Mary Ann exchanged a look, and Reuben reached for his prosthesis.

The security guard fiddled with his watch and changed the subject again.

"Do you like tea or coffee?" Reuben said coffee, but Mary Ann wanted tea.

"I'll be right back." The guard loped off.

By the time he returned, the group of well-dressed strangers had moved around to the left. They had quit observing Reuben and Mary Ann, but they lingered. Reuben felt nervous. *I'm just an amputee,* Reuben thought, frustrated all over again.

They drank their coffee and tea, and the friendly guard motioned them to follow. Gathering their things, they trudged after him, crossing the street. Reuben looked back over his shoulder. Mary Ann took a quick breath, and Reuben jerked his head around. The guard had vanished. Swiveling around, Reuben glanced up and down the street, turning to look behind him. The guard was nowhere in sight. Mary Ann's eyes grew huge, and they both spun toward the men who had been watching them. They were gone, evaporated.

"What!" Reuben said.

"An angel," Mary Ann suggested, her eyes solemn.

Reuben opened his mouth, but just at that moment the bus rolled in.

Reuben had almost dozed off when he felt a familiar slowing of the bus. The border crossing was coming up. Concrete and wire clouded the horizon. Leaving the West Bank was always more difficult than coming in, and this could take long. Reuben dreaded the milling around, the waiting, and the paperwork.

On a recent trip, he had not even been allowed to cross. Because of visiting other countries in the region, he had requested that no Israeli visa be stamped in his passport, and the only record of his visa was electronic. At the West Bank crossings, the guards did not like to check the computers. They had refused him entry, and he had waited on the guardrail outside in the cold wind until one of the team men had come to pick him up and taken him to a different crossing where they had been able to return to Jerusalem. Now he tried to think ahead, wishing he could avoid these crossings.

The passengers were preparing to dismount. Mary Ann stood. Reuben stopped her, raising his finger. "Wait, let's not get down. Lonnie was saying the other day that they can't actually make foreigners get off the bus. Let's see if they'll take our passports from the bus here."

Mary Ann flashed him an open-mouthed look and then sat down, looking brave. "Well, if that's the way it's to be . . . if they shoot us, they'll have to shoot us together."

"Mary Ann!" Reuben exclaimed.

"Well, they will!"

Reuben laughed. "Oh, I doubt—"

"Dear!" It was Mary Ann's turn to exclaim. "Those guards would shoot you on sight!"

"I don't think they'll shoot us," Reuben replied. He took her hand and they waited together. The other passengers had gone.

The soldiers stepped on the bus, ready to do their checks, and saw Reuben and Mary Ann. One of them barked something, and the soldiers advanced on the foreigners. "Heh!" The guttural sound sprang from the point man. More soldiers boarded, only glancing out of the corners of their eyes. They spread out to sweep the bus. The first three concerned themselves with the foreigners.

"What are you doing here?" two of them said in heavily accented English. "Why did you not get down?"

Reuben explained, and the first man tried to argue. "You should have gotten down. You must always get down!"

The second man, however, brushed him aside, reaching out for the proffered passports, and disappeared. The other two followed in his wake. A bit of time passed before they were back, unhappy. "You do not have an Israeli visa. Get out of the bus. How did you get into the country?"

"I flew in," Reuben told them. "They didn't stamp my passport. I have an electronic one, though. Check the computers."

The first soldier began to gesticulate, losing himself in Hebrew. The second man, the one who had taken the passports first, crossed his arms and observed Reuben for a minute, his head cocked. Then, without a word, he left again and was gone for a long time.

By then the other passengers had boarded and were back in their places.

Reuben waited. Everyone waited. Tension climbed in his throat. Mary Ann looked at him occasionally and went back to praying.

Reuben himself prayed. "God, I need my passport. Maybe it was foolish of me to try staying on the bus."

As time dragged on, Reuben prayed again. "It was foolish of me, and I am sorry for not trusting you earlier. I know you don't need me to do your work, and I know that whatever I can do for these people is out of love, and I know that love is the only solution. I'm sorry I was cynical. I need to get my passport back, please."

He had barely opened his eyes when a big soldier—a big, big soldier—stepped out of the building by the crossing and made his way over to the bus. He was different than the other border guards. He looked more elite, more honed to his job. Watching him come, Reuben remembered the dangerous job these men had. At these borders between the Palestinian West Bank and Israel, anything could happen—any violence at any minute. It was the concern of these men to sort through people and find these threats. Dark glasses guarded his profile; a knife swung from his neck. His assault rifle hung on a strap over his shoulder. Sidearms poked at the insides of the man's brown arms. He ascended into the bus, striding back through. The passengers hushed.

He had American passports in his hand. Closer he marched, closer, closer. Reuben swallowed convulsively. The soldier reached out and handed the passports to Reuben, who received them numbly. The guard drew up to his full height, his chest expanding, and snapped, "Be careful; be watchful."

That was profound, Reuben thought. He blinked at the guard. Spinning on his heel, the soldier was gone.

Darkness had fallen by the time they reached their apartment. Mary Ann began to fix a late meal. Reuben tucked his clay pot into the little micro oven to bake.

"Mary Ann," he asked, "how hot should the oven be?"

"Oh, I don't know." Mary Ann stirred at the soup, tasting it. She wasn't listening. "350. Everything gets baked at 350 degrees."

"This," Reuben said, "is not a cake. I think it's supposed to be pretty hot."

He turned up the heat in the oven as high as it would go and went off to his computer to work on a report. Mary Ann brought him his soup in a bowl and sat with him, eating hers also. They talked of the day as they ate.

"Oh, that man who talked to us when we were waiting for the bus must have been an angel!" Mary Ann opened her eyes wide, remembering. "I think God sent him just for that special purpose." She waved her spoon, thinking about it.

"Maybe so," Reuben admitted. He took a bite of soup and considered. "I think he was sent to minister to us. We were so tired, and I was discouraged. Off and on I was tempted to think none of this is worth it, that we can't make a lasting difference, and that God wasn't going to look after our passports. Even that man—it was hard to have him asking all about my handicap after such a long day. But God sent him as an angel, and he ministered to—"

Ka-poooww! A sharp explosion perforated the air. Mary Ann jumped as if she'd been shot. Reuben leaped up, and though he always maintained that his running days were over, he covered the distance to the kitchen at a clip. Mary Ann followed, "Reuben! Do you think it was a gunshot? Be careful!"

Reuben knew what it was. Ruefully, he removed his clay pot from the oven. "Oh, no! Now *that* is ruined. It blew the bottom right out." He stared at the broken little clay pot, and Mary Ann took her husband by the elbow and smiled up at him. Reuben returned the affectionate look with a wry expression.

Reuben went back to his computer and took a bite of the cheese he had been eating. He wagged his finger at Mary Ann. "You know, there's a lesson in this."

She giggled, but he held up his hand, continuing, "When I took the pot from that potter, he smiled as if to say, 'Wait and see. There is more to this than you think. Maybe you'd better let someone who knows what he's doing bake that pot, but if you want to try, go ahead and see what happens.' It just so happens that I ruined the pot. I think God is saying something about this ministry and all the questions. He's saying, 'Wait and see. There's a lot more to this than you think—a lot more than you can see. I know what's going on. I know how to bake the pot. But if you think you know how, go ahead and see what happens. After all, it's my pot. I made it.' " Reuben chewed, thinking.

Mary Ann thought it over. "Well, God uses broken vessels, doesn't He?"

Reuben pushed aside his plate and stared at his computer. He looked back at her, "What?" Then he grinned. "Well, yes."

Early the next week Reuben returned to the bus stop. He took the pot along to show to the potter, telling his story.

The potter listened, directing his gaze into the rafters. When Reuben had finished, the potter reached for the pot, turning it over in his hand. When he looked up, his eyes smiled, but his mouth was sober. "Your oven was too hot."

CHAPTER 21

West Bank Ministry

ASIF WAS ONE OF THEIR first connections in the West Bank, but Reuben and Mary Ann found many more with little effort. The concentration of handicapped children in parts of the West Bank climbed high. In pockets of the population, 5 percent of the children were handicapped. Close intermarriage caused a huge amount of birth defects and genetic diseases in what was sometimes referred to as the "world's largest prison."

The West Bank was not a funny place. Surrounded by miles of concrete wall sometimes as high as twenty-five feet and topped by barbed wire, it was regulated by checkpoints. Crossings were guaranteed to be finicky, and once inside the walls, many reminders of bondage met the Yoders.

The West Bank and the Gaza Strip were largely populated by Palestinians who had fled as the nation of Israel came to power. When the Jews had returned to Israel as part

World's largest prison, the West Bank.

of the Zionist movement that roughly coincided with the two World Wars, skirmishes among Jews and Arabs and the resultant war of Israeli independence had crowded many of the Palestinian Arabs from their homes and into these two territories. Although the territories were controlled and patrolled by the Israeli forces, the Palestinians did have a government structure functioning in most of the population centers. Fighting without and within made that government structure unstable. The conservative Islamists clashed with the secular Palestinian nationalists, and they all hated the Israelis, who promptly returned the sentiment.

Social service agencies were available in the Palestinian cities and were quite helpful in locating families with special needs children in the villages. While willing to work with Reuben and Mary Ann, these agencies were nonetheless concerned that this was not a front for proselytizing.

"Just don't embarrass us by praying," a worker once said as they were arriving at a home.

Reuben grinned. "I think we can honor that." He knew that their jobs would be in jeopardy if their work became associated with proselytizing.

Yusef, their companion and interpreter, was nearly always with them too. He was a Palestinian who had spent a lot of time in the Gaza Strip. Formerly an agnostic, he had come to Christ through an incredible experience. Now he proved a huge asset to Reuben and Mary Ann's work with the handicapped. He knew the culture of the West Bank and had a heart for the Palestinian people.

One day when Reuben and Mary Ann met with the caseworker in the town of Seer, the lady hearkened to their cause and her face lit up. "Why, here is just the man you should meet." She presented a tall Palestinian by her side whom they had scarcely noticed before. "He was just in here to discuss something with me. His daughter is physically handicapped." She addressed the man in rapid Arabic. He nodded in response and moved off.

"Come, sit down," the caseworker invited. "We'll go to visit his family in a moment. Now tell me about yourselves."

Reuben told her about their work among the handicapped, how he himself was an amputee and wished to see what he could do for others. In a bit the man returned, and the caseworker gathered them all up to go. They walked together down the street to a tiny home set back from the roadway. The man ushered them in, and the caseworker introduced the family.

The daughter, Korina, was an imperious little thing. She sat in her bed, her flaring eyebrows and arched nostrils giving her a royal air. "I am Korina. My legs don't work. And who are you?"

Korina had many younger brothers and sisters, well-behaved youngsters who all looked as if they might cry. Demure as kittens, they stood together along the wall, taking the visitors in with big eyes. The family was poor but clean. The home was down a dusty street of the small town of Seer, and olive trees grew at two corners of the house. The father said little, and they did not see the mother immediately.

The social worker led the conversations, telling Reuben about Korina. "Korina would love to be in school, and she would do well, but we have no way to get her there."

Mary Ann placed herself by Korina, and they communicated with the little Arabic that Mary Ann had picked up—and with a lot of gestures. She taught Korina a finger game that soon had them both pealing with laughter.

Korina had a genetic muscle disease, and her muscles were wasting away. Her legs were already paralyzed, and she could not walk. The sight of her listless limbs broke Mary Ann's heart, and she debated what her life expectancy could be. The child's family doted on her; it was plain to be seen. When not talking with the other adults, her father's eyes rested on her, a patient lament in his eyes. The little children running to and fro trusted no one but Korina. Like a queen, she reigned from her couch, and they scampered to do her bidding. The eldest one brought in some tea for them all to drink and a little pudding-like desert with pistachios sprinkled on it for the guests to eat.

The social worker stopped and smiled as she watched the communicative dance between Mary Ann and Korina. In response to a question from the caseworker, the little girl burst out with an ecstatic deluge. The lady addressed Mary Ann, her dimples showing. "She says she feels something coming from you."

Love, Mary Ann thought. *Love. Funny how God's love just pours through you at times like these.* Mary Ann hadn't thought that she had been particularly loving, but she was fond of the little girl already.

Reuben had an idea. He had the perfect wheelchair for Korina back at the warehouse. It was the right size and even a purple color to match her ladyship.

"I have the perfect chair," he told the worker. When this was interpreted to Korina's father, he only nodded slightly. The social worker pressed him more, and at length he replied, his words brief. A cloud settled over the caseworker's face.

Yusef leaned over and said, "He says they don't believe a word you say. They don't believe you will come back."

"Won't come back!" Mary Ann exclaimed. "Why does he think we came?"

The social worker was apologetic. "It is actually common, ma'am. So many foreigners come, promising aid. These foreigners just come in for evaluations and take pictures to solicit funds. They exploit the children, using them to get money. And they never come back."

"I see." Mary Ann pressed her lips.

Reuben was grave. He had never thought of that. Standing, he stepped over to shake hands with the father. "We will be back."

The worker did not interpret this, and Reuben was uncertain how much English the man understood, if any. The pause breathed awkwardness into the departure, and Reuben and Mary Ann walked away, Reuben silently declaring that he would show this family something different.

"Well, I never . . ." Mary Ann was still troubled. "I don't understand what good they think it will do us just to come visit them and tell them we will be back with a wheelchair. We didn't ask for anything or even take pictures."

They did have the perfect wheelchair back at the shop, just as Reuben had remembered. The shop was Reuben's domain, the place where he could whittle away hours fiddling with the parts and pieces of equipment. His ingenuity was self-taught, and he loved to take a piece of equipment, maybe a broken wheelchair, and fix it. From childhood, Reuben had been handy with his fingers, straightening and fixing and welding and creating. He loved craftsmanship, and the wheelchair shop was dear to his heart, for the handicapped people were also Reuben's own special realm. Mary Ann helped him too, cleaning the pieces and polishing. Sometimes sewing was required. Together they spent many happy hours.

Reuben bought used wheelchairs or other equipment that he could find. Without being able to totally explain the difference, he felt that the used equipment was something he would feel more comfortable giving, sensing that perhaps the gift would be better understood. The labor of love that went into those chairs spoke volumes. Although many of their beneficiaries never knew the time and effort the couple spent on the chairs they received, perhaps it was unconsciously recognized. Anyone can give a new gift, shiny and smelling of plastic, but a piece of equipment, softened by use and restored by goodwill, fitted just for them—who could resist it?

The next day they were back to fit Korina to the wheelchair. To Reuben's disappointment, the father was not at home. This time the mother of the

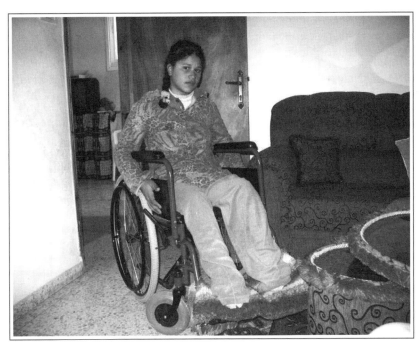

Korina and her family are convinced that people of "the Book" keep their promises.

family poked her head out, and after a moment, slipped into the room to join in the children's excitement. They had just lowered Korina into the chair when the next child, a boy, grasped it by the handles and whirled his sister off. He gunned her about the room, and Korina shrieked with laughter while the little ones loudly rejoiced.

"Come." Korina held out her arms to her baby brother. The baby was lifted into the chair to join his sister and stuck his thumb into his mouth before beginning to wail. His soft little mother gathered him up to comfort, and Korina paused, flushed, to chatter to her family. Reuben took advantage of the chance to kneel down and examine the fit of the chair.

"Look," he pointed. "It's a little short here. Not a big problem; she's a growing girl." He directed Korina's attention and gestured to show her the problem. The hilarity faded into a glow, and she became business-like, nodding to show she understood. Reuben had just accomplished this circuitous conversation when a shadow fell across Korina's lap, and they looked about. Her father stood in the doorway, his head nearly reaching the doorjamb and his face hardened into stone. His eyes were like deep pools of water that a person peers into, trying to see beneath the surface.

"Well," Reuben drew a deep breath, nodding. He stood to acknowledge the man. The return greeting was adequate, but gruff. Reuben turned back to Korina. "Well, then, let's get you back in bed." Reuben didn't know why, but he felt as though he had been caught trying to steal a prize calf. He avoided looking at the father's face. Mary Ann studied it, though. The man was looking at the dangling legs of his daughter, limp in the air and draped over the bed, and his expression was bruised like the petal of a flower when insistent fingers rub over it, ripping the thin skin.

It went nearly a week before they returned with the adjusted chair. This time the tumult met them. The children no longer huddled in doorways as they arrived. They ran out to meet them. Korina maintained her poise this time, welcoming them with a carefully practiced phrase of English. "How are you?" She motioned to chairs with a majestic wave of her thin hand and did not look at the wheelchair Reuben carried. Her nostrils quivered and her lashes batted.

Almost immediately Korina's father strode in. Today there was no wounded expression. Although still reserved, his salutation was warm, and he stood near them, a spark in the dark eyes. He watched as Korina tried the chair. It fit as though it were made of elastic, cupping Korina's proportions.

An elaborate snack was spread out, and Mary Ann called the children to her, convincing them to take also. They capitulated with little show of politeness, and the adults did not reprimand them at all.

Korina's father put down his tea and spoke deliberately. A dim twinkle of something rose in Yusef's face before he interpreted the man's words. "Why do you keep your promises when no one else does?"

Reuben wiped his fingers on a napkin, considering. "We have a book," he said, "and by this book we live. Would you like to see it?"

~~~~~~~~~~~~~~~~~~~~~~~~~~~~~~~~~~~~~

It was wintertime, and Reuben drew his jacket more tightly about him as he and Mary Ann made their way into the second house they had visited that day. The social worker was coming behind them, having stopped to collect a pencil she had dropped. A raspy shriek like the call of a wounded animal startled them. Again the screech rose from somewhere to the side of the house, extinguished with a breathy gasp.

"What's wrong with him?" Mary Ann clapped her hand to her face as they approached, horror creeping into her soul. A boy writhed on the cold concrete in front of the house, his legs jerking. Drool leaked out of the stubbly mouth, and the irises of the eyes were just visible. The sobbing wails crept out of his throat, arrested by a sporadic intake of air. He moaned, thrashing.

Reuben knelt down by the side of the boy and felt his arm, rigid like the sinew of a bowstring. Another moan beyond them made them jump, for it did not appear to have come from the boy. Just then the boy flailed, striking Reuben. Reuben slid back a little.

"He's having a seizure," he commented.

"What can we do for him? Oh, dear, where can his parents be?" Mary Ann wrung her hands.

The social worker had come up by then. "Let him be. Don't restrain anyone in a seizure. He has them a lot, unfortunately."

"Does no one care for him?"

"He's got parents." The social worker sighed. "Come. We'll find them." Out of the corner of her eye, Mary Ann caught sight of a brief movement at the side of the house, and her hair prickled in her scalp. She claimed Reuben's arm.

Through the silent house, they followed a dark passage. The small house would have been cluttered had there been any items to strew around, but there was little besides a few odd pieces of furniture and some dishes flung on the floor. One was broken. An unclean but oddly human odor of filth and body waste entered their nostrils. Mary Ann was beginning to be able to identify the smell after months here in the West Bank. An open door admitted them to the view of an old man humped under a thin cover on the floor. It was the father, the social worker said, sleeping away the chill of winter. Going out behind the house, they found the mother hunched over, sitting against the house wall, rocking back and forth.

The parents were old, in their nineties. The three handicapped children, said the caseworker, were all in their fifties. Two of them suffered from severe epilepsy; all three were mentally handicapped with various physical limitations.

The old mother looked up with a glaze on her eyes that had settled there fifty years ago. Her face was pitted and creased, and rivulets of grime were etched in her skin. During the wintertime in the West Bank, many of the poorer people went without bathing rather than brave the cold water, and the sight of her was repulsive. Reuben tried to kill the feeling, telling himself that it was a human who needed help. He glanced backward compulsively but gathered himself in hand. A slight flutter at his side made him remember his wife, but she had left, skimming up to the old woman. Mary Ann put her arms about her, exclaiming the Arabic greeting. Twisting in Mary Ann's arms like a small child who had suddenly been picked up, the old lady pushed away. Surprise drew itself all over her face, and she revolted against the agape touch. Mary Ann crooned and pulled her nearer.

Reuben sensed that the woman had not felt love in years—maybe never—and felt his own involuntary convulsion of disgust melt. *Mary Ann is an incredible woman,* he thought, admiring his wife of forty years.

The social worker was speaking with the woman, who muttered hoarse replies. "She says the son we saw having a seizure screamed all night last night. She and her husband are exhausted. Unfortunately, I think these kinds of days are pretty common."

The rangy grasses, bunched at the side of the house, parted, and two old faces with drawn, childlike expressions inserted themselves. "Ah," said the worker, "there are the other two." As quickly as they had appeared, the faces were lost again among the grasses, but the moan that had echoed earlier uttered again from the direction of the grasses. They were gone, like wild things.

"What is the government doing for these people?" Reuben asked of the social services worker. "How has the situation deteriorated to this point?"

The worker shrugged. "This is bad today. It's always worse in the wintertime. For years the parents could care adequately for these children, but both parents and children are getting older, and the children's health is getting progressively worse. Soon something will have to change."

With little to do and little to say, Reuben and Mary Ann soon left. The old lady had drifted back into her world and resumed her rocking. "What could we have done for them?" Mary Ann asked Reuben. "A wheelchair? What difference would a wheelchair make?"

They went back to see about the wheelchair a few days later, concluding that the boy with the seizures would be able to use one. The wheelchair fittings took them back several times, but the deadness of the place always oppressed them.

Mary Ann put forth special effort to shower the mother with affection—with true love. The old woman shied away at first, but by the last visit, she reached out with her arms when Mary Ann entered, a shy gleam in her faded eye.

These visits to the West Bank were worth something somehow, Mary Ann was sure, although for many of the visits they would never see results. She remembered Jesus and His ministry among the poor, the destitute, and the unclean. He had given them His all even if they'd never sail to Rome to testify before Caesar or lead a church in Jerusalem. Among the lowly, where numbers could not be tallied, His ministry had taken root. Kind words and a loving touch have no numerical value and don't change the smell of the dirty children, but Christ had held them in His arms anyway.

~~~~~~~~~~~~~~~~~~~~~~~~~~~~~~~~~~~~~~

Vivian's name is beautiful, Mary Ann thought. Beautiful in more than name, the girl's animation fueled Mary Ann's admiration. The long, dark curls tucked under her veil had come loose about her face as she expressed herself. They were talking about Mary Ann's children, and Vivian had volunteered stories of her own childhood. The memories cheered them to mirth, for the women laughed easily.

Friendship is a powerful tool for evangelism.

Reuben and some of the other BOL men had been traveling to other parts of the West Bank that day, and they had dropped Mary Ann off to spend her day with Vivian and her mother. Vivian's mother loved Mary Ann. She wanted to keep Mary Ann, she said.

A degenerative muscle disease had been gradually claiming Vivian's motor skills and affecting her coordination. Originally, she had functioned well, going to college and operating with normal capabilities. Now the genetic monster had bought her life and her plans. She could no longer stand, and even lifting her hands required phenomenal effort.

College had enlivened Vivian's already active mind and channeled her many interests. Her brain worked like lightning, and her wit twinkled through her conversation. She had been a mathematics major, and her brilliance came from somewhere. Vivian's mother, a vivacious wisp of a lady, was bright too. They both spoke clean, clear English.

"Come, I want to show you something." The mother whisked Mary Ann to the back room. Nothing of interest appeared, but she pelted Mary Ann with questions.

"Why do you dress like you do? Why do you wear a cloth on your head? Do you ever wear makeup? Why not?"

She frowned when Mary Ann explained how women should submit to their husbands. "You have to listen to your husband?"

"I want to!" Mary Ann cried. "If it wasn't for Reuben, I don't know where I'd be. I thought Muslim ladies must listen to their husbands too. Don't you?"

The lady ducked her head, grinning, and didn't reply.

"Why don't you wear jewelry?"

"It adorns my outside when I want to concentrate on making my inside beautiful."

"But your inside *is* beautiful!"

"Maybe," Mary Ann admitted. "The part that is beautiful is where Jesus is."

By this time Vivian had joined them, and she and her mother considered this with cocked heads. "Okay," they agreed, "maybe so, but after your inside is all beautiful, why can't you make the outside pretty?" Vivian patronized jewelry, and her mother retrieved some of these items now, draping necklaces over Mary Ann until she looked like a jewelry tree. The three pealed with laughter, and Mary Ann removed them.

"Now," Vivian said slyly, "Reuben will like you better."

"Yes, much better. He doesn't like jewelry." Mary Ann folded her hands and put them in her lap, a smile quivering on the edge of her demure expression. "No, no makeup." The mother had brought out a pot of rouge.

Vivian laughed again, but it faded away into a frown. "Why?" she asked, and the words formed slowly. "Why do you say Jesus made you beautiful inside? How could someone else make your soul good?"

Mary Ann put her hands to her cheeks, thinking and praying. She did not want to mess up the question. "Sin came by one man, and that affected the entire world. In the Bible it says that as Adam brought evil into the world by his sin, so Jesus brought life into the world by His death. That death was for me so that I don't have to die because of my sin. I can live a holy life without first having to atone for it by my death. Only in my heart do I have to die. Mary Ann is not a good person, you see. But if I let what Mary Ann wants to do die, then Jesus can live in my heart, and that makes it beautiful."

Her heart sagged as she saw Vivian's drawn expression. These things were never easy to say right, and the girl was confused. *Lord, in spite of me, make her be able to understand. Oh, Vivian! Vivian, don't you see the death that is in you?*

Mary Ann hunched in her chair. She wished for Reuben. He could say these things so much better. He knew how to explain so that a person could understand. She raised her eyes to Vivian's face. "Would you like to understand better? It's such a hard thing to explain. I'm so sorry."

"No, no." Vivian waved her concerns away. "I understand your words. It's just such a big idea. Where did you learn this?"

"Why, from the Bible."

"Bible? That's the Christians' holy book, right?"

"That's right."

Vivian lifted listless fingers and set them down again. Her mother rubbed her face. "I see."

They were quiet. Mary Ann stared into the glass of water, wondering what to say next. "Would you like to read one?"

Vivian was gazing at the floor, her brow stern. A minute passed, and she raised her shoulders in some sort of agreement with herself. "Okay." She did not look up. "I think I would like to."

~~~~~~

"Ameerah!" Mary Ann called out to the girl bouncing up and down in her wheelchair near where the driver had parked the car. They had decided to swing by, having been in the village to see someone else.

Ameerah's stumpy black braids bounced up and down on her shoulders. She was exuberant, noises burbling out of her instead of words. She was a big girl, bigger than Mary Ann. In the excitement of seeing Mary Ann, she struggled to her feet.

"Ameerah!" Mary Ann called again and raised her hand to shield her eyes from the sunlight slanting from the west. "Ameerah, how are you?" Mary Ann claimed the girl in her arms. "Ameerah, look." She lifted one of the braids. "See how pretty your hair is in the sunlight?" The wind caught the wisps of loose hair and blew them into Ameerah's eyes. They both laughed. Ameerah didn't understand English. She couldn't speak her own language either. This made the language barrier disappear.

Mary Ann took Ameerah by the hand, and they made their way to the house.

Beyond the house, the shadows of sunlight dropped across the stones of a sepulcher. Seeing it, Mary Ann's heart knotted, and she hugged the girl a little closer. Ameerah was one of twelve children, of whom seven had died. Ameerah's father, Nasser, had shown the family burial site to them the last time they had come. The tomb was laid up with stone and block, and a little wall divided the place. .

"On this side I laid my boys," he had explained, running his fingers over the mortar between the rocks. "And here are my girls." Mary Ann recollected the patient creases in the man's face as he had stood there viewing the graves of seven of his children. All seven had been handicapped. Out of the living five, two were handicapped. The other three had married by now.

Reuben and Yusef caught up with the Mary Ann and Ameerah by then. "Ah, Ameerah." They proceeded into the house. A grunt from the corner made them look. "Salmar!" Reuben moved closer to say hello. Salmar, Ameerah's brother, had received a wheelchair on a previous visit. "How does the chair fit?"

"Ar-howahy-ah," Salmar garbled, and he watched Reuben to see what Reuben would think.

"That's good." Reuben felt the feet on the footrest. "That's a good fit. Feels good, doesn't it?"

The boy only gazed at him and made no more sound. The children's mother bustled, clearing three chairs for the men to sit down. The ladies sat on the floor.

Nasser looked worn as he joined them and sat down on the floor opposite from the visitors. Adjusting his legs, he began, "I had a dream last night that you would come to see me today."

Reuben froze. "Is that so?"

"Yes, and I saw you sitting right where you are sitting now. Please be comfortable. I want your presence very much."

The men exchanged glances. "What else did you dream?"

"I didn't. Not much. Mostly I could not sleep. I fought in myself all night long, and early this morning I fell into sleep, and there I dreamed that you would come."

"Nothing else?"

"Nothing else."

The group became quiet, except for Salmar, who yawned and tried to tell everyone something. Reuben waited for Nasser to explain more, but he said nothing, his shoulders drooping.

"Suppose we sing," Mary Ann suggested. "Ameerah likes to sing."

They sang. Reuben was thinking hard about Nasser, anxious to question him. He found it hard to keep his mind on the songs, but Mary Ann and Ameerah enjoyed themselves and sang on. Ameerah had learned, or at least they pretended Ameerah had learned, some English songs.

Nasser listened, and Reuben kept an eye on him, trying to decide what was in his mind.

"*Be*, Lord," he implored. "This is beyond me. I don't even know what is going on here."

Yusef pulled his jacket around him and sat forward. "Nasser, can we pray for you?"

Nasser unfolded his hands, scratched his head, and sighed. "Yes."

The men gathered around Nasser, and Mary Ann wrapped Ameerah in her arms. Yusef prayed that God would visit their country, that village, that specific household, and every person within that household in a redemptive way by His Holy Spirit. He prayed that God would bless the workings of Nasser's spirit as God's Spirit ministered to him.

Nasser heaved a deep breath as they finished, and he clung to the men, not releasing them from the circle. "Ah, my brothers. If I could only feel the Spirit of God in peace as you do, I would count myself blessed. But God is distant, and in my heart I only experience the conflict of a man trying to survive a world of evil. If I could understand God and what He really wants from men like me, I would be able to have some peace!" His voice rose in a wail, and his chin sank onto his chest.

"Nasser." Reuben touched the man's arm as he rubbed it across his face. "Nasser, we have a book. If you would just read that book, it would tell you ever so much more about God. Do you want to see it?"

"Please."

When Reuben carried the New Testament in from the car, Nasser seized it in his hands as a man cradles his firstborn. He raised it to his lips, kissed it, brought it to his forehead and cried, "In three days, I will read this book."

"We will be back, Nasser," Reuben promised. "First you read this, and then we will talk."

Reuben and Mary Ann returned to visit Nasser a few weeks later. While the others finished their tea, Yusef and Nasser drifted away to a little side room. Reuben slipped to the doorway a few minutes later. Yusef and Nasser were sitting side-by-side. In Nasser's lap reclined the New Testament. No longer crisp, the pages fluttered in the breeze, but Nasser didn't mind. He was listening to Yusef explain the path to salvation.

"From heaven did the LORD behold the earth; to hear the groaning of the prisoner; to loose those that are appointed to death" (Psalm 102:19b–20).

Reuben thought back over the handicapped people they had worked with. Most had received wheelchairs, and in one way or another, he and Mary Ann had been able to make a small difference in their lives. These people had seen friendship and love and fulfilled promises. Some of them had received Bibles—a chance at truth. Nasser had watched his children in wheelchairs become friends with the Christians, and now he wanted more.

Minnesota · Virginia · Pakistan · Ukraine · Afghanistan · Israel · Haiti · Bangladesh

Tahreer

IT WAS WINTER, DREARY AND chilly. The bushes of the barren land they drove through stood forlornly against clouds churning in turmoil. Out with Yusef to investigate a need in the West Bank, Reuben and Mary Ann were wearing jackets against the chill. Yusef was explaining Palestinian politics and the difference between Fatah and Hamas, the two predominant Palestinian parties. He was telling Reuben and Mary Ann about Hamas, the more radically Islamic of the two groups, and some of the terrorizing tactics they used in dealing with those who disagreed with their ideology. The discussion had been triggered by graffiti they had spotted on the wall while crossing the border into the West Bank.

"Oh! Here we are," Yusef said suddenly. He executed an abrupt turn, parked, and the conversation was over. Reuben replaced the cap on his thermos and swung out of the van. "Be careful there," Yusef called over his shoulder. It was raining lightly, and Yusef had learned how precarious mud and wet stones were for an amputee.

Reuben did walk carefully as they made their way down a few steps and onto a narrow path that led to a lean-to on the side of a small ramshackle house. The tin roof held the sagging poles of the lean-to against the rest of the house. A hole in the northeast corner funneled a tiny drip down into that corner of the room. An elderly grandma huddled in the room on a bed beside which a small wood fire crackled in the confines of a makeshift fire ring. Bedsores festered on her frail body. Her curly iron-gray hair streaked the bed beside her.

Reuben and Mary Ann took this in silently and said a warm hello to the lady, who only peered at them through glazed eyes. A young woman with pointy eyebrows had entered the lean-to, coming from the house across the street. She appeared to be in her mid-twenties. Tucking a wet curl of hair under her head wrap, she greeted them warmly and curiously. Mary Ann's attention was caught by her right eye. It was small and shriveled in the socket and did not coordinate movement with the left.

Yusef stepped up and spoke to her in Arabic. The eyelashes fluttered in the direction of Reuben and Mary Ann, who stood back, waiting, but the eyes did not turn. Yusef's guttural voice ceased, and the girl's voice came in clear English. "Sit down, please."

"You speak English!" Mary Ann was delighted.

"Yes," the girl replied, pulling up a chair by the bed. "My name is Tahreer."

Mary Ann paused to put her hand on their young hostess's shoulder. "Oh, that's a pretty name. My name is Mary Ann. This is my husband."

Reuben said hello just as the noise of a jackhammer from across a rocky valley caught their attention. White buildings with red roofs stair-stepped down the horizon, and in the hollow below, more construction was underway.

"Rich Jews encroaching on Palestinian land are developing that area," Yusef told them.

Tahreer agreed and added that the settlement had been built over the last two years. "One minute." She slipped away to another room, returning with drinks and some fruit.

Reuben brought up the subject of the grandmother. "We help handicapped people."

Tahreer wilted. "I don't know what to do about her. She insists that she wants to be out in the little lean-to. She used to sleep there, and in the summer it's okay. But in the cold season, she suffers. I try to bring her in at night, but she is still so strong I can barely manage. My brothers say we should let her be. I think her mind is not correct. Now she has sores."

Mary Ann put her hand on the girl's arm. "I tell you what," Reuben said, setting his glass aside. "We're going to try to help her, but let me think about how to do that. We'll come back in a few days."

Tahreer sat up straight, her eyes widening. She opened her mouth, looking to Yusef, and then closed it.

A minute of silence passed and then Tahreer spoke again. "It is hard for me to take care of her. I had cancer in my left eye as a young girl. They tried to treat it, but in the process I not only lost my left eye, but my right eye was stunted. I have only 30 percent vision in it now, and it seems to be getting less."

Mary Ann sighed and squeezed the girl's hand. "I'm so sorry," she said.

Reuben and Yusef measured the bed frame, and by the next time they visited, Reuben had found an air mattress for the grandma. It was a nice air mattress with a pump and controls on it. When they took it to Tahreer's house, everyone was enthusiastic, including the neighbor children who piled around to look. One of them had a stick and whacked it excitedly. Reuben looked at the air mattress, and Yusef did too.

"This isn't going to work," Yusef said. "No, please," he said to the child who was poking the mattress with the stick now. The child poked it again.

"No, it's not," Reuben admitted. "It'll be flat before nightfall."

They took the air mattress away, and Reuben hunted up an egg crate foam mattress. "I want to give her something that won't immediately break and cost a bunch of money to keep working. The air mattress was too fancy anyhow."

Tahreer was grateful for their interest and help, absently so. She came and went while they adjusted the mattress.

Roused, the grandmother fussed and fidgeted. When Mary Ann asked her how she liked the new mattress, the grandma only replied in a reedy voice, "No one loves me; no one listens to me." She turned her mournful old eyes back to the tin, and the blanks in her eyes returned.

Tahreer smiled and shrugged. "She's losing her mind. Grandmother," she called, bending over the old woman, "doesn't the mattress feel nice?"

A moment passed before she stirred in the direction of her granddaughter's voice. "It does all right."

Mary Ann visits Tahreer and her grandmother.

Tahreer pulled the little group into the house for a snack. "Come again," she said, "and come for lunch." She was smiling. She was pleased to have someone do something for her grandmother. Perhaps she appreciated the gesture more for its kindness than for the comfort it gave her grandmother.

They returned for the lunch another day. Mary Ann was excited about returning because she thought she might be able to slip a Bible into Tahreer's hands. "I know she'd study it, Reuben," she told her husband. "She's so sensible and intelligent, and I know she thinks about these things."

It was Friday, the Muslims' holy day, when they went for lunch. This time they stayed all afternoon. Tahreer's father joined them for the meal. He was talkative and jolly, curious about America. "I am a good man," he said once, complacently. "I have only one wife. My sons have many wives, and they are bad."

Mary Ann's eyes opened wide at this statement, and Tahreer stared at her plate. Reuben, to whom this was addressed, replied, "It's better with just one, isn't it?"

"Yes!" Tahreer's father was vehement. Tahreer glanced at Mary Ann, and for just a second, her eyes twinkled.

After the meal was cleared away, Tahreer began to talk, and they watched through the big window as the weak winter sun plodded toward the horizon.

She talked of many things, telling about her treatment for her eyesight, about her parents' journey, and her own pilgrimage to India in search of usefulness for life. "There I learned English. But my real purpose was to receive special training on how to make life better for others with disabilities," she continued. "I was trained as a social worker. It is good that I have a good job. Not only can I support myself, but I can contribute to our household. Otherwise, I would be an unbearable liability for my family."

She continued the topic effortlessly. "So it is good that I can work because I will never get married. You see, no one wants a blind wife. Who would want to join in my darkness? I always knew this, and now I have learned what a good thing this is. Even if I could change my blindness, I wouldn't. You see, I am not like others. I am not blind to other people's pain, and I am not scared of their struggles. Because I myself struggle, I know what it is like, and I know they are good people inside. I have many friendships with people no one else will bother with. I have discovered a secret treasure with these people. Should I have my eyesight and should I have gotten married, I would be busy and normal, and I would not care."

Reuben listened, lost in thought. He understood. These were all battles that he had fought, victories he had won. He remembered the evening he had crossed the brook Jabbok. He had walked away from Jabbok with a limp. *It's funny,* Reuben thought. *People walk away from encounters with God with a limp. To the world, they look crippled, but inside they know and God knows what actually happened.*

A fire filled Reuben as he thought about it. With effort, he called himself back to the living room with the misty winter rain outside and Tahreer's gentle speech. Amazed, he watched her, wondering how she had stumbled upon the truth of her handicap. She was so close to the truth, yet so far.

He yearned to show her the whole truth.

Tahreer was not done with the topic, but just then they were interrupted. Three men shouldered into the house casually, as though they belonged. Tahreer spotted them, and her eyes lit up. She introduced them as her brothers.

They were big men, with pointy, trimmed beards, but smooth looking. All of them wore the look of men busy with other things—bigger and more important things. Polite to the point of coolness, the conversation stalled after they arrived. Tahreer, already a refined conversationalist, spoke to them respectfully, careful of their wants.

Mary Ann got the impression that Tahreer loved and feared them. The brothers heard about the new mattress with little comment, but afterward the second to eldest scooted his chair a little nearer and began to ask Reuben questions about where they lived in Jerusalem and what they did. The others listened, interested.

Tahreer brought juice, and everyone drank. Drinking together relaxed the atmosphere. The brothers asked for more juice, teasing Tahreer. Mary Ann noticed that in spite of the frosty heights of respect the family relationship reached, it could melt into camaraderie.

When the time came to leave, Mary Ann felt an insistence to make sure Tahreer had a chance to have the Bible in her hands.

Mary Ann tugged at her husband's shirt sleeve. "Reuben," she whispered. "Reuben. What about the Book?"

Reuben had forgotten about the Bible when the brothers had entered, and now that he did remember, he wasn't sure. He took Mary Ann's hand, stilling her. Something was wrong. He did not have a good feeling. Was it all the big men? Tahreer herself posed no alarm. However it was, Reuben did not want to bring up the Bible in front of those brothers.

Mary Ann looked at him, waiting. Slowly, Reuben shook his head. Mary Ann sat back.

As they took their leave, Tahreer and her brothers trailed them out to their car, still talking. Mary Ann thought of the Bible again, right inside the car. She wished she could slip it into Tahreer's hand.

As they drove away, Mary Ann turned to Reuben, despairing. "Why, oh, why? I so much wanted her to have it."

Reuben shook his head. "I don't know. Something wasn't right. I don't know why."

Yusef listened to the conversation a while before he remarked, "It's best that you didn't give her the Bible this afternoon. Those brothers are all with Hamas."

Minnesota Virginia Pakistan Ukraine Afghanistan Israel Haiti Bangladesh

The People

REUBEN SAT IN THE CIRCLE of believers and marveled at the group before him. The gathered BOL volunteers, a Muslim imam, a nun, one of the two Jewesses who attended this service regularly, and two Protestant ladies all waited for him to open the service. He was reflecting that one of the things that made Christianity so interesting was the diversity it attracted. People from every nation, culture, and religion conglomerated under the provision of Christ. It was a beautiful mosaic of God's creation, but the diversity added to the challenge of leading a united church service.

Among Reuben's duties on the BOL team was his responsibility as a spiritual leader. Sundays he led out in a worship service for the BOL volunteers and others who chose to attend. Now he was thinking, *How do I conduct a service with this incredible mix?* Normally it wasn't quite this inclusive, and taken aback, he was having trouble pulling his thoughts together to welcome everyone.

The door opened a crack, and a pair of bright eyes peeked in, capped by a crest of wildly waving hair. Gilbert was here, not even very late. He bounded into the circle, his shirt half-buttoned and a rip in the knee of his blue jeans. Gilbert had brought a friend, whom he towed in now as he whispered good evening in all directions. The friend appeared coolly skeptical as he glanced around. Reuben supposed he was hunting an escape route. Gilbert had a knack for getting people to church. Often on his way to the service, he saw a lost soul who needed some sound encounter with the truth. In one way or another, Gilbert arrested them, making it impossible to get away politely.

This newcomer was taking it in stride. Reuben had seen more shell-shocked versions.

Gilbert Dawson was an American, a renegade of radical theology, and he was writing a book targeting what he referred to as religious legalism. Jesus didn't start a religion, he argued. Away with church structure and rules. Be free in the Spirit to build the kingdom of God.

Gilbert was shrewd with his doctrine. He loved to argue, caring little about what or where or when. Thriving on controversy, he patronized the BOL worship services.

After the service was over, Gilbert stood in a corner chatting inattentively to one of the team members when he caught sight of Reuben. Raising one finger in an "aha" sort of manner, he scurried over, clutching his torn jeans.

"Ah, Reuben," he chortled.

"Gilbert," Reuben replied, tilting his head back, "now how are you?"

"Fine! Just fine! Now as I was just telling Lonnie, I feel that you had the third and fifth points of your talk wrong, concerning the ascension of Christ. Now has it ever occurred to you that perhaps . . ." and off Gilbert went. He gestured a lot while he talked, and he had a habit of standing sideways from his listener. Many thoughts and feelings flickered over his profile as he waved and gestured.

"I see how you feel," Reuben admitted after the topic had been thoroughly discussed. "Let me think about that, okay?"

"Ah, Reuben, I tell ya what," Gilbert said, cocking his head. "I tell ya what, why don't you let me preach next Sunday?"

"Hmm," Reuben said, "hmm. Gilbert, now why don't you do this. You go home and study out the Scriptures. You see, I have done some study on this particular subject, and it would be good to hear your viewpoint."

Gilbert said he would do that.

"Well, now, that's good." Reuben glanced around. "I think my wife needs me, so I'll catch up with you some other time."

"But you never answered my question!"

"What question?"

"Why, about preaching."

"Well . . ." Reuben stalled, thinking fast, "tell you what. I'm already planning on doing the topic next Sunday, but let me talk to my team about it."

That exchange had been friendly enough, but the next Sunday Gilbert was antsy. Reuben spoke on practical Christianity, about the sanctification of the Spirit becoming outward in righteous works. Gilbert grew jumpy. He angled himself this way and that. He adjusted his bill cap. He hunched his shoulders. Reuben observed this but ignored it. After the service, Reuben slipped into another room for a drink, and as he poured himself a glass of water, he heard the conversation in the other room begin.

"We need to pay more attention to the person of Jesus Christ!" It was Gilbert. "In paying such minute attention to the details of the Holy Writ, I've reached the conclusion that we miss the big picture. We lose sense of where we are going. Christ is the Word of God . . . that's John 1 if you recollect. We must attempt to imitate His character and the rest will fall into place. See, we too often become arrogant in the middle of our tradition. Tradition makes us safe, makes us believe in ourselves, and pretty soon we have a religion!"

Reuben didn't want to get dragged into the discussion, and he busied himself elsewhere. But before Gilbert left, he sought Reuben out. His mind seemed to be working overtime, but he only mentioned that he wanted Reuben and Mary Ann to come to his house for supper sometime that week. "Maybe Wednesday."

Reuben promised that he would check with Mary Ann but agreed that likely it would work out. Inside he was thinking, *Gilbert is not happy.*

On Wednesday Reuben and Ryan rode the bus to visit some friends. At five o'clock, waiting for a bus, Reuben realized that he wouldn't be able to make it for the 6:30 appointment at Gilbert's house. He called Gilbert.

"No biggie." Sometimes Gilbert was very American. "How about tomorrow night?"

So it was arranged. As Reuben ended the call, Ryan hesitated before asking, "Gilbert?"

"Yes." Reuben explained the plans, adding, "I can't help but feel that he has something waiting for me. This is not going to be just a social chat. He wants to preach sometime, and he didn't like my sermon on Sunday."

"Oh, I doubt it will be social." Ryan returned his little day-planner back to his shirt pocket and settled back. "He wants to preach pretty badly. He talked to me about it too. He's got some strong feelings about our traditional beliefs."

"I'd like to know why he keeps coming if he thinks we're so off the wall," Reuben said. "We're not forcing him to come and listen to us."

Thursday it poured rain. Reuben kept his eye on the weather and phoned Gilbert about mid-afternoon. He was anxious lest Gilbert would think he didn't want to talk, but he wouldn't be able to go if the rain did not stop. "I don't think we can make it. It's too wet to walk far on the streets."

"No problem," Gilbert said, "I will come pick you up in my car. You just walk out of the Old City and wait at New Gate, and I will be there at 6:30."

"Okay!" *We're not to be let off the hook so easily.* Reuben tried to think ahead about how to explain his traditional beliefs. He dreaded being alone with Gilbert's arguments. Given a chance, he thought he could answer all of Gilbert's points pretty well, but once Gilbert got going, there was no stopping him.

Six-thirty came, and Reuben and Mary Ann made their way carefully along the wet, treacherous streets to New Gate, Mary Ann holding the umbrella. Gilbert was waiting there in his car. They climbed in, shaking water off cheerfully.

"Thanks so much for picking us up," Reuben told Gilbert. "With my leg, it is difficult to maneuver these streets."

"No problem." Gilbert wasn't paying attention. Then he paused, looked over, and asked carefully, "Is there a problem with your leg?"

"My leg?" Reuben was startled. "Why, I'm an amputee. Didn't you know that?"

Gilbert didn't reply. He looked at Reuben with eyes the size of saucers. Reuben tugged his pant leg up. Gilbert took in the stump and the prosthesis before he answered. "No, I didn't know. I had no idea."

"It happened years ago in a farming accident," Reuben explained.

The ride was quiet after that. When they reached Gilbert's apartment, Gilbert followed Reuben and Mary Ann up the stairs, watching anxiously. Once in the apartment, he procured the best chair for Reuben.

The evening was pleasant. Gilbert regained his tongue and a bit of his habitual enthusiasm, but he remained more subdued than usual.

Over their snack, he began to ask questions. "What happened to your leg?"

Reuben told the story.

"But why did you come to Israel then? You're handicapped, man!"

"Israel! Oh, we've been to more places than that."

"You have?"

"Well, yes, Pakistan for instance, and Afghanistan." Reuben described what they had been doing in those countries.

Gilbert picked at the grapes on his plate for a minute after Reuben finished. "You lived in Taliban country?"

Reuben assented laconically, but Mary Ann exclaimed. "We lived in tents too! Nights, I would lie awake thinking, *God, just be with us.* And the landslides, now they were something."

"Well, yes," Reuben laughed.

Mary Ann continued, "They would come roaring down the mountain. Huge rocks bigger than our tent!" She indicated the size with her hands.

"Well . . ." Reuben caught her hand. "Well, now, I wouldn't say . . ."

"Oh, but they were! They were something." Mary Ann shook her head severely at Gilbert. Gilbert only listened, stricken.

"In Afghanistan and Pakistan, we would drive those mountains! And beside the road, it would drop down for thousands of feet. Sometimes we couldn't make it up those hairpin curves, so we would put rocks behind the wheels of the jeep and then gun it.

"Once, when we were out in a village in Pakistan, Reuben disappeared. I couldn't find him anywhere. I could have drowned in fear. We were right on the edge of Taliban country, and no one knew where he had gone.

Someone had seen him leave the village and go up the mountain with a man. It was a long time, oh my, at least half an hour—"

"Ah," said Reuben, "fifteen or twenty minutes at the most. I was not gone long. I had just gone to take some pictures."

"Well, finally he came and he wasn't even worried! I was so scared. I mean, if we had been kidnapped together, it would have been one thing. But I told him the next time I wanted to go with him."

"Well, be that as it may." Reuben snagged her hand and looked her over, still laughing.

Gilbert looked green and excused himself to go get some more tea. When he returned, they all had some more, and conversation dwindled to a murmur. Reuben brought up the topic of Gilbert's family, encouraging him to talk.

Gilbert began to tell about his upbringing, of a mother who worked a lot and a father who did nothing but read and spin tales to tell the rest of the world. "He was a smart man," Gilbert mentioned. Silence fell for a moment, and he continued. "I get my interest in philosophy from him. I love to read, and he taught me that. But I guess he didn't do much for the world. He never lifted a finger to help anyone, not even Mom."

Once the evening had been spent, Gilbert drove the Yoders back to New Gate, chatting cheerfully. He parked the car and walked with them to their apartment, stopping to say good night, but he did not linger. No mention of sermons or church had been made.

～～～～～～～～～～～～～～～～～～～～～～～～

Gilbert was not the only one who dropped in to hash doctrine. One Sunday morning when the BOL team had gathered for their service, a band of youngsters from the neighborhood marched past the door, drawing the team to the street to watch.

A young couple was following in the crowd that trailed the band. They had spotted the American team and stopped to chat with them, asking if they could take a picture. The girl was Pakistani, and the man was from

Germany. Intrigued, they lingered. "What are you doing here?" they asked.

The team invited the couple inside. The girl said she was Muslim, and the man said he was an agnostic. An interesting discussion ensued as the team spent the morning telling about their work and describing their faith. The service was never finished. This was more valuable, Reuben felt. He liked that his team was flexible enough to drop their service and instead spend the time explaining the Gospel to this young couple. As it was, after eating lunch together, the young couple walked away with their minds churning.

Another time, Reuben was already speaking in the service when an older couple came by. Mary Ann invited them in and got them seats. The two seemed of European descent, dressed like hikers. The man wore a little back-pack strapped to his chest instead of his back. Reuben thought little about it, supposing the man wore his backpack in front so he could sit more com-fortably. The pouch bulged. Several times the man lifted a small flap on the pouch and peeked in. The woman was also restless, and Reuben couldn't tell if she was bored or agitated. Finally she jumped up, whispered something to her partner, and left the apartment. The man sighed, stretched his legs out, and opened the pouch. A little dog peeped out.

Another Sunday, Lonnie joined Reuben and Mary Ann before the ser-vice. "I invited an imam to come tonight, Reuben. I met him at another church service that I attended recently, and we talked for a while. He had some interesting questions, so I thought it would be good to have more contact with him. He speaks pretty good English. He called me today and said he intends to come."

"Not a problem." Reuben's mind skipped back to the topic he was plan-ning to speak on.

Lonnie introduced his friend, the imam, when he arrived, a sad-looking man of about fifty years old. His name was Khaled, and he said he had been a student of Islam for forty years. Separated from his wife, he lived alone.

Reuben preached on giving, and Khaled listened shrewdly but made no comment. The next Sunday when Reuben spoke, the subject was Christ, the cornerstone. Again Khaled attended. Reuben watched him. Khaled came a third time, and a fourth. That time Reuben spoke on being born again, starting with the virgin birth of Christ. Beside him, Khaled seemed relaxed. Reuben had just reached the passage on Nicodemus when Khaled raised his hand. Turning, Reuben looked at Khaled.

Khaled smiled. "May I have a piece of paper please?"

"Of course," Reuben said, scrounging around a bit. He came up with a pad of yellow, lined paper. "Here."

Khaled took notes. He wrote and wrote, even stopping Reuben once to clarify the reference of a verse.

One night a month or so after meeting Khaled, Reuben entered the Old City through the Damascus Gate. It was early evening, and pleasant. Soldiers milled about, and the raspy cry of the vendors rose at the sight of a foreigner.

"But I am not a tourist," Reuben explained to one persistent shopkeeper. "I live here."

The shopkeeper scowled and returned to his wares, grumbling. The others saw that Reuben was being difficult, and their attention drifted elsewhere. Just beyond the immediate crush of the shops inside the old gate rested a little mosque, buried between two apartment buildings. A man was sitting bolt upright on the front steps leading into the mosque. The golden light of the sun's last rays lay in stripes across his headdress, shadowing his eyes, and a streak lay across his hands and across a yellow paper.

It was Khaled. Absorbed in his paper, his surroundings were lost to him. Reuben stole across the street to the entrance. Khaled saw him then, and tucking the paper in his pocket, he stood to receive the intruder. "Reuben! Come in and sit."

He ushered Reuben into his small, empty mosque. It was a brief tour, and Reuben thought his friend seemed distracted. "What was the paper you were looking at when I came?"

The imam studied Reuben for a second and then drew him off to the side by a pillar. "It's the paper you gave me." Tugging it out, he showed it to Reuben. It was covered in Bible verses. "I can't bring a Bible here. That would be dangerous for me. You know most people of my religion don't like Christians. But your people are my friends. So I brought this paper to think about the things you have said."

Months passed, and the time came for Reuben and Mary Ann to go back to America.

Khaled was surprised to learn that they would not be staying. "Reuben, I need to talk to you before you leave," he told him over the phone.

"Well, come on over to our apartment," Reuben said. "How about tonight?"

"And Lonnie. I want Lonnie to be there."

Khaled arrived at the apartment not long after that. Smiling, he shook hands as though they were all meeting for the first time. Mary Ann brought some juice, but he waved it away. Reuben talked easily of different happenings in the city. Khaled made little answer and then stepped away to take a call on his cell phone.

Lonnie exchanged glances with Reuben, and when Khaled returned, Lonnie addressed the imam. "Khaled, is there a problem?"

Khaled considered. "No," he said at last, "only this. I have a need in my heart for your Christianity. I want salvation, and I want to understand this new birth. My religion is old."

The room was quiet, and Mary Ann appeared in the archway leading to the kitchen.

"But I have some questions."

Reuben collected himself. "Well, then. Let's have them."

The conversation ranged widely. There weren't so many questions, but it seemed that Khaled just wanted to talk. He spoke of the trash he observed in the lives of Muslim people. "They aren't honest. They lie and cheat and steal. But sometimes, in places like Saudi Arabia, they cut off thieves' hands. They love money. There are many, many beggars on the streets that no one helps."

"Khaled, the problem is that even the good things people do are worthless in the long run," said Reuben. "Suppose every Muslim were honest, suppose there were no thieves, suppose everyone had enough money. Would that close the gap between people and God?"

"No," Khaled muttered. He dropped his head in his hands and shook it. "No."

After a bit, he began on terrorism. "Look at this country. It's torn up by fighting between Jews and Arabs. The Jews are greedy; my people try to bomb them. They kill us back. Someday it will all become a huge war. Maybe both races will be destroyed!"

The windows in the apartment had blackened by the time Khaled looked at the clock and exclaimed, "I need to go! The last bus will be leaving soon. I thank you for the evening. Good night." Almost before the Americans had stood to their feet, he had shaken their hands and walked out the door.

Reuben hurried after him, stopping outside the door. He called down the stairwell, "Be safe, and pray to God for answers, my friend! Don't be afraid to ask."

Only the empty stairwell echoed back.

CHAPTER 24

Minnesota Virginia Pakistan Ukraine Israel Afghanistan Haiti Bangladesh

Bind Up

IT WAS THE END OF June 2010, and the smell of death rose from the city of Port-au-Prince as Reuben and Mary Ann sat in their *tap tap*,[2] sweltering from the heat and sick from the stench. Over six months had passed since the January earthquake, but the sensation of disaster pervaded the narrow corridors through which traffic skulked along. The rubble of the city lay where it had landed. Heaps of garbage and children mixed as freely as though the children had grown there. Goats clambered through the worst of it, and women skirted the decay without looking down.

Six months earlier, January 10 had caught Haiti by surprise. On that day many lives became statistics at which the rest of the world stared in horror. Figures in the hundreds of thousands only estimated the extent of death. No one ever knew for sure how many people had died that awful evening, but ten thousand here or there scarcely seemed to make a difference.

"My friend is buried under that building," one Haitian would say to another, or, "Look. That is where my father and two little brothers died."

Six months later not so much had changed. The traffic jams in Port-au-Prince complicated transportation. From one end of the city to the other, cars and trucks and vehicles of all sizes sat for hours, waiting for some little

2 Small, often brightly painted pickup trucks used as taxis

nucleus of humanity to begin to move and free them all from the road trap.

The scene reminded Reuben of a different time and place. He thought of Nehemiah who had returned to Jerusalem to rebuild the city. At night, Nehemiah could not sleep and rose to ride around the city on his horse. Destruction surrounded him.

Those who had remained in Jerusalem had no vision for rebuilding the city. Rebuilding was a huge job. No one could drum up the inspiration. They had families to feed. The people had sunk into quarreling and feuds, huddled in hovels among the disarray of their lives. They hated the ruined city, blaming it for their problems, not realizing that it reflected them, an embattled and embittered people. Other men had destroyed Jerusalem, the inhabitants theorized. *Let those people rebuild it. We have lives to live.*

No one had cared until Nehemiah, living in a faraway land, had dreamed of what the city of Jerusalem could be restored to. As it was, Nehemiah had a good reason not to rebuild Jerusalem. He was a servant to the king, carrying his wine. Nehemiah, however, had dreamed of more, and he had done the impossible, securing the king's consent and freeing himself to return to Jerusalem to build again.

Reuben looked around him and wondered what could be built from Haiti's ruins. A vision rose before his eyes of a country of men whose knees bowed at the name of Christ and whose tongues told the story of love. Haiti needed a Nehemiah to come and rebuild.

Beggars loomed in the streets, knocking on car windows and crooning their woes. "Give us . . . give us . . ." Reuben watched as a woman in an orange skirt and a brilliant pink blouse carried a basketful of chickens from one side of the road to the other. The crossing was tricky since the vehicles sat bumper to bumper, and they pulled close as soon as there was an inch of cleared space to thread through. Reuben watched her work her way through the breathing vehicles.

He leaned back, fishing behind the seat. Sweat had beaded out on his thin cheeks, and his stump was out, exposed to whatever air could move amongst the exhaust of the traffic. "I brought a whole box of books today, Mary Ann. Let's give some of them to these beggars."

"That's a good idea." Mary Ann's face brightened. She turned around on the seat and knelt to reach into the box. "Just leave it there. I will dig the books out." She handed a stack of *25 Bible Stories* booklets to her husband and stretched her own arm toward the open window.

"Here!" she called. "Here!"

A beggar, hobbling on a twisted leg, had finally given up on their *tap tap* and wandered off. He spun too fast now, catching himself on his one crutch.

Mary Ann waved the book at him. "Hurry!" she cried. "There are only so many, and there are a lot of you!"

The beggar appeared uncertain, but the grunt of a little boy, appearing between two truck bumpers, stirred him. The little newcomer and the hobbling beggar both set out for Mary Ann's book. The little one reached her first and snatched the book from her hand. The hobbler let out a howl and groped at the side of the taxi.

"Oh!" Mary Ann squealed, startled and half-terrified at the success of her gift. She took one from Reuben. "Here! There's one for you too, but you'd better tell your buddies fast because we've only got one box." She tugged another book out of the box and passed it out the window to a third beggar who appeared on the other side of the taxi.

"Let's give one to the driver of that vehicle." Reuben's eyes began to twinkle.

"Oh, let's." Mary Ann leaned over the front seat.

Slowly their taxi pulled up until at last they were even with a truck hauling some sort of tin. The truck driver was nodding asleep, his chin sunken on his ebony chest and his short, curly lashes turning upright from his cheeks.

Reuben leaned out his window with the *25 Bible Stories* and tossed it into the truck. The booklet glanced off the sleeping driver's shoulder and struck the gearshift, waking the driver. He sat straight up as though he had been hit by lightning. Rubbing his eyes and head, he spied the book and reached for it. Shaking his head again, he began to page through it. Reuben and Mary Ann watched eagerly.

At last the man glanced over and saw them. A grin broke over his face, and he waved the book at them. Just then, traffic opened up, and the taxi lost ground beside the truckload of tin.

Reuben glanced at their driver, "Can we catch up to him?"

After three or four minutes, they gave it up. They had lost sight of the truck. It took them another twenty minutes to clear the traffic, and then finally they were moving again. A breeze lifted their hair and eased the heat on their skin.

"It feels just . . . lovely!" Mary Ann said, opening up her arms to the breeze.

"Doesn't it?" Reuben agreed.

"There goes the truck driver who was sleeping!" Mary Ann exclaimed. It was, and he was reading the Bible story book they had given him.

"Praise the Lord," Mary Ann said, but then she added, "But he shouldn't be reading while driving!"

~~~~~~

Although hundreds of thousands had died in the earthquake, even more had been injured. Immediately after the disaster, the hospitals had been swamped with patients. Most people had sustained trauma injuries that, if not cared for properly or operated on immediately, could take their lives. Outside the hospitals, patients had lined the grounds, waiting for a doctor to become available. The doctors and nurses were scarce, too scarce to meet the demands of the massive number of patients.

Beacon of Light had operated a base in Haiti before the earthquake. The base included a warehouse, staff housing, and facilities for teacher-training conferences. A large part of BOL's focus had been education—supporting schools throughout Haiti. After the earthquake, when the hospitals had overflowed with patients, BOL had set up temporary care facilities to receive patients, and volunteer medical staff had flown down from the United States and Canada to offer medical assistance.

Doctors of every strain and specialty from many different organizations had worked endless hours to help the people, with barely time to pause for breath. They did not have time to do the intricate surgeries required to save wounded arms and legs. Many, many more ill and dying were lying on the ground outside, too many to reach. The doctors had done the best they could in the time they had, cutting limbs off where good tissue remained. The doctors amputated one and brought another in. The numbers of amputees had grown by leaps and bounds.

Amputations, however, were not like other wounds. They needed special surgery and continual oversight during the healing process to insure that stumps were shaped to fit a prosthesis comfortably.

Reuben had learned a lot about amputations in his life as an amputee, and Beacon of Light had asked him and Mary Ann to come to Haiti for three months to follow up with the amputees who had come through their clinic. Reuben had sighed after he had gotten the call. There were days when it was easier to imagine that he was the only amputee in the world. He had suffered enough with his own amputation. Why involve himself again? Again there would be the flashbacks, the phantom pain, the anguish that came with being around so much suffering. But again, he would go. Few people knew what they needed to know to help the amputees, and the doctors were busy anyway.

The hospitals of Haiti had set up big white hoop tents in empty parking lots to accommodate the excessive number of patients. Reuben spent his days there, under the rounded white ceilings. He took cases of *25 Bible Stories* to the patients and sat with them, trying to encourage them.

One of the clinics they visited was next to the small town of Titanyen in a field a short ways north of BOL's base. The clinic had set up a hoop tent, like so many others, and Reuben and Mary Ann often went there. This clinic specialized in helping amputees. They had an interpreter who called himself Pastor Emmanuel.

"Good morning!" Reuben called out as they strolled into the tent one morning.

A lot of little boys stayed at this clinic, and they claimed Reuben as personal property. They had all become great friends.

We don't have to figure everything out;
rather, we need to learn to trust God.

"Reuben!" They came, some running, some hobbling. Some had to be carried. The children gathered around, and in their brown eyes, big and sad, small flames of life sparkled. For the moment, the little boys and girls forgot about the pain and the death they had seen. Again they were children, children who squabbled over who got to sit next to Reuben and who tried to snatch a second book when no one was looking. They pinched and tickled each other and shouted back and forth. Reuben loved this part of the day, but that day he did not stop to joke with the children. They trailed him as he continued inside.

Inside the clinic was a prosthetics ward. Here Dr. Neil from Vermont worked to fit the amputees with prostheses. Dr. Neil, a big, boisterous man whose hands were always busy fixing prostheses or wrapping bandages, looked up as Reuben entered. "Mr. Yoder!" he boomed. "I thought you'd come in today. I could use a hand here."

Reuben gladly offered his hands to help hold things in place. He and Dr. Neil often held involved conversations about prostheses or the best way to wrap a stump to shape it.

The little boys followed Reuben through the door, and Reuben started talking to them. He picked up one child named Prince and held him on his lap. "Look, Prince, how does your leg feel?" Prince had lost a leg in the earthquake. It had been broken, and several days had passed before he had received any medical care.

Prince looked at his leg and shook his head. Several moments passed as he worked to get the words out. "Hurts," he said finally.

Reuben pulled up his pant leg. "Look, Prince. I don't have a leg either."

Prince looked at it and then looked away.

It troubled Reuben that the children acted so matter-of-fact about his prosthesis. The children of America reacted more or less dramatically, but these Haitian youngsters only glanced at it and away again. They had seen much worse, and disfigurement was so common that the little ones had adopted these sights as normal.

Reuben plunged on with his story, hoping it would help somehow. "I lost it in a farming accident . . ."

"Mr. Yoder!" Dr. Neil was listening. "Come out of that corner and sit down and tell all these people your story. They need to hear that there's hope."

Reuben grinned at his friend and stood. He carried Prince with him, and they sat down in the middle of all the amputees gathered in the ward. Some were practicing walking or using their prostheses; others were doing therapeutic exercises. Some were being measured and fitted to receive prostheses. Others were just sitting about, watching. They gathered around, their shining faces sober. Reuben had seen the joviality of many Haitians out on the streets, and he wished to see these folks cheerful now. Even more, he wished to see them joyful. He started again, hoping that something he said could make a difference.

Pastor Emmanuel sat beside Reuben to interpret.

"I lost my leg in a farming accident. It was not a great big accident like

"My grace is sufficient for thee: for my strength is made perfect in weakness. Most gladly therefore will I rather glory in my infirmities . . . for when I am weak, then am I strong" (2 Cor. 12:9, 10b).

the earthquake here in Haiti. I was the only one hurt. My leg got caught in some machinery." Reuben talked on, finding his rhythm in the speech. It was a familiar story, but it took on a new dimension in the context of this audience.

"God is a good God. His ways are higher than ours." Reuben cringed slightly even as the words were still in his mouth. He believed what he had said with all his heart, but he wondered. Was he supposed to say things like that in these situations? It was easy to walk in on his prosthesis and tell the people that God would work everything out for good. Yet he knew from experience how hard it was to accept that and show by his life that he believed it. A flare of pain in his absent left leg made him catch his breath.

He took a moment and then continued, "Sometimes really awful things happen. We don't always know why. Most times we don't know why."

Reuben fought the helpless feeling that rose inside him until he almost choked. After all, was it any use trying to help these people? They would end up where they could, begging on the streets or groveling in misery somewhere. It all seemed so useless. He knew what recovery was like. Phantom pain stabbed him again, and he clenched his fists.

"God, it's no use!" he felt like crying. He sensed Mary Ann's eyes on him from where she was holding a little girl across the ward.

In the best of circumstances that he had experienced, he had learned how difficult it was to rebuild a life that had been torn and ripped up. He had God, a reason to go on. He had a higher meaning to life. What did these people have?

Remember, a small inner voice said. *Remember, the higher meaning in your life is to share that hope.*

What hope? Reuben asked the inner voice.

The hope of Me. The hope of One who came to bind up the brokenhearted, to proclaim liberty to the prisoners . . . to set at liberty them that are bruised . . .

Right, Lord. The broken people again, the ones whom God always brought him in contact with. To them he owed something. It was a huge responsibility. Ever since he had become an amputee, he could not go about his life and ignore the suffering around him. He knew, and he paid the price of knowing.

Only a couple of seconds had passed since Reuben had stopped talking, but it seemed as though several minutes had come and gone. Pastor Emmanuel was waiting. Reuben wiped the sweat of his palms on his pants and continued talking to the audience.

"There is some reason God wanted you alive. He saved you. You didn't die in the earthquake. You didn't die of your injuries later. So now you have to find out why. When things happen to us, we often don't see the big picture. But God sees it. We need to trust that there is a reason for things we can't understand and see. You need to move on. You need to get better, to learn to walk again, to use your prostheses. After a while, it won't hurt so badly. After a while, you will have learned what it takes to be able to do things. See, this young man has a prosthesis already." Reuben put a hand on the knee of a young man near him. "What's your name?"

"Toussaint," the young man replied in a gravelly voice.

"Toussaint, how is it going anyway?"

Toussaint shrugged. "I am learning to walk, but it hurts a lot."

"Show me where." Reuben leaned in. Dr. Neil had stopped his work, and now he came to look too.

"Right there?" Reuben felt it. "Your liner ought to be able to help that out." Reuben took his own prosthesis off. "See, this is my liner. It's called a gel liner." The gel liner was superior to the scratchy wool socks, and they were so forgiving. Ever since Reuben had started using a gel liner, he had been enthusiastic about it. Gone were the days of the sweaty, scratchy sock liners. The gel liner eased the pressure points and was so comfortable that Reuben wondered how he had walked around with his sock liner for hours and hours before.

Suddenly Dr. Neil was leaning over him. "Put that away," he whispered. "Don't ever show that here."

Surprised, Reuben replaced his liner, looking up at Dr. Neil. Confused, Reuben slipped his leg on once more to demonstrate. "You don't need professional therapy to learn to walk well. Just practice walking in places where you can see yourself—like in front of glass storefronts or mirrors. Don't let yourself favor a certain leg. Try to keep the length of your stride equal, and don't let yourself develop a limp. Work on it until you don't limp."

Later, Dr. Neil pulled Reuben aside. "Sorry I could not explain, but I didn't want you to show them that gel liner. Gel liners are the best. They are much more comfortable and better for the stump too. But they are simply too expensive to even try importing. These people can't have them, so there's no point in even telling them about them. And besides, if they know there is something better and we don't provide it, they will accuse us of not giving them the best we can."

"I see." Reuben fell silent. It felt wrong that he could use such a luxury right in front of their faces.

Reuben and Mary Ann walked on from the ward then, into the hospital. In the wards they ambled up and down the aisles, stopping to chat with the occupants of the beds. Some were up and about, some were visiting, some were sleeping, and others lay with glazed open eyes.

A nurse escorted them some of the way, asking them why they were there. "Amputees!" she said when they told her. "Come here for a minute."

She led the way to the very end of the aisle where the last bed stood alongside the wall. The bed was empty, although the things scattered about indicated that someone stayed there.

"Here." The nurse paused at the end of the bed. Along the floor, Mary Ann saw a little bit of white sticking out beyond the bed.

"What is it?"

"Who is it, you mean," the nurse replied. "Jesula! Here, Jesula." The white piece stirred. Mary Ann bent at the waist and peeped around the corner of the bed.

A girl was on the floor, lying on her side. Her eyes were opened wide, so relaxed they almost crossed as they fixed themselves on the white wall. Her face was blank, and her arms lay limply at her sides. Her right leg was amputated below the knee, and the bandages over it were soiled.

"She hasn't let me change her bandages for the past two days," the nurse explained.

"Why is she on the floor?" Reuben wanted to know.

"She won't stay in her bed because she says people can see her. She speaks English. Go ahead and try to talk to her."

"I see." Reuben wondered what to do. Mary Ann had crawled onto the bed, and now she was leaning down, peeking over the side.

"Hello, Jesula," she called into the narrow cavern between the mattress and the wall.

Jesula stirred again.

"My name is Mary Ann."

There was no response.

"I've come to visit you!" Mary Ann's voice was cheerful. She waited a couple of seconds and asked, "Aren't you going to talk to me?"

The nurse laughed. "Good luck. She hasn't spoken in over two weeks."

Mary Ann reared back. "Why?"

The nurse shrugged. "It's her way of dealing with it. They all have to manage somehow."

Mary Ann leaned down closer. "Jesula. I'd love to talk with you. Don't you want to talk to me?"

Jesula finally rolled over and glared up at Mary Ann.

"I'm not going away," Mary Ann said. "Sit up and tell me about yourself. How old are you?"

Jesula looked her over, her face registering disbelief. She lay back down, turning her back again.

Mary Ann sighed. "How old are you? You seem so young."

Thirty seconds passed. "I'm eighteen."

"Eighteen! Well, that's a nice age. You're almost grown."

Jesula sat up, and her expression was not welcoming. "How do you know my name?"

"Why, the nurse told me. Didn't you hear her? She also said you haven't changed your bandages in a while."

Jesula scowled.

"Suppose I change them for you? My husband here is an amputee, and I nursed him back to health." Mary Ann got down off the bed and knelt on the floor, all business.

Jesula crossed her arms. "What do you want? I haven't got any money."

"Don't need money,"

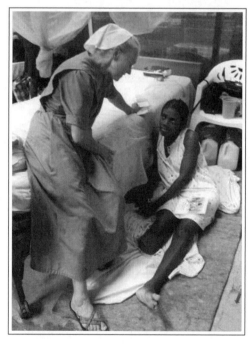

Mary Ann coaxed Jesula into talking again.

Mary Ann said, putting a pin in her mouth to hold. "What do *you* want?"

This caught Jesula off guard, and she laughed. Her whole face changed. It did not look so thin, and her eyes closed when she laughed. Then her face clouded. "I want my leg back," she said, and then her voice got so low that Mary Ann leaned forward to hear. "And . . . my mother."

"Oh, you poor child." Mary Ann gathered the girl in her arms. "You poor child." Jesula bowed her head, and Mary Ann's tears dropped on her head.

They were all silent a minute, and even Reuben's eyes were damp. When Jesula looked up, big, bright drops sparkled in the corners of her eyes. She shook them away and scooted forward, fumbling with her bandages. "Here," she offered.

Mary Ann got to work, once again stern. "These are stuck on awfully hard."

"Soak them off," said the nurse who had been hanging around, watching. She turned toward the corridor.

"If you show me where some water is, I can bring some," Reuben said, following the nurse,

They soaked the bandages off Jesula's stump and bound it up again. *Bind up*, Mary Ann thought. *The Spirit of the Lord God is upon me; because the Lord hath anointed me to preach good tidings unto the meek; he hath sent me to bind up the brokenhearted, to proclaim liberty to the captives, and the opening of the prison to them that are bound . . .* She tried to remember the rest. There was more to that verse about giving unto the mourners beauty for ashes, oil of joy, and garments of praise . . . She sighed and clucked her tongue. Jesula wasn't wearing much of a garment of praise yet, but Mary Ann figured she would. They'd start with the bandage.

Minnesota Virginia Pakistan Ukraine Afghanistan Israel Haiti Bangladesh

Lovelie

THE HEAT OF THE DAY climbed up the back of Mary Ann's neck, prickly in her scalp, even as the sun was setting and the shadows fell across the valley, giving feature to the drab Haitian landscape. Darkness was kind to an ugly place and gave relief to the drudge of the day. Bored, she looked around the parking lot and leaned against the car. She wished for something to eat. She was not hungry, but a piece of strawberry delight made from fresh strawberries from her own garden back in Virginia sounded appealing. Mary Ann smacked her lips and crossed her arms, waiting.

Reuben had gone to find Pastor Emmanuel. When they had left the clinic, they had thought he was following them, but he hadn't been after all. Mary Ann turned and folded her arms over the top of the BOL vehicle, staring in the direction of home. She wished that Reuben and Pastor Emmanuel would hurry. They had a long drive back from Port-au-Prince to the base.

"Mary Ann!" It was her husband calling. She whirled to see him striding toward her across the pavement, the last orange light falling across his shoulders in a garish show.

She faced him. "What?"

"Do you mind if we stay for a bit?" He rushed on, not waiting for an answer. "Pastor Emmanuel just found a girl that BOL treated extensively after the earthquake. She was on the list of people we were supposed to look up, but we hadn't found her yet."

"Okay," Mary Ann agreed. She followed him, arms swinging. "What's her name?"

"Lovelie. She's the one who was pinned under a building for five days before she was rescued. She came into this clinic here just today for a checkup, and we happened to cross ways."

"Oh, yes." Mary Ann remembered the story.

Back in the clinic, now brightly lit with fluorescent light bulbs, the two joined Pastor Emmanuel in the waiting area. He and Lovelie appeared to be acquainted with each other and were talking easily. Lovelie's right arm was amputated above the elbow.

"God must have wanted me alive," Lovelie was saying as Reuben and Mary Ann took seats. "I think about that every day. My friends died. I didn't. Why?"

Pastor Emmanuel looked up, flashing his white teeth at Reuben and Mary Ann. "This is Lovelie. You've heard of her."

Lovelie looked at them with inquiry. "Hello."

"How are you?" Mary Ann scooted closer and took Lovelie's hand. "My name is Mary Ann, and this is my husband Reuben."

"Reuben is an amputee," Pastor Emmanuel explained to Lovelie.

Lovelie seemed surprised. She turned to Reuben. "Were you here during the earthquake?"

"No." Reuben lifted his pant leg and began to remove his prosthesis. "I lost my leg in a farm accident a long time ago."

Lovelie was staring at his prosthesis, but she dragged her eyes away long enough to ask, "Are you with BOL?"

"Yes," Reuben replied.

"Lovelie spent a large part of her recovery time at the BOL base," Pastor Emmanuel told them. "She is used to BOL workers."

"I see." Reuben showed his prosthesis to Lovelie. She examined it and sat back, laying her right arm along the back of the hard plastic chair.

Reuben asked, "Would you mind telling us your story?"

Lovelie shrugged and sat in silence for a moment. Then she began to speak in a low voice, her lower lip poked out and her eyes settled on her feet. She had been attending a Bible study at a church when the earthquake had begun to disintegrate the church building. Lovelie had run in one direction while many of her friends ran in the other. The building had tumbled around them, imploding in one deafening sound. It all happened so quickly. Lovelie had lain stunned on her face.

"The dust came down all around me, and all the concrete and stuff was piled around me and on top of me. I tried to figure out what had happened. It had come down so quickly that I thought it must be some joke, or my head was spinning. I thought in a moment I would sit up, and it would be all right—that I had just fallen or something. I tried to sit up, but I couldn't move. The building was down for good. Something sharp had been driven into my back, and my arm was tight under something heavy. It hurt so bad I could barely think.

"After a while I heard some little noises like a kitten mewing. It was my friend. I called to her, and she talked back for a while. Another friend was also within talking distance. We talked some. We were all hurt bad, and the first friend started sounding weaker and weaker. My other friend was still there though, and we prayed together and waited for someone to come get us out. We did not know why no one came. We thought we were the only ones, and no one came. My second friend was getting quieter too, like she was falling asleep. I wanted her to talk to me. I kept telling her that she must hold together because someone would come for us. But after many hours, she would not answer me. I was all alone.

"It was not always quiet. At times there were voices above me, and I heard the rumble of a machine. I tried to call for help, but all the broken bricks and beams on top of me kept falling together, and the beams shifted in closer and closer. I got pinched tighter and tighter with every aftershock.

"At first I wanted to scream and scream because I couldn't stand being tight. After a while I got used to it, but the pain was worse. After a day or two, I heard voices outside, moving around. I thought they were looking for me, and I shouted at them. My voice wasn't as loud as usual, and they never seemed to hear. Two more days went by. On day four I heard voices again, and I tried with all my strength to scream loud enough to be heard, but the voices faded away. I knew my end was close, and I told God, 'If you don't get me out of here, I am going to die.' I was so sad I cried some. I actually thought I was dying and hoped it would be soon. I hurt all over, especially my arm and back.

"On the fifth day I heard voices again, and I screamed. A man heard me, and immediately they began digging through the rubble to rescue me. It took them a long time to get to me. That was the longest part of the whole five days, waiting while they picked things off the top of the pile till they got to me. I was taken to a hospital, where they cut my arm off. Now I don't have a right arm." Lovelie waved her stump as she finished.

Mary Ann shook her head, and Reuben did too. "That's an amazing story, Lovelie," Reuben said. "I think you are right that God wanted you alive."

"I think He did too," Lovelie said, standing suddenly. "I've got to go."

Lovelie (on left) knew God wanted her alive to help other people.

"Where could we meet again?" Reuben asked, standing also. "I would like to talk with you some more. BOL gave me the job of following up with the amputees from their temporary clinic, and the Lord arranged that we met you here tonight. I don't know how else we would have found you."

Lovelie thought about it. "Maybe I could meet you the day after tomorrow. I have to come here again that afternoon."

That night Reuben fell into conversation with Isaiah Moyer in the base kitchen. Isaiah Moyer, the administrator at the BOL base, was an old Faith Mission Home staff worker whom Reuben knew well. Isaiah had married another FMH veteran, and Reuben found it amusing that he was now under the oversight of Isaiah and his wife.

"You know something?" Reuben asked, reflecting. Do you remember when I used to be behind the desk there, and you were here on this side, in front of my desk?"

Isaiah shrank in his chair a little bit and then grinned. "Yeah . . ."

"Now the tables have turned. Back there, the younger was responsible to the elder, but now the elder has the opportunity to serve the younger, and I consider it a tremendous opportunity to be your servant."

Reuben liked the arrangement. At the end of the day, he could finish up the mowing or repairs that he had been assigned and wander back home. His work was done. Administrators couldn't do that. Their work never ended. Their responsibility followed them everywhere. Yes, Reuben liked the arrangement.

Isaiah and Reuben sat around the table a bit longer, and Reuben told Isaiah about their meeting with Lovelie.

"Interesting," Isaiah said. "After Lovelie had been here for several weeks, one night she started talking to one of the staff girls who stopped to talk with her. She had been pretty quiet, but that night she started talking, and she talked about everything she had been through, and she cried and cried. From then on the staff talked with her often, and one evening several of them took her back to the church where she had been buried. It was still a mess—even a skull lay there, probably belonging to one of her friends. Lovelie started to cry and wanted to be taken home, but then she kept asking why she had been spared. She was convinced that God wanted her alive."

"That's a good attitude," Reuben said. "She's a tough little soul to come through that. God must have really been looking out for her."

Reuben and Mary Ann and Pastor Emmanuel returned to the clinic two days later to find Lovelie. She was not there when they arrived, and they plopped down in the ward to wait.

A nurse, scurrying by, paused for a second.

"Would you take a look at bed six? We're at our wits' ends with her." She ran on.

The three traipsed down to bed six, where they found a young woman lying face down in bed. Both her right arm and right leg were amputated.

Mary Ann looked at Reuben, and Reuben looked at Mary Ann. "Where'd that nurse go?"

Mary Ann scooted up beside the cot and hunched down. "Hi!"

A wasted girl turned her sunken eyes to look at Mary Ann, and her eyes flickered ever so briefly before she looked away. Mary Ann remembered how the same thing had happened with Jesula. She persevered, but try as she might, Mary Ann could not get her to respond. Finally Mary Ann rose to her feet and shrugged. "What can we do?"

"We could pray," Reuben suggested.

"I was," Mary Ann said, sounding tired. "Let's find that nurse."

"I'm still going to pray," Reuben said. Mary Ann wrinkled her nose and went to stand beside him as he prayed, "Lord, give us the words to draw this young woman out. Help us to be sensitive . . ."

After they had finished, Mary Ann poked her head around the corner. "There's the nurse. Hello! Can you come here a second?"

The nurse appeared, and they drew her aside. "What's wrong?" Reuben gestured to the prone figure. The girl hadn't moved since she had looked away from Mary Ann's face.

The nurse sighed. "I don't know exactly, but she's in bad shape. She's a double amputee and has bad burns on the leg that isn't amputated. She has head injuries too, and she's partially paralyzed."

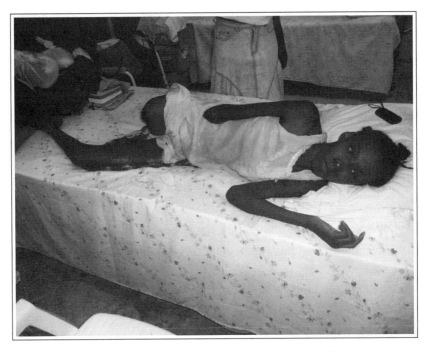

Judette, a double amputee.

"Oh, dear God . . ." Mary Ann buried her face in Reuben's sleeve. Reuben's eyes watered at the thought of such trauma. "Whoa," he said softly.

"Worse," the nurse continued, "she comes from a bad area of Haiti."

"Bad area?"

"Bad for voodoo and witchcraft. She's not been eating. And she lost six of her family members."

"I see," Reuben said.

"Try to talk to her again," the nurse suggested. "She seems like just a shell, but I've occasionally gotten a few words out of her. I think she's under some sort of spell."

"What's her name?" said a low voice at their elbows. They all turned to see Lovelie, who had just walked up behind them.

"Judette," said the nurse, and she was gone. The group exchanged glances.

"Let's pray again," Pastor Emmanuel said. They all prayed hard. A lot of emotion went into Mary Ann's prayer, but Lovelie's voice was distant and gentle.

Lovelie and Mary Ann both approached the bed, and Lovelie knelt down and began speaking Creole into Judette's ear. At length, Judette stirred. Lovelie looked over her shoulder. "I asked her if she would like to change positions." Her voice was weary.

With Lovelie's help, Mary Ann gently turned the girl. Judette's head lolled against the pillow at first, but then she began to hold it up. She looked at her four visitors, her dark eyes fearless but dead.

"How old are you?" Mary Ann asked her, and Lovelie repeated the question.

"Twenty-one," Judette breathed.

Mary Ann dropped down on the cot, careful not to jostle it. She began to chatter about herself and Reuben and the nice day outside. She leaned in confidentially. "Judette, you've got pretty hair. Do you want me to comb it for you?"

Judette shook her head, but a glimmer of a smile broke at the corners of her mouth. They stayed for about five more minutes. "Okay, Judette, we're leaving now, but we'll be back," Reuben said.

Judette looked at him, and Mary Ann patted her on the shoulder. They left.

Outside under a tree, Reuben and Mary Ann sat down with Lovelie. They talked about Judette.

"She's got to figure out that she is supposed to be alive," Lovelie said. Her hand stirred in her lap, and she looked up at them, her eyes flaming. "I had to figure that out. I still don't know why, but God wanted me alive. I know that. He must have something special in mind."

"Yes, He does," Reuben agreed. "But, what about you, Lovelie? What can we do to help you?"

Lovelie spread her fingers and looked the backs of them over carefully. "I wonder why I'm alive. I need help to find that out. I don't know where to go from here. I always thought . . . thought I would get married."

Lovelie stared at her hand in her lap and then shook herself, continuing with a stronger voice. "I wanted babies. I love children. But . . . I think God wants me to help people. Like you are doing."

"Oh, Lovelie!" Mary Ann's heart broke. "God does want you to help people. That's exactly what you can do."

"How can I do it?" Lovelie asked.

"It's like this." Reuben leaned in, touching his fingers together. "I am trying to help others who wrestle with the same things I do. I am an amputee, so I try to help other amputees. God brings things into our lives to make it possible for us to better help others with similar needs. You can do the same. There are people out there who need what you have, what you know, and what you have learned."

Lovelie made no response. They sat in silence for a moment.

Mary Ann was watching her husband. "You know," she said at last, "I'm not an amputee, but in a way, we're all amputees helping each other."

Reuben raised his head and studied her. "How do you mean?"

"Well," Mary Ann explained, "spiritually, we are all amputees striving to help other amputees. We are all sinners, and so we have a message to carry. Suppose God sent only perfect people to minister to others. Who would ever listen to the truth? People would be thinking, *Yeah, it works for you because you're already perfect.* But since we are sinners, broken people too, God can use us to minister to other sinners to show them a way of redemption. I don't know . . . it's hard to explain."

Lovelie looked confused, but Reuben understood. "You're right," he said, startled by the idea. "It takes the pride completely out of who we are and what we do if you look at it like that. Even Christ had to be broken, broken by a cross, before He could save the world. God can't use us if we think we're perfect. In our weakness, He becomes our strength. How about that? It's incredible!"

Lovelie made a small sound beside Mary Ann, and they both looked at her, recollecting themselves.

"For now," Reuben said to her, "would you like to spend some days with us, visiting amputees? You can ride along, and you and Mary Ann can do things together."

"Oh, I would love that!" Mary Ann cried, her eyes sparkling. "Would you, Lovelie?"

So that is exactly what happened, but not right away. The next day Mary

Ann was carrying a load of dishes through the kitchen when she slipped in a puddle of water. The dishes flew everywhere, shattering, and Mary Ann struck her shoulder as she went down, tearing a rotary cuff.

The pain was so intense that Mary Ann nearly passed out, but she hung together as Reuben and a few staff members descended on her. "Are you all right?"

Mary Ann bit her lip.

"Take a deep breath, sweetheart." Reuben was kneeling beside her, supporting her as she struggled to sit up. "Just rest."

Mary Ann rested with her head down for a minute, barely hearing the buzz of conversation around her. *Oh, Lord,* she said inside, *if this hurts this bad, what must Lovelie and the others have gone through for days?*

Mary Ann got help more quickly than the earthquake victims had, but she had to be down for a few days. After she had recuperated somewhat, they did return to Port-au-Prince.

Upon their return, they took Lovelie to visit Jesula and Judette. Reuben and Mary Ann had been back to see Jesula a couple of times since their first visit. She was unpredictable. Some days when the pain, either physical or emotional, ebbed, she was delighted to see them, and chattered. Other days, the pain appeared to overwhelm her, and she almost refused to talk, her lip sticking out and her face glowering. Those days she stayed down on the floor between her wall and her bed.

On this day, with Lovelie along, Jesula acted more even-tempered. She talked with Lovelie about her surgeries and how her stump was healing. As they sat with her, an odd sound of tapping caught Reuben's ears. The sound had an irregular beat to it. He looked around just as a little girl entered the room. She was missing both an arm and a leg. With a crutch under her only arm on one side, she hopped on her only leg on the opposite side of her body. The child was tiny, barely big enough to reach over her head and touch her ear, and her eyes, huge and brown, asked questions of the group on Jesula's bed.

A small sound escaped Lovelie, and she sighed. Mary Ann half-rose with her arms open, but the girl had turned and hopped away again. She reminded Reuben of a little robin with a broken wing. Jesula stared after the little girl and then blinked, looking away.

"Do you know her?" Mary Ann asked Jesula.

Jesula seemed to collect herself, and she replied morosely, "I've seen her before. I don't like to see her." She lowered her head. "I don't know why."

"You are blessed, Jesula," Mary Ann said suddenly.

"Yes, because I am not like her."

"No," Mary Ann said. "You are blessed because God keeps a special watch over you. That little girl is special in God's eyes too. Sometimes parents have a sick child. When they have a sick child, they take special care of that child. They do everything they can to help that child. That's how God is with us. You are in the very center of His care, and so is that little girl."

Jesula gazed at Mary Ann and did not reply.

As they entered the clinic to see Judette, the nurse they had met before passed them. "Oh, I'm so glad to see you. Judette is always better after you are here to see her. She eats now, and I even get her to smile once in a while."

"It's because of prayer," Mary Ann told the nurse.

The nurse brushed hair away from her face and looked suddenly worn. "Probably. You people do that a lot, don't you?"

"We do," Mary Ann said, and she sounded firm. "That's very important."

"I suppose so," the nurse agreed. "I don't do it enough. Of course, I'm not just visiting around in the wards either."

"No, and your work is important," Reuben assured her. "But don't underestimate what prayer can do for someone like Judette."

Someone hollered down the hall, and the nurse looked restlessly in that direction. "You're right. What I do is important. Thanks for the reminder."

"Let's find Judette," Reuben said, glancing at Lovelie who was standing along the wall.

They found Judette draped over her bed in much the same manner that she had been the first time they had met her. She turned her head this time, though, and like before, Mary Ann and Lovelie did what they could to make her comfortable while they talked.

It took some time to draw her back out again, but by the end of the visit,

Judette had warmed up. They asked her a little about her life, careful to steer around painful subjects. However, Judette seemed open. She told them she had been studying to be a pharmacist before the earthquake.

A little bit of the hollow look was leaving her eyes as she wrung Mary Ann's hand. "Come again."

Judette gave Lovelie a hug, managing one word. "Lovelie," she said.

Minnesota Virginia Pakistan Ukraine Afghanistan Israel Haiti Bangladesh

I Am Nothing

UNDER THE OPEN SHELTER, THE day was warm but the shade was pleasant. Outside, the leaves of the banana tree blew in a sultry breeze that came from the ocean. The dark faces, lined on the benches, stared back at Reuben. A few laughed, some smiled, but most just watched him. The heavy weather reminded him of the smoldering culture they were a part of. It was a dancing fire flamed by gaiety and loud music. Sometimes it burned blue with anguish and sometimes white with anger. Sometimes—most days, in fact—it was a heap of glowing coals, waiting to be fanned to life.

Reuben had been reading a book he'd picked off a coffee table at the BOL base. It was about the history of Haiti, about how it had freed itself from French colonialism. The sweeping saga had caught him in its throes, a story of blood and courage and despair.

Haiti had been a dark, dark place in colonial days. The French colony had produced 60 percent of the world's coffee and 40 percent of its sugar. Manning the plantations with hundreds of slaves brought from Africa, the French landowners extorted production through the brutal discipline of their field hands. The death rate among the slaves was so much greater than the birth rate that large shiploads of captured Africans arrived daily to replace the dead.

The slaves held an overwhelming majority in the population, however, outnumbering the whites, freed slaves, and mulattoes ten to one. Enraged by the brutality they suffered, the slaves breathed a real threat to their masters. Voodoo and other practices of African religions were illegal in Haiti. But helpless to stop them, the French colonists cowered in their beds at night, listening to the drumming of the voodoo ceremonies from the hills. Slave revolts were not unheard of in Haiti, and in 1791 one more rebellion swept the country. That one flamed beyond French control. Within days, the revolt had spread like wildfire and immersed the entire land in a bloodbath. A decade had passed before Haiti had been established as a recognized nation, led by the inspirational figure of Toussaint L'Ouverture, a former slave himself.

All this ran through Reuben's mind as he waited for Pastor Emmanuel to finish his opening talk in Creole. Haiti's beginning had laid the foundation for the modern Haiti. The country that had been born in oppression and leapt to freedom through lawless ferocity now hobbled aimlessly under poverty and misfortune. Haiti was a broken country. Its people were a broken people. The fire that had bought their freedom had burned down to ashes. Today the coals only glowed, but someday something would fan that fire to life again, and it would leap high and catch hold in men.

Reuben bowed his head. *I pray this time that the battle be in a different realm, that the revolution be spiritual. God can use these people.* He shook his head, thinking about it. *No, God* is *using these people.*

Reuben and Pastor Emmanuel had gotten together to host a workshop for amputees at a small village church. Some of the amputees had shown enough interest that Reuben had thought it would be worth a try, and seven amputees had come.

Talks with Lovelie had convinced Reuben that they needed to hold this seminar. Lovelie had asked the same questions over and over. "Why? Why me? What do I need to do? What is my responsibility to God since He got me out?"

Mary Ann and Lovelie had become fast friends. Reuben smiled now, remembering. He loved watching his wife befriend hurting people. She adopted them, and they adopted her. Reuben marveled at her ability to mesh with people. He himself found it harder to invest in relationships, preferring one or two that he could take more time for. Mary Ann seemingly loved the whole world, gathering its crippled and sad into her arms, and the whole world seemingly loved her back.

Pastor Emmanuel finished, and Reuben took the stand. Pastor Emmanuel interpreted for him.

"What happened to you was not a surprise to God. God has a plan. Something dramatic happened to you, and God must be interested in you. Many of you are asking why God spared you. That is a good question to ask. To ask why God wanted you alive, to ask what He wants of you will take you on a journey that won't end until you die. It is often hard, but it is a beautiful journey. It won't be comfortable, but it will be fulfilling."

The faces watched him. Reuben searched them for understanding. He saw thirst.

"God wants you. He needs you. He made each one of you with a place in mind for you. He formed you to play a part in the world, and He made you with the personality and the circumstances to play that part.

"There is a verse in Romans that talks about all things working together to become something good for people who love God, who are called to do His purpose. This is true, but it is hard to understand. Out of all the religions in the world and all the things to worship, our God is the only one who can take the bad and the ugly and the painful things and work with them. Every other religion demands perfection to receive blessing. Our God isn't like that. All He asks for is you. He wants you, not what you can do."

Reuben kept talking, caught up in the message. "When I lost my leg, it was a horrible thing. It hurt worse than anything I had ever felt. I didn't know pain could be that bad. My leg looked ugly. All that blood and bone and torn flesh . . ." Reuben stopped, wondering if he had gone too far. All of them dealt with phantom pain. He felt a stab of pain in his absent leg, remembering with vivid recollection just how that leg had hurt. He saw that same flare of pain reflected in the faces before him. They all knew what he was talking about.

"I had a family to take care of who suddenly had to take care of me. I was poor and didn't have money to pay the doctor. Nothing was good about it, but because of that awful accident, I am here today to help you when you need someone who knows something about amputations. That is how God works. He works with broken people, like you and me. He takes the very thing that makes us seem weak and like a burden to other people and uses that weakness to help us understand other people who have the same weakness. This is brotherhood, why God gave us each other. This is why God sent Christ to earth, where He suffered terribly and then gave His life. Christ, of all people and friends, can relate to what you suffer." The faces concentrated, thinking.

"I can look back now and see this, almost thirty years later. But back then I didn't know, just like you don't know. That is what we call faith— knowing the character of God so well that we know what to expect from Him. Something bad could happen to me tomorrow. Tomorrow I could get cancer, and as hard as it would be, I would know that since God had been with me through my amputation, He could use my cancer in the same way. Do you see what I am saying?" He thought they did. Lovelie was nodding her head.

They all sat together and talked. They talked about their amputations, but they talked about more than that. They discussed how they felt about it inside. Over and over, Reuben heard one common fear. "What if I never get married?"

"God knows," Reuben heard himself saying. "It is possible that you won't get married. But in the big picture of life, is that so important? There's got to be more to life than marriage."

Inwardly, he kicked himself. The platitude sounded clumsy. These girls were worried about marriage, about being loved and accepted for who they were, about their support and security in a cruel world. He looked at Mary Ann, almost guiltily. He had wanted to get married too. Where would he be without her?

Mary Ann was on a roll about the marriage thing, though. "Oh, there is more to life than marriage, girls! If you get married, this is good and right.

But don't let yourself get dragged down into thinking that's all that can make your life happy and fulfilled. Oh, my! When you're married, then the babies come, and you're so busy it seems you can't ever do anything for anyone else, and you have to work, work, work. Paul says that a person who is married has to worry about the things of the world and how to please his or her spouse, but if you aren't married, you can think about the things of God and concentrate on doing them."

So much for that, Reuben thought and grinned at his wife. She ignored him.

"How do we know what God's will for us is?" Lovelie wanted to know. She was used to thinking these things through—used to asking questions. The others listened.

"I think," Reuben said slowly, "that there are a lot of right things for a Christian to do, like getting married or obeying some commands in the Bible.

"But if you're doing these things and haven't surrendered your life to God, then you aren't in the will of God, no matter how right those things are. Sometimes it isn't so much what you do as why you do it. God is faithful, and He will show you. He'll open the doors. Just walk through the open doors and step in the light He shines on your way. Most of all, stay connected to God's Word, the Bible. We've brought a Creole Bible for each of you. You have lost something important, but this book will show you how to receive something far greater—the gift of eternal life."

"But how do we know His will?"

Reuben sighed. "The only way you can know is by walking with God in close friendship. If He is your friend, then you will know when He talks. Make Him your friend, and you will recognize His voice, okay?"

After the talk, Reuben looked at the stumps of the amputees and gave advice and explained things. The amputees clustered around each other, listening and offering advice.

After the meeting was over, Reuben and Mary Ann walked back to their house at the base. They were tired. Their three months were almost up. The next day they would return to Port-au-Prince to say goodbye to their friends.

When they reached the clinic where they'd met Judette, she was not in her cot. A nurse told them she was in therapy, so they went to find her. Behind a curtain, they found Judette face down on a table, doing her therapy. Her therapist looked at Reuben and Mary Ann inquiringly.

"We're leaving the country," Reuben explained. "We want to say goodbye to Judette."

"Okay," the therapist agreed. "But make it quick."

As Reuben knelt at the head of the table, Judette raised the upper part of her body with one arm, faltering. A smile crossed her face, drawn with the effort of her therapy and glistening with sweat. "We've come to see you once more before . . ." Reuben paused. Her face warned him. "I'm sorry, we'll return after therapy is finished."

Reuben looked around at the therapist, who stood awkwardly by, closing and opening her hands. "We're going to go see some other people and come by later. Finish your therapy."

Several little fellows on crutches were tagging along behind Reuben by now. They had found a niche in his heart, always begging him to take off that wooden leg. Perhaps theirs would look something like that.

When they returned to Judette's bed a while later, she was sitting in her wheelchair. Judette's mother was lingering near her daughter. They had given Judette a Bible on a previous visit, and her mother had asked for one too. Judette was staring down at her lap.

"Judette," Mary Ann said, her voice soft, "we're here."

Judette did not look up. She bent over abruptly and dropped her head onto her knees, covering her eyes with her one hand. She was sobbing, and then she cried and cried and cried.

"Oh, Judette," Mary Ann said. "It's going to be okay. Judette . . ." Mary Ann's eyes were wet too, and she put her arms around the girl. Helpless, Reuben clenched his fists. "It will be all right." Mary Ann was pleading.

Judette shook her head through her tears. "But you're going back to America. What do I have? I am nothing."

Mary Ann stroked Judette's head and was silent. It all impacted her—the cry of Lovelie and the others, Jesula's moods, Judette's bleak future, even the tales Reuben had told her of the bygone days of slavery in Haiti.

She hugged Judette to herself. Only God knew what would happen to Judette and the others, but that was okay. Another tear fell from her eye and mingled with one of the drops on Judette's cheek.

Minnesota Virginia Pakistan Ukraine Afghanistan Israel Haiti Bangladesh

Bangladesh the Golden

REUBEN AND MARY ANN HAD traveled to Ohio for an international crisis meeting with Beacon of Light the summer of 2012. During intermission, Fred Myers, the BOL representative for Israel, was talking with Reuben about their possible return to Israel for a few months. Fred explained to Reuben that another couple was able to serve for a longer term than Reuben and Mary Ann were, and so the other couple would probably fill the house parent position there. The doors to return to Israel were closed.

Mary Ann listened while Reuben explained it all to her. She pinched her lips together, looking determined. "There's got to be more."

Reuben grinned at her—at the little slogan. He wasn't terribly worried about it. It would have been good to return to Israel, but he wouldn't object to some time at home. Mary Ann, however, was restless. She fidgeted in her seat the rest of the day, listening to reports and discussions. There was such a big world out there. She wanted to go out and save it, pull it into her arms. She stared into the big eyes of the African children on a BOL poster. Those children needed someone to love them. Mary Ann thought of her little grandchildren, glad they weren't alone and neglected.

In the evening, after the meeting adjourned, Albert Lapp, an international crisis worker for BOL, dropped by the guesthouse to visit. They were passing a bag of chips back and forth on the small table, and Mary Ann had brought out some granola bars she had made. Reuben had just told Albert about not being able to go back to Israel. "Now what?" He shifted his coffee cup in his lap. "Now what?" he repeated to the coffee.

Albert took a chip and chuckled, "A BOL meeting is a good place to ask that question."

Reuben laughed too. "I guess so."

Albert stirred his coffee. Mary Ann watched, fascinated, as he added milk. The color of the coffee muted as the milk swelled through it and it turned pale. "Now your coffee won't be warm," she said, clucking her tongue. She stood to heat the coffee in the microwave for him. Albert looked over his glasses at her.

"That's the whole point of the milk."

"Oh." Mary Ann sat down again and pushed the granola bars at him. "Here. Finish these. We've got plenty."

Albert looked carefully at the granola bars. "I can eat one more, but not all of those."

Reuben laughed. "I tell her not to force-feed people."

"Like the Bengalis," Albert said. "They force-feed you. The last day before we left Bangladesh, all we did was go from one house to another and eat rice. I ate five meals back to back that day, and I'm not talking about snacks. I'm talking about heaping bowls of rice—refilled."

"Oh, no." Mary Ann's jaw dropped. "How did you survive? I would have been sick!"

"I was," Albert admitted.

"Oh." They were all silent.

Albert looked up from his coffee. "Want to come to Bangladesh? We need house parents."

There was silence for a moment. Then Albert started talking again. He told them the story of how the work in Bangladesh had begun.

"A cyclone ravaged the southern part of the country in late 2007. The villagers said that in the moments before the storm surge, all the water in the river was sucked out, and then it came back in a sort of tidal wave effect. Whether that's true or not, that's how they described it. Thousands were killed."

That cyclone had brought Beacon of Light into the riot-ridden country of Bangladesh to do rebuilding. When the BOL crew leaders had first arrived in the small village of Kabirhat, they found they were the first white-skinned people the village had ever seen. Women and children thronged the doors and windows, standing ten feet deep on the porch outside the kitchen where the house parents would cook for the crews.

The villagers often talked about a former head schoolmaster, and one day this old man invited Albert back to his place for lunch. Albert walked about a mile to reach his home, and he had a nice time there. The old man mentioned that he had several sons, one of whom was the consul general, representing Bangladesh in Los Angeles.

Albert had not taken the man seriously, but one day he heard a rumor in the village that Abu Zhafar was coming home to visit. Abu Zhafar, it appeared, was the son of the old head schoolmaster and the consul general from Los Angeles. Abu Zhafar did come to visit, and he was indeed the consul general.

In meeting with Abu Zhafar, Albert had asked him what they could do to help his people. The great man shifted on his chair while stray children and villagers, all claiming to be relatives, looked on. Those who were intimate enough to be casual in the great presence of Abu Zhafar bustled and beamed on the world, bringing tea and biscuits for the men to share, and fidgeting under the banana trees by the pond. The childhood home of Abu Zhafar was constructed a bit better, perhaps, than most homes in the destroyed village, but no pomp indicated the caliber of the children who had grown up inside its walls.

Abu Zhafar had answered, seeming to think aloud, "We need English teachers. I had an English teacher in elementary school. I give him credit for where I am today. All of our university classes are in English. English is the language of technology. In our country a man needs a college degree to get a job any higher than rickshaw puller or shopkeeper. Our people need more education, and to have education, we need to speak English. We need English teachers."

That winter, after the BOL rebuilding project had finished, Albert and his father Dale Lapp had taken a team of English teachers back to Bangladesh, and the next winter they went again. After two winters, a man named Sagor, who had worked closely with the BOL crews during the rebuilding project, desperately wanted the Americans to send a second team to his village. The village of Kabirhat was in the southern part of Bangladesh, but Sagor's village, Cumrakhali, was much farther north. The

Abu Zhafar

third year, two teams traveled to Bangladesh to teach, one going north and one south. Now the fourth year was coming up, and the northern team needed house parents.

Reuben and Mary Ann returned to their Virginia home a day or so after their visit with Albert. They had just built a house in Rural Retreat, Virginia, and had moved there after twenty-nine years in the Faith Mission community.

A few weeks later, Dale Lapp and his wife Laura came to visit Reuben and Mary Ann. They came one evening and stayed to talk, and they talked the whole next day. Dale was an inspired man. The next evening as he climbed into his car to leave, Dale called over his shoulder, "You have an official invitation to come to Bangladesh as house parents."

Reuben and Mary Ann did not commit themselves one way or the other, opting instead for prayerful consideration. They *were* interested, though. And the ESL (English as a Second Language) Bangladesh board was very interested.

"Bangladesh!" one of Mary Ann's friends exclaimed. "You're too old to go work in Bangladesh."

As December 2012 drew to a close, the news echoed throughout their circle of friends. "Are you crazy or what?" some wondered.

"An assignment from God as obvious as this," Reuben told the concerned people, "is never crazy, and after all, God knows our age well."

They landed in Dhaka, the capital city of Bangladesh, early one January morning. The airport was hot and singing with mosquitoes. Outside the airport, horns blared. Reuben saw the rows and rows of dark faces pressed against the fence outside the pick-up area. They leaned in against each other, a breathing, pulsing, silent audience to the modern world that was gliding into their turbulent city.

Fresh out of the cold of the Christmas season, Mary Ann felt the humid warmth of Bangladesh hit her like a blast. January was the coldest month of Bangladesh's seasons, but the midday sunshine still warmed up the city. After they squeezed into the microbuses that picked up their crew of twenty-two along with all their luggage, it was almost suffocating. They crept along, pausing here, stopping there. The traffic swarmed around them, vehicles of all types. People swarmed everywhere. Reuben had explained that in Bangladesh it was like cramming half of the population of the United States into a space the size of Iowa.

Mary Ann closed her eyes and wished for her bed in America. *Oh, for the long, cold nights, the coziness of the covers, the soft pad on the mattress . . .* With a jolt, she jerked awake. She had been dozing. Reuben, beside her, was craning his neck to look out the window. They had arrived somewhere. She crawled out, and the young men in their group started to pull the luggage piles apart.

Two girls ran out from the bottom of the tall apartment building to meet them. A small team, led by Albert, had already been in Dhaka for the last three months to study the language. Their eyes were round at the sight of twenty-two new people who had just arrived. Twenty-two people meant eighty-eight pieces of luggage. It all went into the apartment, and the crowd sat sprawled around it to eat lunch.

One of the girls showed Mary Ann a bed where she could rest. Mary Ann followed her, staggering with weariness. Jet lag never got easier—not *any* easier at all. She almost fell onto the bed, but then she couldn't sleep. She was too tired to keep her eyes open, but the racket of horns and horns and more horns on the street outside drifted into her dreams, making her toss fretfully.

Finally, after a couple of hours, she rose. The twenty-two people had disappeared to shop and take care of other details. Only one girl from the language team was still at the flat. She was wandering about with a rag in her hand, looking lost and aimlessly pushing the foreign luggage around.

The girl turned at the sound of the bedroom door and smiled distractedly. "Hello. Did you sleep well?"

"Some," Mary Ann said, looking around. "It's just so noisy. I couldn't really sleep."

"Noisy?" The girl's look was blank. "I'm sorry. I was trying to be quiet. Everyone went shopping, so I thought . . ."

"Oh, no, the traffic."

"Oh, the traffic!" The girl began to laugh. "Yeah, it's pretty noisy. I forgot about it. You get used to it after a while."

Mary Ann frowned. "Well, aren't we leaving late tonight on the microbuses for the village?"

"I think so." The girl was uncertain. "I'm going to the other village, so I'm not sure what your plans are. I'm Dale's granddaughter, you know, so he keeps me down south with him. He doesn't trust me too far, I guess." She grinned.

"Oh, you're Dale's granddaughter!" Mary Ann was delighted. "That's wonderful that they can have you with them."

The group for Cumrakhali did leave that night, stacked into microbuses. Reuben and Mary Ann were used to foreign traveling, but they weren't used to having a team of twelve young people with them. Neither were they accustomed to having luggage poking into every corner and resting below each elbow.

There was a certain sport to night travel in Bangladesh that they hadn't encountered before either. Mary Ann expected to sleep en route, but sleep was slow in coming. Her heart in her throat and her chin perpetually in the seat in front of her, she watched the road race of the night buses. Trucks bringing in rice and bricks and cattle from the villages were only allowed into Dhaka at night. They competed with the night buses who competed with each other for the right-of-way. The narrow roads were built up on dikes, lined by trees, black against the moonlight. They were out of the city at last, and Mary Ann could see rice paddies and fields in the bright night.

Albert, their Cumrakhali team leader, was riding in the front seat with the driver, but he turned around to say something to the group. He smiled at Mary Ann's tense face but said nothing to her.

Mary Ann looked over at the driver. He seemed to know what he was doing. And no one else seemed too worried. She decided she wouldn't worry either and settled in for a long night of driving.

~~~~~~

House parenting fell into a routine. Each new country was not so different from the one before.

Mornings were difficult. Each morning before the bustle of the team had started, Reuben rose to put on coffee. January had indeed lived up to its reputation of being the coldest month in Bangladesh. One of the girls on the team said she wore more clothes to go to bed than she ever wore in the daytime. There was no heat, not even hot water, and the chill settled deep into the concrete-walled flat. Reuben didn't even need his cup of coffee to wake him up. The cold did that before he was dressed.

Mary Ann and Reuben enjoyed their team immensely. Mary Ann was in charge of the meals. Fortunately, the team girls all liked to work, and work they did. Mary Ann had help with almost every meal. The continuous meal planning made her scowl at her cookbooks and tap her fingers, but at mealtimes the food always appeared on the table. Then it disappeared as quickly as she could put it before them.

Every morning, the youth congregated in the bathroom and did the laundry, using buckets and plungers. Suds dripped from the chins and hung from the showerheads. Every once in a while a great shout of laughter would go up, and after a bit, out they would come, wet to the waists. Apparently it was a competition to see who could wring out clothes the hardest. Mary Ann frowned over her wrinkly dresses. They would dry without all that wringing, but the wringing was fun.

The teachers went off to school next, coming and going at various times the rest of the day. Reuben did the market trips and the odd jobs around the place. Shopping in the market was his favorite. There was just something about picking a bird out of the squalling bunch of chickens, tied together at the feet, and then watching quick brown hands dice the bird. In a few minutes the whole live bird would be dead and dismembered. Up the street, a cow, pointy all over from bones, would turn a gentle head to watch the slaughter, only mildly interested in the fate that cows and chickens shared alike.

The dogs lounged around. This Reuben did not like. No one in Bangladesh liked dogs, and maybe that was why they looked the way they did. Reuben had not known that a dog could be bald, but Bengali dogs were, all except for a few hairs curling out of the gray, infested skin. Their tails did not rise and wag like dogs' tails should; they hung, broken, at odd angles behind the slinking animals.

Reuben did not like the dogs, but he felt sorry for them. They didn't get much to eat. Even the chicken bones got eaten in Bangladesh, crunched up by strong white human teeth. The chicken bones at the American flat did not get eaten, however, and Reuben thought that more enterprising dogs would have found that refuse. The jackals ate those, though, and at night retreated to the orchard beyond to howl and bark under the moon.

Once or twice Reuben went to school to see what was brewing, to see where his teachers went all the time. It was easy to see why they spent so much time there. The students ran out, shouting and laughing, to meet them as they entered the schoolyard. They loved their teachers, and they liked speaking English. The bell would drag them away then, and the schoolchildren formed lines in front of the national flag for opening exercises, singing the national anthem. "Sing" was a kind word for it. It was more of an unearthly groan, rising from their stomachs and dragging along about knee level. The children did not really sing, only mumbled and grimaced, grinning at their teachers and pinching each other when no one was looking. The odd one could sing, but that didn't help. A true note in a blast of off-key notes sounded as off as the rest.

Reuben smiled, listening to this, and the children nearest him smiled back, oblivious and indifferent to the tune. *"A-ma-a-ar son-ar-ar Ba-a-angla-uh,"* which meant "my golden Bangladesh."

The children clamored into their classrooms next. It seemed that no one would ever sit down and listen, but sometimes they did. Eventually a signal went forth somewhere, and classes settled into a hum. The team teachers did well, considering they had no curriculum and few resources—only their imaginations. These students were going to learn some English. Even if at the end of three months the only new skill they had learned was proper articulation of "purple" and "Thursday," they would know some English. They needed to. Someday, many of these children would need to pass entrance exams to universities, and then they would need to know English.

Often Reuben and Mary Ann would go visiting or shopping for fruits and vegetables in the afternoon. Mary Ann liked the visiting. Buying vegetables was too close to cooking. She liked to cook, but she liked people better. She liked evenings when the teachers were home, preparing for classes. Sometimes they played games. Sometimes they made popcorn. Sometimes they just sat around and talked. Local youth and children dropped in all afternoon and evening to play volleyball or UNO or to study English. A few of the teachers had started private tutoring sessions after school. There was always something happening, and Mary Ann loved it.

Minnesota Virginia Pakistan Ukraine Afghanistan Israel Haiti Bangladesh

Rana Plaza

APRIL 24, 2013, DAWNED HOT and hazy in Dhaka. In the east, the red sky made the early morning feel even warmer. In the humidity of the approaching rainy season, even nights did not cool down much. The streets, gray with mist, were brightened by the hordes of women and young girls, and the odd man, all headed to work in the factories. The Savar section of the city twittered with the birds, the early hawkers, and the factory workers.

Aroti moved close to her fifteen-year-old friend, Rehana, shivering suddenly in the damp air. "I wish we didn't have to go to work today."

Rehana looked at her friend solemnly. Aroti's words drew her mind from the little home behind the vegetable market where she had left her crippled mother. Her mother had clubfeet but could walk on her knobby ankles. Their home behind the vegetable market, one in a series of connected concrete structures, accommodated them well. It had one room like all of their neighbors' homes. In the old days, her father had done his best to provide for them. But he had died of cancer a few years earlier, and Rehana missed him. She missed having someone to look after her.

Most days Rehana left this trouble behind and bounded on her way. Her sturdy legs and stocky body made it easy for her to work hard, and she liked work almost as much as she liked play. Today, though, she was apprehensive.

She sighed and shook herself, rubbing the stubby nose that was a direct contradiction to Bengali ideas of beauty—Bengalis liked long pointy noses. She tugged at hers, trying to make it longer. "Don't worry so much, Aroti. Nothing is wrong with the building. We were silly to leave yesterday. Every factory in Bangladesh has cracks in it, and whoever heard of a building falling down? There's more of a chance it will burn."

Aroti tripped suddenly on an uneven brick and sat down on a concrete step outside a store entrance, holding her toe. She scowled. "How do you know anyhow? What makes you so sure?" Her toe was hurting.

"I just know." Rehana flipped her short braid over her shoulder. She was not worried about Aroti's toe. "Come on."

They were drawing close to the big sprawling mall and factory complex of nine floors called Rana Plaza where they both worked. Hundreds of workers were streaming in from all directions. Usually at this time of day, the chirping of day laborers filled the streets.

But this morning the workers were not chattering. No one was quite comfortable. The day before, new cracks expanding in the structure of the building had alarmed them, and they had all refused to work. The bosses had ordered them back to their jobs, saying they had checked out the cracks and there was nothing to worry about. That alone would not have brought the workers back, but the bosses had threatened to fire any worker who did not return to work that day.

It was eight o'clock when the garment factory workers went to their machines. Workers were still arriving. The shops and banks on the lower floors were opening. Almost four thousand people were in the building. There was no electrical power on the top floors that morning, and the overseers started the generators. Suddenly Rehana looked up from her sewing machine. Something was wrong. The rest of the workers paused. Everyone listened as a rumble started somewhere deep in the building.

"Get out!" someone yelled, and everyone bolted. It was 8:57, and the building was collapsing. The roar rose all around the fleeing workers. No one was getting away. In seconds, the workers felt the debris falling around them, trapping them—cutting off their escape. With a tremendous slap, the floors fell together, and the entire building caved in as huge pieces of concrete slid like boulders in a landslide. The rebar in the walls snapped. Rana Plaza had fallen.

Over 1,200 people were proclaimed dead. Around 2,500 people were hurt.

The shopping plaza had never been intended to house factories with their heavy machines and vibrating equipment. But it was common for factory owners to be careless about safety concerns. The factory owners who operated in Rana Plaza were no different. Four floors had been added to the building without a permit. The building could not sustain the added weight, and thus the tragedy.

~~~~~~

The ESL team had returned to America a month before the disaster. Reuben and Mary Ann were busy finishing up their new home, and Mary Ann was doing some spring cleaning. Albert Lapp was driving truck, delivering mulch for his brothers' sawmill in the middle of a busy spring season when Rana Plaza fell with a roar that was heard around the world. International concern and support welled all over the world stage. Many NGOs (non-governmental organizations) and other charities poured into Bangladesh to help the victims. In response to the crisis, Reuben and Albert returned to Bangladesh in May to find opportunities to help. Reuben hoped to locate victims with amputations.

The first morning back in Dhaka, the two men took a CNG[3] north to the outskirts of town to the site of Rana Plaza. It was easy to tell when they had come upon the collapsed building. Excavators clawed at the wreckage, lifting the broken parts away piece by piece. Military personnel and other rescue workers swarmed over the lot. Beyond the cordoned parts, onlookers milled about. The heavy smell of death lay over the place, weighing down into the alleys and along the streets. It wormed into a man's lungs

---

3 A three-wheeled motorized rickshaw that runs on compressed natural gas

Rana Plaza

and the pores of his body, finding paths into everything. Under the hazy gray sky of a hot morning, the twisted rebar and lowered concrete piled in a bleak scene. Bagged shapes had been stacked off to the side—body bags. The shrouded feet of the dead pointed back at a world that had claimed the blood of the poor.

Arriving at the military hospital, Reuben and Albert found one place where being a foreigner did not carry any weight. Reporters haunted the place. They were trying to get into the hospital to see the victims—to interview and photograph. The doctors refused Reuben and Albert access to the patients.

But the two men were so persistent that soon they were shown to the military commander-in-chief of the rescue effort. When the men entered his office in a building across the street from the crash site, the commander looked up from his desk and pushed his spectacles up on his nose. A large glass front to the room offered a full view of the rescue work. He smiled in the conscious way that a man of position does and looked at them over the top of his glasses. Busy, he did not rise to greet them.

"I am sorry," he said in pleasant English. "You will not be allowed to see any of the victims. The amputees especially are not to be visited. Here." He shoved a paper at them and stood. "Write down your name and your passport number and your purpose."

They scribbled down the information accordingly, and Reuben said, "I am an amputee. I just want to talk to them, to see if there is any way I can help them."

"Amputee?" The commander frowned at Reuben.

"I do not have a leg." Reuben reached down to pull his pant leg up. "See." The dull look of the wooden leg gave it a dead look. The sock of the prosthesis showed, and Reuben looked up at the commander. The commander was staring at his leg.

"Did you have an accident?" he demanded.

"Yes," Reuben replied. "I was doing farm work." He and Albert stood still, waiting. The commander picked up some papers and adjusted them; he arranged his glasses again. Several men who had followed Reuben and Albert into the room grew silent. Down the hall, nurses called to each other, and beyond in a courtyard, chattering rickshaws rolled in with more patients. Other rickshaws rested, preparing to take them away again when rehabilitated.

The commander-in-chief handed them a slip of paper. "This is my personal phone number. Whenever you want to see the amputees, you call me."

"It's incredible how your prosthesis speaks in places like these," Albert said as they were leaving. "They won't give us the time of day until they realize you're an amputee like those victims."

Reuben nodded. It was not a new experience for him. "It is incredible. I think there's a bigger lesson in it all. If we walk into someone's life as the whole person who knows how to help them get on the right path, we're in trouble. We need to present ourselves as the healed amputee who has learned how to walk again, telling them we have learned how. Then they listen to what we have to offer."

"I suppose so," Albert said, and then he yawned, still fighting jet lag. They had only been back in Bangladesh a day or two.

At another hospital, a trauma hospital, a doctor ordered them out of the ward. He was angry. "The only reason you Americans come here is because you don't think we Bengali doctors know what we are doing. Go. Go."

"Let's find someone in charge," Albert said. They hailed a nurse and asked for the director. She smiled and took them to a man who smiled and took them to another man. That man took them to an office.

"The boss," the second man announced, grinning.

Reuben and Albert said hello to the boss. "Look," Reuben said, not waiting for introductions, "I am an amputee. I came from America to see if I can be of any help. I'm not giving money or gifts or writing a newspaper. I just want to talk to the amputees." He whipped up his pant leg.

The director was taken aback, and he procured a younger doctor to show them around the hospital. "Do what you can to cheer them up."

Going from floor to floor, trailing the young doctor, they met the amputees of Rana Plaza. On every pillow was another pair of blank eyes and sober lips, people wrangling in the throes of pain and loss.

One young woman stared at the ceiling when they approached her bed. Her face had been sunk into an expression of utter hopelessness; even the corners of her mouth sagged. She turned to look at the two Americans, and her face changed. Eyes flashing, she flipped her hair on her pillow. The dark mane of curls brought to mind the glistening coat of a newborn colt Reuben had once found crumpled on the ground. The colt had rocked forward, trying to stand, but staggered back, lurched forward again, and fallen back. The look in its eyes had been the same as this girl's—spirited.

The young woman's expression was wiped empty again, blank and soft. She turned her face up to them. The ward hummed with activity. Patients were sprawled all over, attached to lengths of IV tubing. Family members were coming and going, bringing food for their daughter or sister in bed.

The girl moved a slim wrist ringed with an ID band toward the end of her bed, but Reuben did not sit down. "My name is Reuben. What is yours?"

"Sonia." Her tone was dull.

"How old are you?"

"Eighteen."

"I am sorry about your accident," Reuben said, leaning down. "I know you're in awful pain."

"How?" Sonia slanted her jaw toward him. "How can you know?"

Reuben smiled at the feisty girl. "I also lost a leg." He lifted his pant leg, taking the prosthesis off to show to her and leaving his stump exposed. He explained it rapidly, not knowing if she understood it all, but not caring. He knew without looking that Sonia's eyes were fixed on the stump of his leg. When Reuben raised his eyes to her face, her expression had changed once again. It had hardened, glinting.

"Sit down and then stand up."

Reuben sat and then stood. Caught up in the moment, he laughed a short triumphant laugh. "See."

Sonia did not laugh. *So amputees can sit down and stand back up,* she seemed to tell herself.

"Amputees can live normal lives," Reuben told her, "and they can come from America because they understand what amputations are like and care about the people in Bangladesh who suffer."

Sonia goggled at him, and then she smiled.

The nurses, lingering about, told Reuben later that it was the first time Sonia had smiled since the collapse.

Sonia herself told them that she was married, but that she had no children. Only days before the collapse, her husband had quit his job at Rana Plaza.

They found other

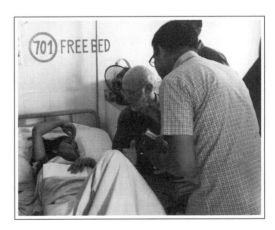

So amputees can sit down and stand back up, Sonia seemed to tell herself.

amputees, mostly girls. Rehana, the stocky girl with stubby braids, was fighting infection in both of her smashed legs. Fifteen years old, Rehana had promised her mother that she would work for two years to support them both, and then get married.

Aroti had lost her right leg below the knee. She was young, only thirteen, and had lied about her age so that she could work to support her family. Her mother had been killed in the collapse, and her father, on the roof at the time of the collapse, had ridden a piece of concrete down nine stories to survive unhurt.

Shilpee was a twenty-year-old mother of a little girl. She had lost her left leg below the knee. Rebekah, the same age, was a double amputee. Pakhi had only six-inch stumps left of her legs.

There were others too—many others. Reuben and Albert continued to visit the city's hospitals daily, combing them for the amputees of Rana Plaza.

Many other people streamed in to give support and money to the amputees too. Their bedsides were strewn with clothes and money, which lay there untouched. The amputees did not care anymore. They wanted their legs back, and they wanted friends in the howling wilderness of their world. This was what drove Reuben. Friendship was what counted.

On the seventeenth day after Rana Plaza had fallen, rescuers found the last survivor. Reshma had been struck on the head in the collapse, trapped in a wide pocket of rubble. She had had some cookies and a little bit of water with her. Another man had been within hearing distance, begging for water. She had tried to reach him, but there was no way to get the water to him. He had died, screaming and pleading, "Save me! Save me!" Numb with horror, Reshma had rationed her little bit of food and water, waiting. Seventeen days later, rescuers heard her banging on a pipe and brought her out into an astonished world. No one dreamed that anyone was still alive in that rubble.

~~~~~~~~~~~~~~~~~~~~~~~~~~~~~~

After two weeks, Reuben and Albert returned to the States. Back in

America, Reuben spoke in various churches about the plight of the amputees. Those who heard him contributed enough money for Reuben to help some of the amputees begin again. Reuben intended to buy sewing machines to help the women support themselves.

In July, Reuben and Mary Ann traveled to Bangladesh for a pastors' conference and stayed a few extra weeks to interact with the amputees.

For some of them, reality had now settled in. Many of Reuben's contacts had fallen into a valley of depression and discouragement. Some were still in the hospital. Rehana had lost both of her legs to gangrene and was struggling with prostheses. Her legs had been cut so short that wearing a prosthesis was difficult for her. Rebekah was still in the hospital undergoing what would be a series of eight surgeries on her legs. At first the doctors had taken only her foot, but the infection could not be stopped. When the last surgery would take place almost a year later, the amputation

Rehana and Mary Ann.

would be just below her knee. The recovery from each operation brought intense suffering.

Rebekah's husband was often in the hospital with her. So many of the amputees' husbands did not seem to care about their wives. Some had even abandoned them. But Rebekah's husband Arif looked after her tirelessly.

"Arif," Reuben said one day as they stood to one side while Mary Ann and Rebekah were talking. "Never, never leave your wife. She is a good woman, and if you love her and care for her, she will continue to be a good wife. It is not her fault that she is an amputee."

Rebekah was talking with Mary Ann. "My mother and brother and sister were all killed when Rana Plaza fell. You are my only family. No one else cares."

Mary Ann gathered the girl in her arms. "I will be your family, Rebekah, and God has given you a husband who did not desert you. Praise Him for that."

Seeing his wife begin to cry, Arif drew close to the bed, patting her on the shoulder. This unusual display of affection brought tears to Mary Ann's eyes too. Arif began to sniffle. Reuben was the only one left with dry eyes, and he said, "Remember, Rebekah, that Jesus, the man whom we told you about, will never leave you either. He is better family than anyone because He never leaves."

"Pray to God," Rebekah said through her tears, and Arif nodded. The young couple looked like a pair of lost children. Reuben and Mary Ann prayed that Rebekah and Arif would feel the heart of a loving Jesus in their lives.

Sonia was doing well. From the day that she had asked Reuben to sit down and stand up, she had tried to get well as fast as possible. She had gotten herself up on crutches soon after that and had swung about the hospital, visiting her friends. Today, she loped in on her crutches, having heard that Reuben and Mary Ann were visiting. Plopping down on the cot beside Pakhi, the one with six-inch stubs as legs, Sonia laid aside her crutches. "Hello." She waved at Reuben, her grin winsome, and accepted Mary Ann's embrace matter-of-factly.

Sonia listened as Reuben told her about the sewing machines he was getting for the amputees. Then she leaned over and tickled Pakhi. "I will make you dresses, and then you can wear many clothes all at once."

Pakhi laughed. Sonia was always making them laugh. After Sonia had moved off to talk with Mary Ann, however, Pakhi drew Reuben to her bedside. "I want to talk to you."

"Okay," Reuben agreed. Someone had just combed Pakhi's hair, and her important manner made him smile. She was feeling good about herself.

"I heard the nurses talking the other day, and I asked them what they were saying. They were talking about what you tell us, that God has a purpose for bad things that happen and can use them to make good things come, and that life can be worth it even for an amputee. The nurses said it wasn't true. They said maybe it is true in America where there is plenty of money and good doctors, but in Bangladesh, nothing can ever be good about an amputee's life." Pakhi stopped and searched Reuben's face.

"Do you believe that?" Reuben asked her.

Pakhi frowned. "No! No, I don't. And I told them they didn't know what they were talking about." She slammed her fist into the mattress. "I think what you said is true!"

Reuben chuckled at her expression and opened his mouth to comment, but just then Mary Ann and some of the other amputees engulfed them. The conversation was lost, but Reuben went away with Pakhi's words ringing in his ears.

Shilpee looked up at him from the cot, her chubby face creased with pain. "Why didn't I die?" she moaned. Listless, she greeted them one day, showing her hair to Mary Ann.

"Soon I will be bald," she mourned. Her hair was falling out because of all the stress and the medications she had taken. "I wish I had just died." For some reason, after all the tragedy, losing her hair was breaking her heart.

Reuben considered. Maybe she just needed a boost out of her own little world of pain, a larger look at life. "Shilpee, may I tell you a story?"

Shilpee shrugged but turned her jet black eyes on Reuben. She was curious in spite of herself.

"One time there was a man named Job who loved God and followed Him. He was also very rich. He had many children, animals, and servants. One day Satan told God that if Job had all his riches taken from him, he would not follow God anymore."

Reuben continued talking, becoming animated as he told the ancient story of tragedy and disaster. He told how Job had withstood the attacks of his friends, but how another battle had raged inside of Job as he questioned God and what He was doing.

Reuben felt the majestic sweep of power when he explained how God had spoken to Job out of a whirlwind. "Where were you when the foundations of the earth were laid? Who stops the proud waves in their course and commands the morning? Do you understand the springs deep in the sea and know where the light goes when the darkness comes? Job, oh, Job, declare if you know these things."

The questions of Job that would be asked by millions of groaning souls for centuries to come had died away in the face of the Almighty. Job had replied. "I am a vile man. How will I answer you? I will put my hand over my mouth."

"You see, Shilpee, Job's troubles weren't insignificant in the eyes of God. But God knew that what Job needed most of all was to see God for who He really was. Job needed to know that God was infinitely greater than he was and rest in that."

Reuben looked down at Shilpee as he finished the narrative and prayed that the disaster would change her life in a way she had never dreamed. God knew where the light had gone in her life when the darkness had come. God had not lost the light, however, and the dawn would rise again on her.

Minnesota · Virginia · Pakistan · Ukraine · Afghanistan · Israel · Haiti · Bangladesh

The CNG Driver
Who Wouldn't

REUBEN AND MARY ANN DESCENDED the steps of a hospital, hunting for a CNG. Noon traffic pulsed around them, breathing acrid fumes. Reuben approached a little green CNG, bending to speak through the bars to the driver. The driver was wearing a purple shirt, and Reuben wondered idly why so many CNG drivers wore purple shirts. The driver flicked away the end of his cigarette and looked inquiringly.

"Square Hospital?" Reuben pointed to the south. "How much?"

"Five hundred *taka*."[4] The man raised five fingers. His square, bristly mustache quaked as he wrinkled his lip, sniffing. "Five hundred."

"Five hundred!" Mary Ann said from somewhere behind Reuben. "Do we look like foreigners?"

"Shh," Reuben said. "Two-fifty, brother?"

The driver removed his cigarette from his mouth and studied Reuben with candor. "Three hundred fifty."

Reuben straightened. It was outrageous. "No, no, three hundred." He turned away.

"Wait!" The purple-shirted driver turned the front wheel into the traffic and reached back to rattle the latch of the door open.

Reuben smiled. "Three hundred?" The driver jerked his head to one

4 Approximately 78 *taka* to one U.S. dollar

side as if it were a silly question, and the couple climbed in. Jolting to one side to avoid a bus reaming into them, the driver gunned the CNG out into the roadway.

"Reuben!" Mary Ann clutched his arm. "The man's an amputee!"

"What!" Reuben leaned forward to see. The driver *was* an amputee. He was missing his left leg below the knee. He shifted gamely, clutching with one foot and stuttering the engine. They lurched forward.

"Sir!" Reuben tapped him on the shoulder as they halted in the frozen traffic. "Leg?" He indicated the amputation, and the driver nodded.

"Look." Reuben tugged at his own pant leg.

The man swiveled to look, and his cigarette sagged. "Leg?"

Sagor, their friend who was with them, looked too. Sagor began a rapid conversation with the driver. The driver had lost his leg when he was hit by a truck three years before. He had a wife and two daughters.

"A man with this much gumption," Reuben told Mary Ann, "is worth investing in. He kept on driving a CNG even though he could have gone out begging. His stump is well shaped. I doubt a prosthesis would be a problem. I wonder . . ."

"Ask him if we may help him buy a prosthesis," Reuben said to Sagor. He shifted about as Sagor went on talking.

"He says yes, he would let you help him with that," Sagor said, breaking away from the conversation.

They arranged that the next time Reuben and Mary Ann visited the Center of Rehabilitation for the Paralyzed, they would hire this driver to take them. While they were there, the doctors could evaluate the driver for a prosthesis. Sagor and the driver exchanged phone numbers, and they promised to stay in contact.

The purple-shirted driver drove them again the next time. The CNG wound out at top speed as it flew along the raised road that traveled from the main city of Dhaka, past the fields of water covered in water hyacinths, past the red-brown brickyards powdery under the dry sunshine. The CNG bucked and galloped as it hit potholes. Huge, yellow dump trucks, spangled with brightly painted pictures, roared at them, and they dove to the sand at the side of the road. Quickly they leaped back onto the blacktop, just missing a rickshaw.

"He's a good driver," Reuben said, delighted. It was rare to find handicapped people in Bangladesh who continued with their lives, working at what they could. Thousands of beggars roamed the streets, some of them much less debilitated than this man.

At the hospital, they were told that the prosthetics doctor had gone home for lunch, but that he would come back, perhaps after a few hours. Reuben shrugged when the nurse told him this. There was nothing to do about it. "Let's go see some of the amputees then." The driver said he would wait with his CNG.

The rehabilitation center was a beautiful place. Reuben and Mary Ann basked in it whenever they entered these grounds. Set off the busy highway, only a mile from what used to be Rana Plaza, it was a refuge of peace and healing. A British woman had started it decades ago and still lived there, overseeing the hospital. It had been built for rest and recuperation.

Beside the hospital, small cottage complexes stood to the side of the main grounds. Here families could stay when the therapy stretched for months. Paralyzed young men lay on carts and used their arms to play carom in an open-air game room. A man with no arms painted pictures with his mouth. The paths were shaded with skimpy trees. A simple fountain bubbled in the receiving courtyard of the hospital. A small pond with benches around it and a footbridge over it waited for troubled bodies to recline beside it. Yet, in all of these thoughtful measures, there was nothing rich and exotic, nothing incongruent with the lifestyles of the broken people who must come there.

Shilpee was out with her walker on the porch of the cottages, shouting across the barren yard and waving her lunch container at a little boy who dug in a pile of sand. She shuffled as if to stomp her foot, but it's hard for an amputee to stomp her foot.

"Shilpee!" Mary Ann cried, running toward the young woman. Shilpee paused in her fit and looked over her shoulder. A smile broke over her face, and her bellowing ceased.

A wheelchair moved into the door and struggled to work its way through the frame. Rehana concentrated and carefully rolled the chair over the threshold. Then she looked up at Reuben and Mary Ann with a shy smile. Her stumps were still hurting her, and the prostheses seemed like a distant dream for the future.

Reuben and Mary Ann spent several happy hours with the girls and their mothers who were staying with them. Before long they settled into serious discussion. Reuben had finally located and bought good sewing machines. They hashed over how best to fix the machines to make them work for women with only one foot, or none. Reuben was going to rig something, he promised. A glow filled him. Afternoon sunshine bloomed around them through the trees. When they left, the girls followed in their wheelchairs a little way, chattering and laughing.

They found the purple-shirted driver again, and together they all went to find the doctor. Reuben watched the driver walk on crutches. He was fast, moving with great kangaroo hops, but Reuben's spirit lifted. "I am going to buy this man a prosthesis. Life will be so much easier for him, and what's more, he's earned it."

The doctor was in from his lunch, and they were escorted directly to him. The doctor examined the stump of the man's leg and said that a prosthesis would work fine for him without any surgery to fit the stump. This news excited Reuben, for he knew how crucial it was for the

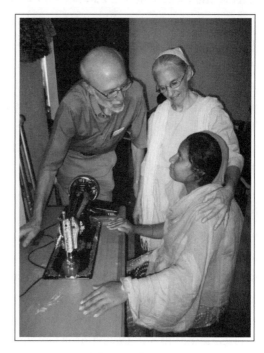

Shilpee at her sewing machine.

stump to first be shaped right. Many amputated stumps had not been prepared for a prosthesis. Next they must arrange for a trial socket. Reuben
sat frowning in a heat of thought, Mary Ann clinging to his arm. He was
thinking it all through, planning how they could meet again. He wanted
to meet the man's family. Perhaps they would have to make an extra trip
to Dhaka from Cumrakhali in January . . .

The doctor and the driver were talking and talking in Bangla. They were
arguing. Anxious, Reuben leaned forward, trying to gauge the temper of
the conversation. Finally the doctor turned and waved his hand helplessly.
He seemed frustrated. "The man wants the money instead."

"The money for a prosthesis?"

"So it seems."

The glow faded from Reuben, and he said, "I'll buy him a leg, but I won't
give him any *taka*."

"I tried to tell him." The doctor turned back to the driver.

The driver wilted when the doctor explained what Reuben had said. He
looked at his hands and shook his head repeatedly.

"Why doesn't he want a leg?" Reuben was disappointed but curious.

"He says he's been without a leg so long that he doesn't want one. He'd
rather be without the leg than try to learn to use a prosthesis, but he would
like the money."

"Try to persuade him." Reuben was on his feet now, pacing.

The doctor shrugged. The conversation continued, but it was short. The
driver shook his head and said something. Then he shook his head again,
looking at the tiled floor. "He sticks to it," the doctor reported. "He says
he doesn't want a prosthesis."

There was nothing more to say or do. They all got up to leave. Stunned,
Reuben watched the man manipulate his crutches around the uneven
bricks in the courtyard. Why would he want to stay one-legged? Was he
just scared of the adjustments? It wasn't as though the man was begging,
using his handicap to get money.

Frustrated, Reuben looked at Mary Ann. "What ailed the man?"

"He didn't want to get better, I guess," Mary Ann said.

"But that's ridiculous." Reuben felt the old helplessness settling in on him, a feeling that they weren't doing enough for the world. This country had millions of unsaved people, and they were all going somewhere. He stood with the message in his hands, and the people toiled by, not knowing—some of them not caring. They had come, taught some English, put a few Band-Aids on people, and made a lot of friends. But was there more they could do? There had to be more!

Reuben and Mary Ann separated from the driver, taking a bus back to the apartment. Reuben leaned into the seat, tired. He shifted, thinking, and an uncomfortable thought struck him. *Maybe the CNG driver isn't so strange after all. There are plenty of people in this sick world who don't want to be healed, and instead, use crutches the rest of their lives. Some people delight in their miseries, preferring to think of themselves as victims. Others are too proud to admit they are missing a leg. Others want the money, but not the gift. I guess Christ dealt with plenty of people who didn't want to receive what He could give. What a world!* Reuben twisted on the scratchy seat.

At that moment another thought gripped him. *Maybe the CNG driver has learned to be content in his present state. Maybe he really doesn't feel he needs a prosthesis.*

"Look," Mary Ann said, poking Reuben.

They looked out the window in the fading sunlight and saw the CNG driver in the purple shirt one last time from the bus window. He sat in a queue of CNGs that were waiting for passengers. They waved, smiling sad smiles, and he waved back. His lips split over flashing, white teeth, and then the CNG driver who didn't want a leg was lost to sight.

The next evening Reuben and Mary Ann took a CNG and went to the north end of the city. They knew a pastor named Zhewel who lived there. Zhewel and his wife were a young Christian couple who possessed a strong vision for Bangladesh. They worked tirelessly for the kingdom of God. Zhewel traveled all over Bangladesh and into India and Nepal by times, shepherding churches and encouraging believers.

Near his home in Dhaka, he nurtured a little group of believers. They met in an apartment every Friday afternoon at four-thirty. Reuben and Mary

Ann were going to visit one of these gatherings. When they reached the little apartment, they sat on the floor with the people filtering in around them. It was hot and stuffy and the room was small.

Reuben looked around him. There weren't many people there, and they were humble people, unimportant in the world's eyes. They sought refuge from the hot, crowded streets, just like Reuben and Mary Ann. The harmonium, an instrument similar to an accordion, began to play. All began to sing, the same style of singing they heard all over Bangladesh—the same instruments, the same flat, wailing tone. On a hot day over speakers, the singing was obnoxious. Now it did not seem a bit annoying. The melody rose and fell. Reuben thought he could listen to it forever.

After the singing was over, Pastor Zhewel rose and spoke, interpreting for the foreigners from time to time.

He spoke about the mustard seed that grew from a tiny seed into a huge tree. Faith was like the seed, like the rice plants they all placed in their rice paddies in the village. At first the plants were small, but then they grew into a great field of rice. The rice fed many people.

"Go out and plant the seeds," Pastor Zhewel told his people. "You've got to take the little seeds and drop them. Maybe it seems that you are throwing all your seeds into just plain dirt, but dirt is where the seeds grow. Every plot of dirt has value. It can all grow seed, just like every person has value and potential. Maybe it seems as though you can never make all the dirt in the world produce a plant. There is too much dirt to cultivate. It's just dirt—dead dirt. But if every man throws seeds out on the dirt where he lives, it will take root. Look at the world, covered in plants, if you don't believe. Believe and throw the seeds out. All it takes is a seed, a little tiny seed."

Suddenly the congregation bowed their heads to pray. They were all praying at once, out loud. The prayer caught Reuben by surprise, but he bowed his head. The fervor around him grew in volume as the people poured out their hearts. For someone from his background, it hardly seemed reverent. For a second he was critical—but then he was ashamed.

I have so much. He mulled it over in his mind. *How can I sit here and question the provision of God? These people have so little, and they don't seem to doubt that God will give the increase. They love God as I do, and they believe Him too. If they think God can change the people of their country, well, they ought to know. If they can go out and sow the little seeds into the muddy streets of Dhaka to be trodden under by the throng, I can too. I am not called to change people. That's God's job—God's worry. I only need to reach out, to touch people, to sow the seed.*

Through the hum of prayer, a familiar sound caught Reuben's ear. It was the evening Islamic prayer call floating out over the town. All over Bangladesh that call was wafting across the land. But here it was hard to hear among the breath of saints' souls. The evening prayer call faded away, drowned out by the friendship with God.

CHAPTER 30

Minnesota Virginia Pakistan Ukraine Israel Afghanistan Haiti Bangladesh

Rasel

AFTER THE VISIT TO BANGLADESH in July, Reuben and Mary Ann returned to the States and then went back to Bangladesh barely two months later. Again, the heat struck them like a dull club. The rainy season was just ending, and the clear autumn weather had not yet come. This time Reuben and Mary Ann were chaperoning a team of young people who were learning Bangla. The Bangladesh ESL board had agreed that steps needed to be taken for a more permanent residence in Bangladesh to work with the many interested people in the country. In preparation for that, ten young people were learning the native tongue.

Mary Ann cooked for the students, and Reuben bought things at the market, did odd jobs, and studied for topics and discipleship classes. Some days they made trips to the hospitals around the city, visiting their amputee friends.

Mary Ann's kitchen window looked into the balcony of the neighboring apartment building, and down to the right, she could see busy Taj Mahal Road and watch its traffic streaming by. Rickshaws, cars, buses, bicycles, trucks, motorcycles, and CNGs all rolled past. The din off the street was incredible, and in the evening it only got worse. Then the schools up and down the streets of Dhaka let out, and the students in uniform strolled down the streets. The shops opened back up after the heat of the midday, and the city came alive. In Bangladesh most of life happened after four o'clock in the afternoon.

One afternoon a thunderstorm shook the apartment building, and rain streaked down into the streets. On the busy sidewalks below the apartment, which were visible through the cloudy kitchen window, umbrellas bloomed all up and down Taj Mahal. The headlights of cars bounced up and down as they bumped over the speed bumps. Rickshaw drivers tucked their passengers in under plastic sheets, and they pumped on through the torrent with heads bent low against the driving water. Some raised their faces, and even two stories up, a person could see the flashing teeth as they grinned at passersby.

It was time to start supper. Mary Ann had begun dicing tomatoes for the coleslaw, and one of the girls was helping her. Tomatoes were a sore point with Mary Ann. One or two of the team members most emphatically did not like tomatoes, and she loved them.

"If I put tomatoes in this, would you eat it?" she had asked Albert one night at supper when they were discussing what to do with the leftover cabbage salad. One of the girls, listening to music while she had made the slaw, had gotten carried away with cutting up vegetables.

"No," Albert said.

"Why wouldn't you just pick the tomatoes out?" Mary Ann asked, playing with the spoon in the slaw. She divided the slaw into two halves in the bowl and let the juice fill up the path.

"No, I wouldn't take any."

Mary Ann sighed and clucked her tongue. "That is just so unfortunate. I like cooking with tomatoes. I just love juicy red tomatoes in food."

"I do not pick through things, so, no, I would not take anything with tomatoes in it," Albert said.

"Oh, I just think there is nothing more refreshing than a nice red tomato." Mary Ann heaved a heavy sigh

"I'm sorry," Albert said.

"So am I," Mary Ann replied. "God created them for us to eat, fresh out of the garden. And tomatoes are one of the best cancer—"

"Cancer," said Albert, "that would about be it."

"No!" Mary Ann gasped. "I meant they're a great cancer preventer."

The number one rule of house parenting was flexibility, and Mary Ann decided to be flexible. She set aside a little salad for herself and put tomatoes in it. Cancer at twenty may not be scary, but Mary Ann was older than twenty, and she wasn't taking chances. She looked out at the rain again and clucked her tongue. The laundry was still out on the roof, but some of the girls had been up there studying. Mary Ann decided to let them worry about it. Reuben had gone to buy bananas for the pudding, and now he was back at the dining room table studying to teach at the pastors' conference. The rest of the team had scattered about, reading, studying, and emailing. Albert was sprawled on the sofa working on his laptop when his phone rang.

"Hello?" Albert's tone was vacant. He was still frowning at his laptop. "Hello, oh, hello. Um, yes . . . Rasel!" He laid the laptop aside and sprang to his feet, striding to stand and look out the sliding door to the balcony.

Reuben looked up from his laptop to stare at Albert's back. Albert's voice floated back, agitated but eager, from the balcony. He wasn't talking much, only asking questions occasionally. The door to the apartment banged open, and some of the girls stumbled through, laughing and wet, carrying a hamper of clothing.

Albert returned suddenly through the balcony door. The lethargy of the wet, hot afternoon had disappeared, and he looked around the room. A light appeared to glow through him. The girls' laughter halted, and Reuben raised his head from his work again.

"That was Rasel." Albert's tone was choked. "He just got out of jail."

"Rasel!"

"Rasel!" the name echoed about the room.

"Rasel!"

~~~~~~

Two winters before, in the village of Cumrakhali, a dying man had needed blood. A villager had come knocking on the door one evening at the flat. "We need blood for a sick man." A few team members had gone, and while at the hospital, the director of the hospital stopped to talk to the Americans, asking questions about what they were doing in Bangladesh.

Not many days afterward, a younger man had stopped in at the English class that Albert taught for the schoolteachers. His eyes were deeply set in his square face. In spite of being almost a foot shorter than Albert, this stranger shook hands, man to man. Albert, struck by the man's conservative attire, suddenly wondered just who this man was.

"My name is Rasel," the stranger said in a soft, throaty voice. "My father-in-law is the director at the hospital, and he told me about you. I write books. Actually, I wrote a book on how to easily learn English, so I want to learn more about the English language from you. I did not know that Americans had come to Cumrakhali."

"Do you live here?" Albert inquired.

"No, but my wife stays here with her family, so I am here often."

It was common, Albert knew, for a woman to move back and forth between her family and her husband's family while the husband worked away. He agreed that Rasel could join the class, and Rasel sat down among the desks. Albert taught well that day. He liked the deeper level of interaction that the teachers' class required, and he enjoyed these men.

Rasel came to class regularly after that, and Albert found him a willing pupil. The classes continued for a couple of weeks, and then one day Rasel said, "I have a question."

"Okay . . ." Albert waited.

"When I was in college, I took a class on world religions. I understand that Christians have an Old Testament and a New Testament. Can you explain what the difference is?"

Albert considered. "Well, that's a big question. I don't think we have time to explain it all, actually."

"Oh, I have time," Rasel said immediately, and the other student in the class nodded. Attendance was sketchy, and none of the others had made it that day.

Albert had been stalling, hoping to have time to arrange his ideas. He bent his head, placing his hands on the desk and leaning on them, searching for a place to start. Then he stood. "Okay, well, it all began when the world was created." He started drawing a timeline on the board. "In the beginning, God created two people, Adam and Eve, and placed them in the Garden of Eden."

"That's correct," Rasel said.

"When God made these two people, they were sinless, and God had a very open relationship with them, walking and talking with them every day. God told them they were responsible to take care of the garden, but they were not to eat of the one tree. Well, they ate fruit from that tree, and . . . do you know what happened next?"

"They hid from God," Rasel said promptly.

"Right. Suddenly they were afraid of God because they had disobeyed. Since that time, people have come up with about four thousand religions, all trying to solve the problem of being afraid of God. They are not sure what they will do when they die and meet up with Him. The Islamic religion teaches that if I do more good works than bad works, then maybe God will take me to heaven. If not, then I will go to hell. So, think about that. Suppose we were best friends and I get a new phone. You want one like I have, so you take my phone when you think I am not looking. Immediately our relationship is damaged. So you leave, and while you are leaving, you see a blind beggar standing by the street. You think of what you can do to fix your sin. You give the blind man a thousand *taka*. That was a good thing to do, correct?"

"Yes, it was."

"Now, explain to me how giving the blind man *taka* solves the problem between you and me after you stole my phone. Would it help?"

Rasel shook his head. "No, it won't."

"Suppose it was ten thousand *taka*. Maybe that would fix things."

"No."

"So how could doing good things to other people solve the problems in our relationship with God?"

Rasel's brow creased. "I understand your point."

"In the Bible, God offers another solution . . ." Albert began. And then, for the next hour and a half, he talked with Rasel and the other student. He told about how animals had died for the sins of people, pointing toward a coming Messiah who would die as a perfect sacrifice. He shared the Old Testament prophecies that told of the coming Christ. Gradually, Albert warmed up, sweeping on in his narrative, trying to explain simply. "The New Testament is the record of the Messiah who came to fulfill the prophecies of the Old Testament."

Albert had expected opposition, arguments, and objections, but neither student stirred. He told then of the birth of Christ and the Sermon on the Mount, in which Christ taught to go not only a mile, as the law said, but the second mile. He talked quietly at the end about Christ being the final and perfect sacrifice. "Jesus is the difference between the Old and the New Testaments."

When they finished, the students rose to go. No one said anything, but Rasel paused by Albert. "Can I talk with you again? I have many questions."

That conversation had led to an intense relationship. Rasel would come to visit often, and he would stay for a long time, asking questions and talking. Albert learned that Rasel was not the average Bengali. Compared to most Bengalis who practiced a more lenient form of Islam, Rasel came from a radically conservative family. Rasel and his father and brothers were all imams and teachers, highly schooled in Islam. Rasel had memorized the Qur'an as a young child. His sister had married into another family of radical Islamic practice. Now she was never allowed to go out of her house unless her vehicle was wrapped in black cloth so that no one could see in. Rasel's home was connected to the village mosque where his father was the imam in charge and where Rasel and his brothers prayed five times a day.

Rasel was full of questions about Christian practice, and through his talks with Albert, he developed even more questions about his own religion. He went to great lengths to obtain answers, asking his father, his brothers, and his brother-in-law. No one could answer his questions. Rasel traveled to quite a number of madrasahs to talk with highly educated scholars. Thirteen madrasahs told him they had no answers. At two of the madrasahs, the scholars grew angry with him.

Rasel told them, "Don't try to prove Islam to me by the strength of your arm; just show me in the Qu'ran or Hadith, and I will be happy. I want to be a Muslim. I want Islam to be correct."

Finally he called the leader of the Grand Mosque in Dhaka. Again, Rasel got no answer. They said, "Don't ask those questions."

Rasel did ask. One night he watched a video where a man explained the differences between Christianity and Islam, addressing questions that many seeking Muslims ask. After he finished watching, Rasel called Albert immediately. "We need to talk."

When Rasel arrived, he sat down and threw open the New Testament. "If this is true, then where does it leave me? I've had it all wrong for years and years. Now what should I do?"

That question had taken Rasel in a path that no one, not even Rasel himself, had imagined. Claiming Jesus as his Saviour, Rasel flung himself into deeper study of the Scriptures. One day, appearing at the apartment, he drew Albert aside immediately and skipped all the normal greetings, preludes to polite conversation. "I was reading in Acts 22 about Paul being baptized," Rasel said. "I want to be baptized."

Rasel was baptized, and in his testimony at his baptism, he said, "For years I've had emptiness inside of me. Almost ten years ago I went to a Catholic church to talk to a priest and ask him questions, but all he did was tell me how wrong and stupid Islam is. He did not answer my questions, so I went away. Then my father-in-law told me about you. I came to your class thinking you were a Christian I could convert to Islam, but instead, I am now convinced that Jesus is the only way for a man to reach heaven. Jesus is the road to God."

After his conversion to Christianity, Rasel's relationship with his family had grown very strained. He told them nothing, but since he lived with them, he could not avoid the questions. "Why aren't you going to prayers? Why aren't you preaching?" His family was suspicious.

Shortly after Rasel's baptism, the ESL teams had left for America. Three months later, Albert and another team member, BJ, returned to spend time with Rasel in Bible study. They met up with Rasel at a bus station one day. Sagor was with them, and Sagor did not like Rasel. "He's a dangerous man. Look how his pants stop right above his ankle. That means he is Jamaat-e-Islami."

Jamaat-e-Islami was the most conservative of the Bengali political parties. They were radicals, believing in violence—activists who caused disturbances. The party was made up of men who had been war criminals in the Liberation War in 1971. Those war criminals were now standing trial for their actions, and the Jamaat were raising riots all over the country. Many Jamaat members were being taken into custody.

A couple of days after meeting Rasel at the bus station, Albert and BJ had gone north to visit the village of Cumrakhali. There, one morning, Rasel came to spend a few hours with Albert. BJ was out and about, visiting friends in the village, but he returned sooner than he had intended, hoping to meet Rasel. Rasel had said that he and his wife were leaving for another village that day, and BJ wanted to say goodbye. When he reached the flat, however, Rasel had left.

"He said he needed to go," Albert said from the table in the corner where he was running his finger around on his mouse pad, glaring at the computer screen in concentration. BJ did not disturb him and stepped outside to call Rasel.

"Rasel, brother, you left. I wanted to see you."

Rasel's voice came through the receiver, thin and distant, "I will stop at your flat on my way out of town. Wait for me, brother."

"I will wait," BJ promised. He went outside and stood by the road. After a bit, Albert joined him, shading his eyes to stare up the street toward the market, toward the bus stand.

"What's up?" Albert wanted to know as a tractor rolled past, pulling a load of bricks. The dust rolled up around them, choking them.

"Rasel's coming to say goodbye," BJ said, rubbing his eyes.

The two stood together in silence.

"He's doing well," Albert said at last. "He's got a passion for Jesus—he wants to take the news to other Muslims. He is appalled at the ignorance and blindness of Muslims, and is raring to preach it across the country." Albert shook his head.

BJ leaned against the wall. "Rasel means 'messenger'; did you know that?"

Albert looked at him sideways, considering. He had just opened his mouth to reply when a motorcycle throttled to a stop in front of them. It was Rasel's father-in-law. The old gentleman's cap had slid back, and he was wearing a lungi under his gown instead of pants. As it slid in the dust, the bike wobbled, but the driver didn't seem to notice, crying out, "Rasel was arrested!"

"Arrested!" Albert took the man by the arm. "What do you mean?"

BJ's jaw dropped. He opened and closed his mouth.

"Do you know where he is?" Albert demanded.

Rasel's father-in-law made an effort to pull himself together. "I don't know. Policemen came and took him away at the house as he was leaving. I am going to the station now to see what I can learn."

That was all they had known for a long time. When Albert tried Rasel's phone, Rasel's wife answered. Her English was poor and labored, and they could drag nothing definite out of her. Rasel's father-in-law didn't know anything for certain, but he blamed Rasel's father and brothers. There was some question of illegal political activity in Rasel's past, and it seemed that other men from his party had been arrested as well. There was no one else to ask, and Albert and BJ were reluctant to go to the police themselves. If there were religious implications, it would be best for Rasel if the Americans stayed out of it. Albert and BJ went back to America, and a vigil of prayer for Rasel began. For fifteen months there had been little word. The name of Rasel had been on hundreds of lips since then as Christians in America had lifted his name in prayer over and over. All had waited and waited for word from him, and no promise had been given that they ever would hear from him again. Rasel had gone to jail.

Albert could hardly believe he was hearing Rasel's voice again over the phone. Rasel was with his wife and daughter in his parents' home. He wanted to come see the American team, but he didn't know when he would get away. His family was watching every step he took.

A couple of weeks later, Rasel phoned Albert. "I'm coming to Dhaka. My bus is coming in after midnight tonight."

"See you then." Albert hung up, and late that night he and one of the other team members slipped away to the bus station to meet him, bringing Rasel back to the apartment to spend the night.

The next morning Rasel stumbled out of the room where he had spent the night, blinking and looking about him uncertainly as if surprised by the walls and the furniture. The team was already sitting down to breakfast, and for a moment they regarded Rasel in silence. His gown and prayer cap had disappeared, and he was wearing pants and a yellow and black T-shirt. His eyes were bloodshot, and in the ugly, brilliant lighting of the dining area, Rasel's skin, lighter than that of most Bengalis, looked almost yellow. The group at the table took it all in. Here was the man they had prayed over for so many months, a man whom God had found faithful, whom God had sustained through months of imprisonment.

Rasel joined the team at the table, but he did not speak of his imprisonment. He only stared uncomprehendingly at the dishes that were passed to him. The team members recovered their hospitality. Albert was jovial, stirring his coffee, but beside him, Rasel did not speak.

Once breakfast was over, the group broke up to do laundry and dishes, and then they left for Bangla class.

"Be safe out there," Rasel said to them as they were scattering. His manner was earnest. "The roads are dangerous this morning."

They were. They always were. Reuben didn't think the young people realized it completely. The country was fraught with political friction, terrorized by strikers. The team joked about catching the petrol bombs that were being thrown into overloaded buses these days, and they talked about bailing out of the broken windows in case of attack, dramatizing possible escape routes. Out on the streets, however, people went about their

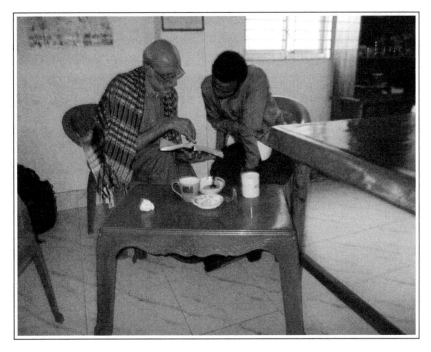

Rasel and Reuben share together in Bible study.

business with quickness and alertness. Some mornings when the opposition parties had declared a strike, the Dhaka streets echoed in stillness, remarkable in a city of several million. By midday, some buses would be out, a few people trotting up and down the sidewalks, but the city was wary.

Rasel shook his head as the door closed. "Bangladesh is in trouble."

After the others had gone, Reuben and Mary Ann sat down to talk with Rasel. He had many months of bottled-up thoughts to spill out. He talked and talked, and they listened. Mainly he talked about his work. "I want to write a book," Rasel said over and over. "People need to know what the problem is with Islam. I need to tell them."

Rasel had a lot to say about Islam and its prophet Mohammad. "It is an evil. It is the reason the people of Bangladesh are in such trouble all the time," Rasel said tensely. "No one realizes it. They are all in blindness, worshiping Mohammad. They don't know who he really was, that he was an evil man who deceived his people."

"Think of it this way," Reuben said. "You are correct about the deception of Islam. We believe that Muslims have been duped into a lie, but we need to focus on how good and right Christ is, on following Him. Telling Muslims that their religion is bad won't convince them to become part of our religion. If they are seeking truth, in time they will come to realize the truth. We don't want people turning to Christianity because Islam is bad. We want them to become followers of Jesus because Jesus is right."

Rasel agreed with this, but he looked troubled. Still close to the grips of Islam, he felt that he had to remind himself that it was wrong. Then he talked about his time in prison, about the contacts he had made. Rasel had found some other men who were seeking the face of God. He had told them truth, holding Bible studies with them, and he reported that five of them had claimed Christ as Saviour. "People need to know," he said restlessly.

Rasel was especially burdened with a desire for his wife to know Christ. "I talk to her about Jesus, and she listens. Someday, I think . . ." His expression grew yearning. "She is a beautiful woman—a beautiful person. Her name means 'key of paradise.' "

Minnesota Virginia Pakistan Ukraine Afghanistan Israel Haiti Bangladesh

We Want Hanging

IT WAS OCTOBER 2013 IN Bangladesh, and the first in a thick storm of strikes and blockades that would last until the elections had begun. The Bangla students trudged to school through the parliament park and past the home of the prime minister where the security shift had been doubled. The prime minister had instated her own personal military unit to guard her and her premises solely. They stood watch all along Parliament Avenue, pointing their guns carelessly and gazing at the passing traffic.

The elections for prime minister were approaching, to be held in December. The tensions around the city were rising. There had been strikes off and on all year. Two women were campaigning for the position. Both of them—Sheikh Hasina, daughter of the man who had founded the country, and Khaleda Zia, wife of the second prime minister who had been assassinated while in office—had switched in and out term after term for the last few decades.

One night the gentlemen of the language team had disappeared on a night stroll, and Reuben and Mary Ann had retired to their room. The girls were studying and reading in the living room when the apartment door exploded and one of the young men burst through the door. "Come quick if you want to see what's happening! The Jamaat just came through, threw gas around, and lit it!"

Everyone in the apartment bolted for their sandals. Reuben and Mary

Ann emerged from the bedroom. Down the stairs and out onto the streets they ran, hoping to see the fire. Up and down Taj Mahal Road, a shouting crowd was gathering to see what was going on. The mechanic and tire shops were hustling equipment into the shops. All along the streets the metal-slatted rolling curtains were rattling as shop owners jerked them down, closing their shops. The fires had burned out, quick but hot. No one knew if more strikers were coming.

"Jamaat, Jamaat, Jamaat." The word was on every tongue. The Jamaat-e-Islam were out and about. So were the policemen. The police trucks rolled slowly along, stopping to talk to the people on the corner, and then they drove on in the direction the rioters had gone.

A few days later the team was moving from the Mohammadpur section to Mirpur 10 in the north of the city. Mirpur 10, the old-timers on the team whispered, was a hot spot for strikes.

It certainly seemed so the day they moved to Mirpur. As the first load of household goods arrived at the new apartment, they waded through thronging crowds on the street outside the new apartment. The apartment was just forty feet up the street from a stand where vendors sold tickets to games held at the huge Mirpur stadium. A new series of cricket matches between Bangladesh and Sri Lanka was about to begin, and the people wanted tickets. Restlessly, the men and boys in line romped and shouted. The ticket counters were selling out, but hundreds still waited.

By the time the language team arrived with the third load of furniture, they drove to the apartment through clouds of tear gas. The cricket ticket picketers were rioting. They bashed in the fronts of banks with bricks and ripped signs, yelling and dashing about.

The police were trying to disperse the hordes. Not every policeman in Bangladesh had a gun, so the police with clubs went first, beating the picketers back. Police officers with tear gas guns came next, followed by those carrying guns with rubber bullets. Last of all came the guns with real bullets. Armored trucks sat nearby on the corners with ominous cannons on top, carrying tanks of hot water. In an emergency, the police would hose the throng down with hot water.

Will true peace be shot from the barrel of a gun?

Someone threw something from a second-floor restaurant next door. The police whirled and returned fire, shooting out the lights on the restaurant's sign. The street emptied, and the Americans on the balcony of their new apartment stepped back from the lattice with a sigh of dissipating excitement. This was their new home.

Several nights later, the crowd was back. They were buying tickets again. The stand didn't open till eleven o'clock the next morning, but by ten-thirty the night before, the line stretched out of sight around the corner of the street. The young men and boys in line stretched and yawned and sat down on scraps of newspaper to wait out the night. They didn't intend to sleep either. All night long, roars of camaraderie washed in waves over the language team members who were trying to sleep in their bunks.

In the morning the team rose with bloodshot eyes to face the day, trying to orient themselves. Laundry—they needed to do laundry. The moment the girls stepped out on the balcony to do laundry, a cheer went up from the ranks below. The crowd was definitely interested.

Some of the girls retreated hastily. "Oh, that's awful!"

Some of the girls turned their backs and kept on working, not to be deterred.

The gentlemen of the team stepped out on the balcony and rolled up their sleeves. "Why don't you go inside?" That day the laundry kings did it themselves, and the girls went inside to help Mary Ann clean up from breakfast.

The big goal in life should not be to solve all our problems, but to follow and obey God.

In 1971 Bangladesh had fought for its independence from Pakistan when Pakistan had tried to enforce Urdu as the official language. During that war, members of the political party Jamaat-e-Islam sided with Pakistan and committed war crimes against their own people. They targeted Bangladesh's leading intellectuals—doctors, scientists, professors, artists, and poets. The war criminals themselves had been left to roam at will until just that year. Off and on under some regimes, they had been imprisoned, only to be released when the power changed hands. Now Sheikh Hasina, the prime minister, had vowed to bring about justice forty years late for the victims of the genocide, and with the help of her government, she established the International Crimes Tribunal. The war criminals were hailed before the tribunal, and in 2013, Kader Mullah, nicknamed Mirpur Butcher, was convicted on five of six charges and handed down two life sentences with an additional fifteen-year sentence.

There were mixed reactions to this sentence. Kader Mullah had supporters, and the Jamaat was furious. However, at the Shahbhag intersection in Old Dhaka, thousands of protesters, mostly young people, gathered to hold a vigil round the clock demanding that Kader Mullah be sentenced to hanging, not a measly life in prison. Protesters marched all over Bangladesh, crying, "*Kader Mullah phasi cay, Kader Mullah phasi cay*" (We want Kader Mullah hung).

Seven months later the life sentence was changed to a death sentence, and Kader Mullah was slated to be hanged. December 11 was set as the execution date. That date gave the Jamaat-e-Islam party and other collaborating parties a chance to demonstrate at length.

Daily, Reuben and Mary Ann watched their team go out the door into a city where there were strikes more days than not. Some of these strikes lasted for five or six days at a time. A strike meant that any protester of the striking party could carouse through the streets, throwing petrol bombs and other explosives, terrorizing anyone who was out and about. Buses were burnt, and with them, drivers and passengers. A small boy was mortally injured when he picked up a cricket ball that turned out to be an explosive. Police deployed everywhere in the city, and there was talk of martial law. Lawyers of prestige gathered outside the house of a minister to protest rulings on the war crimes trials, and the police hosed them down with hot water from cannons on the tops of tanks.

Another war criminal of the Jamaat, not as illustrious as Kader Mullah, was tried. The Jamaat grew upset over the impending verdict, supposing it to be conviction and a life sentence. During the trial, the Jamaat rampaged throughout the city, burning buses and throwing bombs. On the second day of the trial, the news came that the tried man had been cleared of all charges and let go free.

"We want hanging!"

The Jamaat stopped in their tracks and thought quickly. *If we burn things and make a riot, then, see, you listen to us.*

December 10 arrived, but the Jamaat was sure Kader Mullah would not be hung that midnight. The time drew closer and closer to the appointed time. Kader Mullah's party members grew more and more apprehensive as they realized that 12:01 a.m. would eventually come, the time scheduled for the execution. They scribbled some papers claiming that Kader Mullah's trial had been incomplete and hurried to the judge's house to submit the plea. Disturbed in the midst of a social function, the judge looked over the papers to stay the execution and said, "Oh, no, a lawyer must sign these papers first before they can be submitted."

They scurried to the lawyer's house, but the lawyer wasn't home and didn't answer his phone. Just as they were getting desperate, they found the lawyer and got the papers signed. They galloped back to the jail, served the papers to stay the execution and stopped to wipe their brows. "Whew, that was close."

A hearing was scheduled for the next morning and then delayed and then rescheduled. The plea was denied. On the evening of December 11, in a burst of uncharacteristic efficiency, Kader Mullah was executed. Riots followed. The Jamaat and the police clashed again and again.

Into this heated political tension, the ESL teams returned at the beginning of 2014, just a few days shy of the general elections. Reuben and Mary Ann had returned to Virginia for a few weeks to attend to some things and were back as house parents for the winter ESL team in Cumrakhali.

While home over Christmas season that winter, Mary Ann had become ill. Fever had burned in her body, and she grew thin. The doctors in America were not helpful. They did not recognize foreign diseases. The mosquitoes of Dhaka carried dengue fever, and Mary Ann supposed that she had contracted it.

"You're not going back, are you?" friends asked, scandalized as January drew nearer. "You're sick, and it's dangerous!"

"Of course we're going back," Reuben and Mary Ann said. Mary Ann was still weak, ravaged from the fever when they landed in Dhaka again in January in the middle of a strike.

The team leaders hired several ambulances to come pick up the twenty-five team members arriving with four times that many pieces of luggage. Ambulances were the only vehicles that strikers would not harm. Normally the group would have split into their respective teams and traveled on to the villages the day after they flew into Dhaka, but this year travel was impossible. Elections for prime minister were taking place three days after the winter ESL teams arrived, and the military had restricted all travel for the week. No buses, boats, or trains were running.

Thirty-two people, three teams' worth, sat down in the four-bedroom apartment and rented guesthouse rooms to wait out the elections. In the mornings the streets were eerie—dead for Bangladesh. And the camouflaged uniforms of the soldiers could be seen everywhere, dim in the winter mist. For days the city was silent. On January 4, Sheikh Hasina was reelected. The other party had withdrawn from the election.

While they waited in Dhaka for travel to begin again, the team members went out in the city, shopping and preparing for months in the villages. Many items such as bleach or ground hamburger would not be available in the villages. Those of the team new to Bangladesh went sightseeing and souvenir shopping, and in one way or another, most of the team members got a lot of mileage out of Dhaka.

Reuben took Mary Ann to the doctor for blood work. The doctors weren't sure whether or not she had dengue fever, but they prescribed her some pills, and she began to improve.

~~~~~~

The day was clear and a Bengali, one of millions, drifted about the markets in Mirpur 10, idly observing the passersby. Bangladesh was his country, but he had visited foreign countries and had spent considerable time in Australia. He wished to return there. He did not want Bangladesh; he wanted something more. Daily, his mother dropped more hints about marriage, and he was petrified that one day the awful accident of marriage would happen to him. He did not want to marry a Bengali girl and stay in this fossilized city for the rest of his life. This was no place to raise a family. As he stopped to finger some orange gladiolas on a stand, a flash of white caught his eye, and he looked up. Two girls, foreigners, strode past. He would have known them by their walk even if their skin had not been white. Shoulders squared, chins up, they moved among the pushing, sweaty crowds of late afternoon. They wrinkled their noses against the stink of rotting vegetables, but they did not cover their noses with their scarves like delicate rich girls. They were American, all right, and they were wearing dresses and white cloths on their heads.

He followed them aimlessly at first, but the longer he trailed them, the more interested he grew. They bought some ornas[5] and sandals, turning at the Mirpur stadium. Anxious not to alarm them, he stayed back, out

5 A scarf

of their notice. They were turning down a street now, and he stopped at the corner and watched as they disappeared into an apartment building. He wanted to talk to them but was shy.

Standing in the shadows, he watched the building. Americans came and went. In his time standing there, he counted eighteen. Half a dozen young men arrived on rickshaws, apparently having a riotous time. The rickshaw driver did not know they wanted him to stop and did not seem to understand when his passengers asked him to stop. Finally one of the young men whacked the driver on the shoulder to get his attention. "Stop!" The one watching decided these Americans were not used to Bangladesh.

More foreigners came out on the balcony of the second floor, gathering clothes off the line. From the amount of clothing on the line, the man judged there must be a dreadful lot of people. Two older men exited the building. He nearly worked up the courage to approach them, but they were gone on down the street. Ten minutes later they were back, and he walked up to them, introducing himself as Mr. Fragrant.

"Who are you?" he demanded. "What are you?" Mr. Fragrant was intrigued by these foreigners.

Reuben and Dale Lapp spent their evening visiting with him, trying to answer that question. Mr. Fragrant was curious, and he spoke excellent English. In fact, he claimed he had spent so many years studying in Australia that in some ways he preferred English to Bangla, his native language.

"I didn't know there were people like you. I didn't know there were Western women who dressed the way your women do. I, too, am a believer."

"You are!" Reuben was astonished.

"Yes, I had a girlfriend from Australia at one time. She gave me the name of Fragrant. She was a Christian and gave me a Bible. I became a Christian after she introduced me to the faith. We were engaged to be married when she went skydiving. Her parachute did not open, and she fell to her death. I was crushed, but I am still searching, seeking for meaning in life. There was such emptiness in me after her death that I began to read the Bible, looking for something to fill me."

The evening passed quickly for Mr. Fragrant as he told them about his life. An hour after supper was over, he said his goodbyes and walked out the door.

A few days passed and the political turmoil in Dhaka lessened. The buses began to run again. Mary Ann was feeling better, and she was able to travel with the team to Cumrakhali. The winter ESL teams went their way to three different villages, and another winter in Bangladesh began.

Minnesota Virginia Pakistan Ukraine Afghanistan Israel Haiti Bangladesh

Soil

IN CUMRAKHALI, THEY WERE BUSIER than in Dhaka. The team was more active, coming and going from classes, interacting with the hordes of students and children. The community had discovered that the American flat was a great place for social life. People came and went constantly. More than children came. Adults visited too.

Midway through the term, three men from the Bangladesh ESL board in America arrived to help with the weeklong pastors' conference. Dale Lapp came from southern Bangladesh, and he, Reuben, and the three visitors prepared to hold the pastors' conference.

These conferences were held twice a year for young men who had become Christians largely through the work of Pastor Zhewel, the pastor Reuben had visited with in Dhaka in the fall. Zhewel had requested more teaching for himself and these men. They were all new Christians. They had had milk—now they wanted meat.

The conference meetings lasted all day. Pastor Zhewel interpreted for them all, and so the topics took a while. One evening they were finishing late when Dale got a call from his wife Laura in the south with their team. She wanted them to pray. A young boy, a believer Dale was discipling, had fallen sick and unconscious at their gate, and was now gripped in a seizure.

Dale stopped the entire meeting. "Men! Brothers!" In the corner, Reuben looked up.

"There's a young believer who is terribly sick. We call him Nelson. My team is taking him to the hospital right now. My wife wants us to pray for God to spare him."

Bangladeshi culture loved drama of any kind, and these young pastors were no exception. They threw themselves into prayer, voices rising all over the room. Reuben joined in, but he did not try to compete in volume. "Oh, Lord!" one was shouting, "Lord! Raise him up, raise him up! Lord!"

Reuben exchanged an expressive glance with one of the other teachers. Their eyes twinkled, but Reuben loved the ardor of these young men. Bowing his head, he prayed for the young man in the south. Then he prayed for the young pastors who prayed for Nelson—that the seed fallen into their hearts was not sown in stony soil. Reuben also prayed that the men teaching would have the Spirit of the Lord to nurture these seedlings.

The prayer time ended after several minutes, and the discussion continued until Dale's phone rang again. Laura said that she had just heard from the group who had taken Nelson to the hospital. He was conscious now, and the doctor was with him.

"He's better," Dale said, closing his phone. "He is conscious now. Let's thank God."

They gathered close in prayers of rejoicing. God had raised Nelson up. He may have used a doctor to do it, but that was enough in the minds of the pastors. They knew when God had answered a prayer. God had raised Nelson up like they had asked, and they thanked Him.

At the end of February, after the pastor's conference, the ESL team helped at a youth conference that Pastor Zhewel held every year. Some of the men taught, and the team sang. Pastor Zhewel allowed for a lot of singing time between preaching and prayers. The teenagers loved it, for Bengalis loved to sing.

Reuben and Mary Ann invited two sisters, Rima and Rimpi, whom they had met the previous month, to come to the youth conference. The girls had been crippled from birth. Their legs were permanently deformed, bent at the knees, making their lower legs stick straight up behind them while they walked on their knees. They were sweet girls, and Reuben and

Mary Ann and some of the team girls had become friends with them. Reuben and Mary Ann had given them sewing machines to help them support themselves.

When Rima and Rimpi arrived at the conference, Mary Ann went to sit with them. The girls were shy in public places, self-conscious of their deformity. With Mary Ann, however, the girls relaxed.

Reuben watched them over his shoulder for a bit to see how they would settle in. Together, the girls bent over the Bible Mary Ann had given them, following along with the topic. Reuben's heart warmed as he turned back to face the front. Maybe they had been able to introduce a life of something more to these girls.

~~~~~~

In spite of Mr. Fragrant's sensational beginning to his search for truth, Reuben found himself inclined to invest more in this man. After the teams had been in the village a few weeks, Reuben and Mary Ann returned to Dhaka to visit the Rana Plaza victims and set them up with sewing machines. There they met with Mr. Fragrant again. This time Reuben gave Mr. Fragrant a book called *Doctrines of the Bible*.

Mr. Fragrant announced his intention of coming to visit. "I need more fellowship. I am all alone. I live with my parents, but they don't know that I am a Christian. There is no one I can interact with. I need a body of believers around me."

"Well, come on over," Reuben said.

Mr. Fragrant wanted to stay for a long time, and with a little encouragement, might have moved in altogether had not Reuben specified that his invitation was for several days. Mr. Fragrant arrived on the bus late one afternoon, and Reuben walked down to the bus stand to meet him. "Hello, Mr. Fragrant! How was your bus ride?"

"Hi!" Mr. Fragrant replied, but he seemed ill. "Not so well. I don't like buses at all. I was too nervous to eat all day because I didn't want to be sick on the bus, in case I threw *out*. Now I am very hungry."

"Well!" Reuben smiled to himself over Mr. Fragrant's terminology. "It's too late for lunch at our place, but we'll have supper at 6:30."

Mr. Fragrant didn't think he could wait that long for food, and Reuben took him up to town to eat rice at one of the restaurants.

"Do you know what day this is?" Mr. Fragrant asked as they took seats at a greasy table.

Reuben calculated. "It's the seventh, isn't it?"

"It is!" Mr. Fragrant was enthusiastic. He ate a handful of rice and stopped to work the chicken curry into it, thinking. "February seven is a significant day, I think."

"Oh?" Reuben asked.

"Yes. Seven is the perfect number, which makes the perfect day. This is the perfect day to be baptized."

"I see." Reuben sat back and thought. "Maybe the day isn't so important as being ready. Baptism is a serious step."

"Oh, I know," Mr. Fragrant replied.

"In fact," Reuben said hastily, "the Bible has direction for baptism."

By the time Mr. Fragrant had finished his rice, Reuben had convinced him that he would not be baptized that night. The two men returned to the flat and went up on the roof. While the sun set, they opened the Bible and talked.

"See," Reuben explained, "I don't really know you yet. I don't understand your heart—haven't seen your life. This can't be jumped into lightly. For there to be a body of fellowship among us, it's important for us to be open to each other and know each other's lives, you see. You need to take a little bit of time to think about whether you really want to be a part of this, considering what it will require of you. You need to think about how ready you are to make this your life."

Mr. Fragrant agreed to sit back and just fit into team life for a few days and see what he thought. Reuben took time to study the Bible with him and invest in his spiritual growth over the next couple of days, but Mr. Fragrant was not ready to let the subject of baptism drop.

"You just don't want me to marry one of your girls," Mr. Fragrant said one morning. "That's why you won't baptize me."

Reuben was taken aback by this. It hadn't occurred to him that Mr. Fragrant would marry one of "his" girls. Thinking it over, he began to understand the pressures in Mr. Fragrant's life a little more. He was a lonely man. Having tasted romance with his Australian girlfriend with whom he had developed his interest in the Bible, he would not be satisfied with a Bengali woman. He wanted fellowship. To Mr. Fragrant, fellowship was something a man needed all the time in the form of a Christian woman.

"His ideas aren't completely faulty," Reuben admitted to Mary Ann that night, "but there needs to be more to Mr. Fragrant's drive for Christianity than marrying a good Christian woman."

"And his mother is calling him all the time, worrying about who he's with and what he's doing," Mary Ann added. "I heard Mr. Fragrant tell one of the girls he couldn't sleep because of all these worries. He says his parents want him to get married."

Reuben discouraged Mr. Fragrant from going to the girls on the team for spiritual advice, which highly incensed Mr. Fragrant.

"I don't understand how you believers can say no to another part of the body that is struggling," he complained. "How can the body reject the hand? I need these relationships to keep my relationship with God alive in my difficult situation. I only want to discuss the Bible with them. What can be wrong with that?"

"Everyone on our team is your friend," Reuben told him. "If you have questions, you are more than welcome to talk to me or any of the gentlemen. But the girls will not be expected to disciple you. C'mon, Fragrant, you know that is not appropriate. In your own culture this would not happen."

Mr. Fragrant said sadly that he could not have anything more to do with the team. "I cannot continue this relationship. I am angry. Goodbye, my friend. You meant well."

Reuben was sorry to see him go, but he thought maybe it was for the best. Mr. Fragrant had a lot of vested interest in his relationship with the team, and perhaps they all needed a little time apart to sort things through.

Later, after Mr. Fragrant had cooled down, maybe they could reopen the subject on a different foundation. He was a smart man, and Reuben believed he honestly was seeking.

Meanwhile, Reuben and several of the other men on the teams kept contact with Rasel. Sometimes Rasel was in Cumrakhali visiting his wife's family. How he managed to contact the Americans without arousing the suspicions of his father and brothers, Reuben was never quite sure. He seemed comfortable coming for Bible studies, however, and after all, his father and brothers lived in another distant village.

One day Reuben was out in the market. He was beyond the bus stand, walking toward the flat, when a rickshaw rattled up beside him. Looking over his shoulder, he spotted Rasel seated in the vehicle.

"Rasel!" Reuben was delighted. He offered his hand.

"Reuben!" Rasel was genuinely pleased too over the encounter. He gestured to a veiled woman beside him. "This is my wife. Her name means 'key of paradise,' remember? And this is my little girl." He picked up the mite, a beautiful child with tea brown eyes and pale skin.

Reuben was glad to meet them and he asked Rasel, "Would you bring them to our flat for a visit sometime? My wife and the girls on the team would love to meet them."

"Okay," Rasel agreed, "and we must have another Bible study."

Reuben wondered what Rasel's wife would make of that, but he only said, "Of course."

A few days later Rasel arrived with his wife and their little girl. The team visited with them for a bit, and then Rasel straightened in his chair. "Let's study the Bible."

They brought their Bibles out, and Rasel chose verses from 1 Corinthians 11 and Ephesians 5 to read. He picked one of the team girls who could speak and read Bangla. "Carla, would you read it in the Bangla version for us?"

Amazed, Reuben listened to the words halting from Carla's lips and wished he could understand them in the context that they would strike Rasel's wife. *Rasel is a smart man,* Reuben thought, appreciating his strategy.

Rasel was intelligent, and he wasn't done yet. "You did good, Carla," he said when Carla had finished, "but how about you . . ." Rasel turned to his wife. "Read the next couple of verses."

So she did. Without comprehending it, Reuben heard the beautifully liquid sound of the Bangla language coming from the woman's lips. Reuben marveled at how Rasel had drawn his wife into the Bible study. Reuben knew that she was seeking truth, listening to her husband. He also knew that Rasel spent many hours pouring the Word into her, explaining and presenting. Soon she would have to make a choice. Watching the couple, Reuben marveled, praising God. This seed had not fallen onto stony soil, but good soil. He wondered what the future held for the young couple. He suspected that God had more in mind for them.

CHAPTER 33

Ukraine
Pakistan
Israel
Minnesota
Virginia
Afghanistan
Haiti
Bangladesh

There's Got
to Be More

TEAM LIFE HAD ITS UPS and downs, but it was one of the things that Reuben enjoyed the most about Bangladesh. It could also be the most challenging. Reuben had had enough experience with people to know that. He watched the team members get to know each other and fall into a relationship that was mostly "just one big, happy family," and it often struck him just how much like church life team interaction could be.

A team needed each other, depended on each other. They were the sojourners in a foreign land. They spoke each other's language. Each day, the members went out into the world of Bangladesh and taught and built relationships. At night, they returned to each other to rest and build each other up. They shared their best teaching tactics and worked together on planning lessons, regaling the others with stories of their successes and failures in the classrooms. Sometimes hilarity rocked the room, and next they gathered together in a circle, sharing deep insights and experiences. They cried together and shared the things that hurt them.

The team was family, church, and friend all in one. When there was a common enemy, they drew together. Sometimes there were robberies or relationship problems in the community to deal with. Other times they engaged in spiritual warfare, spending time with someone who was seeking truth. In those times the team was strong and close.

Sometimes nothing significant happened for a long time, and everyone grew bored. When they rode on a plateau, wrapped up in their own lives, problems arose much more quickly. Then people struggled to get along and petty issues began eating at friendships. When the team did not involve itself with the Bengalis around them, they grew focused on themselves. Problems among the team, those little things that came from living together, compounded and mushroomed into real issues. Such was the reality of team life.

The young people liked to play the Un-game, a series of cards that had questions for everyone in the group to answer. Reuben joined them one evening just in time to get asked the question that was making its rounds. The question was, "What is something old that you own and that you value?"

Reuben had quite a few of those items. He was describing them when Mary Ann happened onto the scene.

"What is going on?" she inquired.

One of the girls explained the game. "The question is about something old that you own. Reuben is telling us about old valuable things that he has."

"Oh!" she said. "Like a wife?"

Reuben gazed at her. "Now what am I supposed to do with a question like that?"

Mary Ann sat down beside him to listen in.

The next question was, "Tell about a difficulty you overcame in childhood."

"Well," Mary Ann said, since it was her turn, "when I was in first grade, I was Amish. I couldn't speak any English, and I was sent to public school."

"Really!" one of the girls exclaimed. "How could you even learn?"

"I was fine," Mary Ann insisted. "The teacher liked me. I guess it was because I was Amish. And I made out fine."

Reuben looked at her appreciatively. "The teacher liking you had nothing to do with you being Amish."

Team life might be very encouraging, but no team could ever take the place of his wife. She was the dearest person on earth to him, and if it hadn't been for her, moving on after his accident wouldn't have seemed worth it. She had upheld him through all their trips abroad, game to go anywhere with him. Some men had to choose between a life of service or getting married, but Mary Ann had allowed him to do both. Together they had served God, and together they would serve God for the remainder of the time He gave them breath.

~~~~~~~~~~~~~~~~~~~~~~~~~~~~~~~~~~~~~

The first winter they had been in Cumrakhali, a man and his wife had come to the door of the flat. It was morning, just as the teachers were rushing to get to school, and Mary Ann called to Reuben that there were visitors. There were always visitors, it seemed. Reuben thought it was a particularly bad time for visitors, but time never kept anyone away in Bangladesh. He went out into the main room where Mary Ann had seated two people on plastic chairs.

The man had a cane in his hand, and he stared over Reuben's shoulder in the general direction of the wall when Reuben approached to shake his hand. Unnerved, Reuben glanced behind him and then looked back when the man did not take his hand. Leaning in closer, he observed the vacant eyes and understood. The man was blind.

"This is Sediq," said BJ, who had come up to talk to the visitors in Bangla. "And this is his wife."

The blind man's wife was a thin, withered woman with a sharp little nose and mournful eyes. She adjusted her wrap over her head, tucking it behind her ears, which made them stick out.

"How can we help you?" Reuben wanted to know. BJ switched to Bangla again, repeating the question. The two did not respond for a second, seemingly mesmerized. Sediq turned toward the voice and said something in a high, reedy voice. BJ looked appalled and then laughed.

"What did he say?" Mary Ann asked.

"He said that I'll have to speak Bangla to him because he doesn't understand English," BJ explained.

"But you *were* speaking Bangla."

"I *thought* I was." BJ turned to the couple and tried again. This time he got on much better. The woman began to talk, and she went on for quite some time in a toneless voice. Then the voice rose, pleading, and she clasped her hands together.

"What does she want?" Reuben demanded.

BJ sighed. "She wants money. They're poor. Her husband can't work, so he begs. They can't support themselves."

"I see." Reuben shifted where he stood. "Well, explain that we don't just give out cash. Tell them, though, that if there is a medical need, we would be glad to help out. You know our policy."

"Okay." BJ settled in to explain, and Reuben left them there.

A week or so later the poor couple appeared on their doorstep again. Sediq had been hit by a vehicle of some kind along the road when he was out begging. The story and injuries were not immediately clear, but one thing the team understood: Sediq had been to see a doctor and needed medication.

"Well," Reuben said, "let's go buy him some medicine." He prepared to go, and BJ and one of the other boys traipsed along. They all went up to the market to buy the medicine.

BJ talked to them off and on throughout the trip, and when they left the pharmacy, he said to Reuben, "I am going back with them to their house. I want to find out where they live."

"I'll go too," Reuben said. "Let's swing by the house to get Mary Ann."

They all went. Sediq's home was stark and barren. There was no corner table cluttered with keepsakes like there was in so many Bengali homes. One side of the house was open, the mud crumbled away. The hard bed had no mattress, only a cover. One thing they had, and that was a cow. Reuben and the others met the cow right away as it was quartered in the house, just beyond the bed. During the day it was often pastured out in the orchard behind the flat where the team lived, but that day was grayish, cold, and damp, so the cow stayed home.

"Does your cow give milk?" Mary Ann asked the poor wife. BJ

interpreted, and the wife nodded.

"Oh, I would just love some fresh milk!" Mary Ann exclaimed and sighed. Fresh milk rated with juicy red tomatoes with her. The teams had only powdered milk and milk from boxes, which lasted for months at room temperature.

"Well," Reuben said, "maybe we could buy it from them."

"Oh, but do you think it would be any good?" Mary Ann hushed her voice. Sometimes they were served milk when they visited a home. If it wasn't blue and sour, it was stringy with globs of cream in it. Sometimes it was heated with salt in it.

BJ considered. "If we asked for it fresh, like every morning after she milks, it would probably be fine."

It was arranged. Every morning, Sediq's wife brought a quart of fresh milk, and Mary Ann paid her fifty *taka*. This became a daily rite until one day the cow disappeared, stolen. The loss of the cow devastated Sediq and his family, but the cow had left something in her absence—a relationship. The cow had kept the pair from destitution, and now a friendship added richness to life.

Reuben stopped to chat whenever he passed by Sediq, begging in the market.

"Good morning, Uncle!" Reuben would call out, seeing him.

They could not talk much because of the language barrier, but they tried. Exchanging pleasantries was enough. A smile always lit up Sediq's face when he heard Reuben's voice.

One time Reuben came upon Sediq standing by the street. Sediq's head was cocked, listening, hesitating to cross the street. On the busy road through Cumrakhali, many big trucks and tractors and smaller vehicles passed. A yearning expression crossed Sediq's face, one of sadness and fear. Then he set his jaw and turned toward an approaching sound, listening and waiting.

"Uncle!" Reuben called, coming from the market, "Uncle! Wait." Reuben took Sediq's arm, and together they started walking across. Suddenly a truck appeared, sending them both skittering back to the shaded eaves of

Will the blind man find his way home?

the teashops. Traffic really did travel at indecent speeds along that road. Eventually they both made it to the other side. Reuben disengaged his arm and continued on his way. "Stay well, Uncle."

Reuben went up on the roof of the flat one morning with his coffee in hand. Every year the team had been here, construction had been going on over their heads. Another floor or two had been added on top of the building. He wove among the rebar that stuck out all over the roof like bouquets of rusty sticks and around the piles of sand and bricks.

Reuben stood to watch the town come to life. Downstairs, most of his team was still sleeping. Some of them would sleep till the last minute before breakfast, he knew. Reuben did not mind the thought of them in their warm beds. House parents must be up early, and he liked the quiet blue of morning shadows.

Below him and all around him, people were filtering out of their houses. They were wrapped in scarves and sweaters. The worst of the winter chill had passed, but it was still cold to the Bengalis. Housewives pumped water. *Creak-creak, creak-creak.* Men wandered about with toothbrushes in their mouths. Some teashop keepers were sweeping the packed dirt in front of their doors. Fires were being lit at the restaurants, and people were baking bread. The early buses loaded up at the bus stand, and a tractor or two putted down the road. Some vehicles pulled into the gas station beside the flat, filling up for the day. Over the orchard to the east, the sun was coming up, lighting the misty green of the world.

Reuben was holding his Bible by the spine, and now the pages fanned open. He turned it over in his hand, and it fell open to Hebrews 11, the "faith chapter." The page was creased and marked, a corner turned down. He skimmed it, seeing the familiar blur of names: Abel, Enoch, Abraham, Isaac, Jacob, Joseph, Moses, Rahab. By faith, by faith . . . He ran his eye over it again, feeling the thrilling sweep of the words.

And what shall I more say? For the time would fail me to tell of Gedeon, and of Barak, and of Samson, and of Jephthae; of David also, and Samuel, and of the prophets: who through faith subdued kingdoms, wrought righteousness, obtained promises, stopped the mouths of lions, quenched the violence of fire, escaped the edge of the sword, out of weakness were made strong, waxed valiant in fight, turned to flight the armies of the aliens. Women received their dead raised to life again: and others were tortured, not accepting deliverance; that they might obtain a better resurrection: and others had trial of cruel mockings and scourgings, yea, moreover of bonds and imprisonment: they were stoned, they were sawn asunder, were tempted, were slain with the sword: they wandered about in sheepskins and goatskins; being destitute, afflicted, tormented (of whom the world was not worthy:) they wandered in deserts, and in mountains, and in dens and caves of the earth.

Whoa, Reuben thought, *whoa.* It was charismatic language, so strong he felt almost nauseated. The power of the words gripped him, and he read on.

"And these all, having obtained a good report through faith, received not the promise." Who then? These worthy men and women . . . what were they lacking?

"God having provided some better thing for us, that they without us should not be made perfect."

That they without us *should not be made perfect!*

Blinded by the flash of inspiration, Reuben looked down the street and saw a familiar figure scuffling down the street. Sediq was approaching. His cane was tapping, and the ends of his scarf swung about his neck, coming loose. Even from the roof, Reuben could see the grizzled beard, the empty eyes seeing nothing.

My blind friend, Reuben thought. *Sometimes I feel as blind as you.* He stood, looking down, feeling a strong affection, a binding kinship with the man. *I know what you're doing. You're seeking. Like me. Tap-tap, tap-tap,* Sediq came closer. Mesmerized, Reuben watched the slow but even progress.

Tap-tap, tap-tap. Sediq was almost opposite the rooftop where Reuben stood. *Tap-tap, tap-tap.* Sediq hesitated, turning his head toward the street.

Is he thinking about crossing? No! A bus is coming. Sediq, don't! Reuben moved closer to the edge of the roof.

Sediq heard the huge bus bearing down upon him. He shrank back. With a whoosh of air that lifted the ends of the scarf and blew his beard about, the bus rushed past. One step to the side and Sediq would have been dead.

It's dangerous for Sediq to be out. He should go back home! There are big buses and trucks that might hit him. He might stumble and hurt himself. Sediq can't see where he is going. He doesn't even know what is in front of him. Reuben gripped a piece of rebar.

At home, Sediq's house was barren. There was nothing there to feed him—to comfort him. He had to go out, to find something. So Sediq walked on down the street. *Tap-tap, tap-tap.* He kept on, driven by faith that there would be more. He couldn't see where he was going, but still he went on. *There's got to be more!*

Epilogue

REUBEN AND MARY ANN LIVE in southern Virginia in a cabin surrounded by woods shared by wild turkeys and whitetail deer. They are still active in the work in Bangladesh, which usually takes them away for at least four months of the year. When they are in America, they spend a lot of time on the road, sharing about their international experiences and attending seminars and meetings. They also enjoy spending time with their five children and twelve grandchildren.

After their marriage, Darrell and Tamseela moved to Charlottesville, Virginia, where Darrell attended four years of college in preparation for international ministry. He graduated in the spring of 2014 amid the stress of Tamseela's newly-discovered ovarian cancer. In early 2015, Tamseela passed away in Pakistan where she and Darrell had gone to spend time with her family. Darrell returned to Charlottesville and is pursuing employment possibilities, stepping forward with God in the midst of life's big changes.

Darlene and her husband Joe live in Catlett, Virginia, with their three daughters. Joe works for a general contractor in housing construction.

Lavonna and her husband Jonathan live in the Faith Mission community of Virginia. Following a four-year term of service in Kenya, Jonathan began serving as assistant administrator at Faith Mission Home. The couple and their family of three sons and one daughter live in the little log house where Reuben and Mary Ann spent their Faith Mission years.

Connie and her husband Daniel live in Middlefield, Ohio, with their three sons and one daughter. Daniel works as a counselor in youth ministries.

Celena and her husband Nate live just down the road from Reuben and Mary Ann's present home in southern Virginia. They have one son by adoption.

BOL continues its work in Ukraine, Haiti, and Israel and the Palestinian territories. The projects in Pakistan and Afghanistan were initiated in response to emergencies, and the organization does not have regular operations there at present.

The work in Bangladesh continues and is growing. Reuben and Mary Ann still have contact with the victims from the Rana Plaza disaster. Rasel's wife gave her heart to Jesus in the summer of 2014 and was baptized. She and her husband are pursuing their new faith together. There are now three teams of English teachers working in three locations in the country from January to March every winter. From October to December, a smaller team studies the language in Dhaka, the capital city, to further their ability to relate with the people, especially in discipling believers. In the spring and summer months, leaders in the work visit the country and hold conferences for a group of pastors. All of these efforts provide valuable opportunities to speak Christ's love to seekers.

Afterword

IT WAS TIME FOR A new leg. The life span of these manmade ones is substantially less than the one God provided originally. Being of the persuasion that God desires to use situations He brings into our experience to accomplish His purposes, I began to visualize possibilities. My thoughts raced to Haiti, Israel, and far away Bangladesh—to bedside encounters with people attempting to deal with the reality of tragedy. *So amputees can sit, stand, and walk? Will there be another day?* they wonder.

As my prosthetic doctor and I discussed possibilities for my new prosthesis, I asked, "How about an idea?"

"Sure, go ahead," was his friendly response.

"How about we laminate a few words onto the knee socket?"

"I'll give it a try," he assured me. "Here's what you can do. Get iron-on letters and attach them to T-shirt fabric and I'll stick it on."

My goal in ministry needed to be narrowed down to a few words. JESUS IS THE ANSWER fit just right.

Getting a new leg is not an easy process. A new socket

calls for adjustments and conformity to a new mold. After thirty-three years as an amputee, the small stump below my knee still occasionally resists being used as a foot. So I agonize with the continuing finality of being an amputee and wonder how the Master designs to use this as a tool. The whole process of molding, shaping, and fitting the prosthesis helps me understand anew that usefulness comes as a result of allowing God to thrust us into places we would never go by our own choosing. In these places He shows us who we really are in relation to who He is and gives us understanding into His greater purposes.

My prosthetic doctor seemed more quiet the day I arrived at his clinic to receive my new leg. As he handed it to me for my ultimate approval, his eyes seemed to return to the words on the socket. He had probably read them many times as he was working on the contraption. As I began to explain the correlation of the words and the contraption bearing them, suddenly he understood.

"Oh, ministry," he said softly.

I replied, "Yes, do you believe Jesus is the answer?"

—*Reuben Yoder*

About the Author

MELISSA EBY LIVES WITH HER family in Bean's Cove, Pennsylvania. She works at her family's sawmill as a secretary and has spent her winters in Bangladesh the past several years, teaching English. She loves the opportunities that Third World cultures present for spreading the Gospel, but she also recognizes how crucial it is that those in America, including herself, reach out to people around them. Melissa recently started serving part-time with a local ambulance service as an emergency medical technician.

Melissa was on a team in Bangladesh when she met Reuben and Mary Ann for the first time. Later she was privileged to have them as her house parents. From the start, she appreciated and admired Reuben and Mary Ann. She thought their stories were fascinating. The more she learned to know them, the more she realized what motivated their stories—their tireless burden to reach out to people.

They were traveling home from Bangladesh together after serving there for three months when Reuben and Mary Ann asked Melissa if she would consider writing their story. She loved to write but had never written a book. She listened to them in disbelief, but the more Reuben talked, the more she began to see their vision for the story.

Reuben and Mary Ann said they did not want to just "tell their story," but rather, they wanted to inspire other people to get involved in ministry through their stories. Based on their vision, Melissa agreed to write.

The Yoders and Melissa welcome response from readers and can be contacted at reubenjyoder@juno.com and theresgottobemore.mje@gmail.com respectively. You may also write to them in care of Christian Aid Ministries, P.O. Box 360, Berlin, Ohio 44610.

The Way to God and Peace

WE LIVE IN A WORLD contaminated by sin. Sin is anything that goes against God's holy standards. When we do not follow the guidelines that God our Creator gave us, we are guilty of sin. Sin separates us from God, the source of life.

Since the time when the first man and woman, Adam and Eve, sinned in the Garden of Eden, sin has been universal. The Bible says that we all have "sinned and come short of the glory of God" (Romans 3:23). It also says that the natural consequence for that sin is eternal death, or punishment in an eternal hell: "Then when lust hath conceived, it bringeth forth sin: and sin, when it is finished, bringeth forth death" (James 1:15).

But we do not have to suffer eternal death in hell. God provided forgiveness for our sins through the death of His only Son, Jesus Christ. Because Jesus was perfect and without sin, He could die in our place. "For God so loved the world that he gave his only begotten Son, that whosoever believeth in him should not perish, but have everlasting life" (John 3:16).

A sacrifice is something given to benefit someone else. It costs the giver greatly. Jesus was God's sacrifice. Jesus' death takes away the penalty of sin for everyone who accepts this sacrifice and truly repents of their sins. To repent of sins means to be truly sorry for and turn away from the things we have done that have violated God's standards. (Acts 2:38; 3:19).

Jesus died, but He did not remain dead. After three days, God's Spirit miraculously raised Him to life again. God's Spirit does something similar in us. When we receive Jesus as our sacrifice and repent of our sins, our hearts are changed. We become spiritually alive! We develop new desires and attitudes (2 Corinthians 5:17). We begin to make choices that please God (1 John 3:9). If we do fail and commit sins, we can ask God for forgiveness. "If we confess our sins, he is faithful and just to forgive us our sins, and to cleanse us from all unrighteousness" (1 John 1:9).

Once our hearts have been changed, we want to continue growing spiritually. We will be happy to let Jesus be the Master of our lives and will want to become more like Him. To do this, we must meditate on God's Word and commune with God in prayer. We will testify to others of this change by being baptized and sharing the good news of God's victory over sin and death. Fellowship with a faithful group of believers will strengthen our walk with God (1 John 1:7).